Tramping on Life

THE AUTHOR OF
Tramping on Life

Tramping on Life

AN AUTOBIOGRAPHICAL NARRATIVE

HARRY KEMP

GARDEN CITY   NEW YORK
GARDEN CITY PUBLISHING COMPANY, Inc.
1927

Printed in the United States of America

All in this book that is good and endur-
ing and worth while for humanity, I
dedicate to the memory of my wife,

MARY PYNE

Waterbury, Connecticut,
May 20, 1922.

TRAMPING ON LIFE

Now I am writing these things just as I was told them by my grandmother. For I have utterly no remembrance of my mother. Consumption ran in her family. And bearing and giving birth to me woke the inherited weakness in her. She was not even strong enough to suckle me.

. . . .

I was born in the early eighties, in Mornington, Ohio, in a section of that great, steel-manufacturing city which was neither city, suburb, nor country,—but a muddy, green-splashed, murky mixture of all three.

. . . .

They told me, when I was old enough to understand, that my mother was English, that her folks lived in Cleveland and owned a millinery and drygoods store there . . and that my father met my mother one day in Mornington. She was visiting an uncle who ran a candy store on Main Street, and, she girl-like, laughed and stood behind the counter, ready for a flirtation. . .

My father was young, too. And he was employed there in the store, apprenticed to the candy-maker's trade. And, on this day, as he passed through, carrying a trayful of fresh-dipped chocolates, he winked at my mother and joked with her in an impudent way . . and she rebuffed him, not really meaning a rebuff, of course . . and he startled her by pulling off his hat and grotesquely showing himself to be entirely bald . . for he had grown bald very young —at the age of sixteen . . both because of scarlet fever, and because baldness for the men ran in his family . . and he was tall, and dark, and walked with rather a military carriage.

. . . .

I was four years old when my mother died.

When she fell sick, they tell me, my grandfather did one of the few decent acts of his life—he let my father have a farm he owned in central Kansas, near Hutchinson. But my father did not try to work it.

He was possessed of neither the capital nor knowledge necessary for farming.

He went to work as clerk in a local hotel, in the rapidly growing town. Crazy with grief, he watched my mother drop out of his life a little more each day.

.   .   .   .

My father and mother both had tempers that flared up and sank as suddenly.

.   .   .   .

I had lung fever when I was a baby. That was what they called it then. I nearly died of it. It left me very frail in body.

.   .   .   .

As soon as I could walk and talk my mother made a great companion of me. She didn't treat me as if I were only a child. She treated me like a grown-up companion. I am told that I would follow her about the house from room to room, clutching at her skirts, while she was dusting and sweeping and working. And to hear us two talking with each other, you would have imagined there was a houseful of people.

.   .   .   .

My father's anguish over my mother's death caused him to break loose from all ties. His grief goaded him so that he went about aimlessly. He roamed from state to state, haunted by her memory. He worked at all sorts of jobs. Once he even dug ditches for seventy-five cents a day. He had all sorts of adventures, roaming about.

As for me, I was left alone with my grandmother, his mother,—in the big house which stood back under the trees, aloof from the wide, dusty road that led to the mills.

With us lived my young, unmarried aunt, Millie . . .

My grandmother had no education. She could barely read and write.

And she believed in everybody.

She was stout . . sparse-haired . . wore a switch . . had kindly, confiding, blue eyes.

Beggars, tramps, pack-peddlers, book-agents, fortune-tellers,— she lent a credulous ear to all,—helped others when we ourselves needed help, signed up for preposterous articles on "easy" monthly payments,—gave away food, starving her appetite and ours.

When, child though I was, even I protested, she would say, "well, Johnnie, you might be a tramp some day, and how would I feel if I thought some one was turning you away hungry?"

.   .   .   .

My Grandfather Gregory was a little, alert, erect, suave man, —he was a man whose nature was such that he would rather gain a dollar by some cheeky, brazen, off-colour practice than earn a hundred by honest methods.

He had keen grey eyes that looked you in the face in utter, disarming frankness. He was always immaculately dressed. He talked continually about money, and about how people abused his confidence and his trust in men. But there was a sharpness like pointed needles in the pupils of his eyes that betrayed his true nature.

Coming to Mornington as one of the city's pioneers, at first he had kept neck to neck in social prestige with the Babsons, Guelders, and the rest, and had built the big house that my grandmother, my aunt, and myself now lived in, on Mansion avenue . .

When the Civil War broke out, that streak of adventure and daring in my grandfather which in peace times turned him to shady financial transactions, now caused him to enlist. And before the end of the war he had gone far up in the ranks.

After the war he came into still more money by a manufacturing business which he set up. But the secret process of the special kind of material which he manufactured he inveigled out of a comrade in arms. The latter never derived a cent from it. My grandfather stole the patent, taking it out in his own name. The other man had trusted him, remembering the times they had fought shoulder to shoulder, and had bivouacked together. . .

My grandfather, though so small as to be almost diminutive, was spry and brave as an aroused wasp when anyone insulted him. Several times he faced down burly-bodied men who had threatened to kill him for his getting the better of them in some doubtful business transaction.

For a long time his meanness and sharp dealings were reserved for outsiders and he was generous with his family. And my sweet, simple, old grandmother belonged to all the societies, charitable and otherwise, in town . . but she was not, never could be "smart."

She was always saying and doing naïve things from the heart.   And soon she began to disapprove of my grandfather's slick business ways.

I don't know just what tricks he put over . . but he became *persona non grata* in local business circles . . and he took to running about the country, putting through various projects here and there . . this little, dressy, hard-faced man . . like a cross between a weasel and a bird!

He dropped into Mornington, and out again, each time with a wild, restless story of fortunes to be made or in the making!

Once he came home and stayed for a longer time than usual. During this stay he received many letters.   My grandmother noticed a furtiveness in his manner when he received them.   My grandmother noticed that her husband always repaired immediately to the outhouse when he received a letter.

She followed after him one day, and found fragments of a torn letter cast below . . she performed the disagreeable task of retrieving the fragments, of laboriously piecing them together and spelling them out.   She procured a divorce as quietly as possible. Then my grandfather made his final disappearance.   I did not see him again till I was quite grown up.

All support of his numerous family ceased.   His sons and daughters had to go to work while still children, or marry.

My Aunt Alice married a country doctor whom I came to know as "Uncle Beck."   My Uncle Joe, who inherited my grandfather's business-sense, with none of his crookedness, started out as a newsboy, worked his way up to half-proprietorship in a Mornington paper . . the last I heard of him he had money invested in nearly every enterprise in town, and had become a substantial citizen.

My father still pursued his nomadic way of living, sending, very seldom, driblets of money to my grandmother for my support . . my uncle Jim went East to work . . of my uncle Landon I shall tell you later on.

.   .   .   .

The big house in which my grandmother, my Aunt Millie, and I lived was looking rather seedy by this time.   The receding tide of fashion and wealth had withdrawn far off to another section of the rapidly growing city . . and, below and above, the Steel Mills, with their great, flaring furnaces, rose, it seemed, over night, one after one . . and a welter of strange people we then called the "low Irish" came to work in them, and our Mansion Avenue became "Kilkenny Row." And a gang of tough kids sprang up called the "Kilkenny Cats," with which my gang used to fight.

After the "Low Irish" came the "Dagoes" . . and after them the "Hunkies" . . each wilder and more poverty-stricken than the former.

. . . .

The Industrial Panic of '95 (it was '95, I think) was on . . always very poor since the breaking up of our family, now at times even bread was scarce in the house.

I was going to school, scrawny and freckle-faced and ill-nourished. I had a pet chicken that fortunately grew up to be a hen. It used to lay an egg for me nearly every morning during that hard time.

. . . .

My early remembrances of school are chiefly olfactory. I didn't like the dirty boy who sat next to me and spit on his slate, rubbing it clean with his sleeve. I loved the use of my yellow, new sponge, especially after the teacher had taught me all about how it had grown on the bottom of the ocean, where divers had to swim far down to bring it up, slanting through the green waters. But the slates of most of the boys stunk vilely with their spittle.

I didn't like the smell of the pig-tailed little girls, either. There was a close soapiness about them that offended me. And yet they attracted me. For I liked them in their funny, kilt-like, swinging dresses. I liked the pudginess of their noses, the shiny apple-glow of their cheeks.

It was wonderful to learn to make letters on a slate. To learn to put down rows of figures and find that one and one, cabalistically, made two, and two and two, four!

It always seemed an age to recess. And the school day was as long as a month is now.

We were ready to laugh at anything . . a grind-organ in the street, a passing huckster crying "potatoes," etc.

I have few distinct memories of my school days. I never went to kindergarten. I entered common school at the age of eight.

My grandfather, after his hegira from Mornington, left behind his library of travels, lives of famous American Statesmen and

Business Men, and his Civil War books. Among these books were four treasure troves that set my boy's imagination on fire. They were *Stanley's Adventures in Africa*, Dr. Kane's Book of *Polar Explorations*, *Mungo Park*, and, most amazing of all, a huge, sensational book called *Savage Races of the World* . . this title was followed by a score of harrowing and sensational sub-titles in rubric. I revelled and rolled in this book like a colt let out to first pasture. For days and nights, summer and winter, I fought, hunted, was native to all the world's savage regions in turn, partook glee-fully of strange and barbarous customs, naked and skin-painted. I pushed dug-outs and canoes along tropic water-ways where at any moment an enraged hippopotamus might thrust up his snout and overturn me, crunching the boat in two and leaving me a prey to crocodiles . . I killed birds of paradise with poison darts which I blew out of a reed with my nostrils. . . I burned the houses of white settlers . . even indulged shudderingly in cannibal feasts.

The one thing that pre-eminently seized my imagination in *Savage Races of the World* was the frontispiece,—a naked black rush-ing full-tilt through a tropical forest, his head of hair on fire, a huge feather-duster of dishevelled flame . . somehow this appealed to me as especially romantic. I dreamed of myself as that savage, rushing gloriously through a forest, naked, and crowned with fire like some primitive sun-god. It never once occurred to me how it would hurt to have my hair burning!

. . . .

When Aunt Millie was taken down with St. Vitus's dance, it af-forded me endless amusement. She could hardly lift herself a drink out of a full dipper without spilling two-thirds of the contents on the ground.

Uncle Beck, the Pennsylvania Dutch country doctor who mar-ried Aunt Alice, came driving in from Antonville, five miles away, once or twice a week to tend to Millie, free, as we were too poor to pay for a doctor. I remember how Uncle Beck caught me and whipped me with a switch. For I constantly teased Aunt Millie to make her scream and cry.

. . . .

"Granma," I used to call out, on waking in the morning. . .
"Yes, Johnnie darling, what is it?"
"Granma, yesterday . . in the woods back of Babson's barn, I

killed three Indians, one after the other." (The funny part of it was that I believed this, actually, as soon as the words left my mouth.)

A silence. . .

"Granma, don't you believe me?"

"Yes, of course, I believe you."

Aunt Millie would strike in with—"Ma, why do you go on humouring Johnnie while he tells such lies? You ought to give him a good whipping."

"The poor little chap ain't got no mother!"

"Poor little devil! If you keep on encouraging him this way he'll become one of the greatest liars in the country."

A colloquy after this sort took place more than once. It gave me indescribable pleasure to narrate an absurd adventure, believe it myself in the telling of it, and think others believed me. Aunt Millie's scorn stung me like a nettle, and I hated her.

In many ways I tasted practical revenge. Though a grown girl of nineteen, she still kept three or four dolls. And I would steal her dolls, pull their dresses for shame over their heads, and set them straddle the banisters.

.   .   .   .

We took in boarders. We had better food. It was good to have meat to eat every day.

Among the boarders was a bridge builder named Elton Reeves. Elton had a pleasant, sun-burnt face and a little choppy moustache beneath which his teeth glistened when he smiled.

He fell, or pretended to fall, in love with gaunt, raw-boned Millie.

At night, after his day's work, he and Millie would sit silently for hours in the darkened parlour,—silent, except for an occasional murmur of voices. I was curious. Several times I peeked in. But all I could see was the form of my tall aunt couched half-moonwise in Elton Reeve's lap. I used to wonder why they sat so long and still, there in the darkness. . .

.   .   .   .

Once a grown girl of fourteen named Minnie came to visit a sweet little girl named Martha Hanson, whose consumptive widower-father rented two rooms from my grandmother. They put Minnie to sleep in the same bed with me. . .

After a while I ran out of the bedroom into the parlour where the courting was going on.

"Aunt Millie, Minnie won't let me sleep."

Millie did not answer. Elton guffawed lustily.

I returned to bed and found Minnie lying stiff and mute with fury.

.   .   .   .

Elton left, the bridge-work brought to completion. He had a job waiting for him in another part of the country.

It hurt even my savage, young, vindictive heart to see Millie daily running to the gate, full of eagerness, as the mail-man came. . .

"No, no letters for you this morning, Millie!"

Or more often he would go past, saying nothing. And Millie would weep bitterly.

.   .   .   .

I have a vision of a very old woman walking over the top of a hill. She leans on a knobby cane. She smokes a corn-cob pipe. Her face is corrugated with wrinkles and as tough as leather. She comes out of a high background of sky. The wind whips her skirts about her thin shanks. Her legs are like broomsticks.

This is a vision of my great-grandmother's entrance into my boyhood.

I had often heard of her. She had lived near Halton with my Great-aunt Rachel for a long time . . and now, since we were taking in boarders and could keep her, she was coming to spend the rest of her days with us.

At first I was afraid of this eerie, ancient being. But when she dug out a set of fish-hooks, large and small, from her tobacco pouch, and gave them to me, I began to think there might be something human in the old lady.

She established her regular place in a rocker by the kitchen stove. She had already reached the age of ninety-five. But there was a constant, sharp, youthful glint in her eye that belied her age.

She chewed tobacco vigorously like any backwoodsman (had chewed it originally because she'd heard it cured toothache, then had kept up the habit because she liked it).

Her corncob pipe—it was as rank a thing as ditch digger ever poisoned the clean air with.

Granma Wandon was as spry as a yearling calf. She taught me how to drown out groundhogs and chipmunks from their holes. She went fishing with me and taught me to spit on the bait for luck, or rub a certain root on the hook, which she said made the fish bite better.

And solemnly that spring of her arrival, and that following summer, did we lay out a fair-sized garden and carefully plant each kind of vegetable in just the right time and phase of the moon and, however it may be, her garden grew beyond the garden of anyone else in the neighbourhood.

.   .   .   .

The following winter—and her last winter on earth—was a time of wonder and marvel for me . . sitting with her at the red-heated kitchen stove, I listened eagerly to her while she related tales to me of old settlers in Pennsylvania . . stories of Indians . . ghost stories . . she curdled my blood with tales of catamounts and mountain lions crying like women and babies in the dark, to lure travellers where they could pounce down from branches on them.

And she told me the story of the gambler whom the Devil took when he swore falsely, avowing, "may the Devil take me if I cheated."

She boasted of my pioneer ancestors . . strapping six-footers in their stocking feet . . men who carried one hundred pound bags of salt from Pittsburgh to Slippery Rock in a single journey.

The effect of these stories on me——?

I dreamed of skeleton hands that reached out from the clothes closet for me. Often at night I woke, yelling with nightmare.

With a curious touch of folk lore Granma Gregory advised me to "look for the harness under the bed, if it was a nightmare." But she upbraided Granma Wandon, her mother, for retailing me such tales.

"Nonsense, it'll do him good, my sweet little 'Johnnie,'" she assured her daughter, knocking her corncob pipe over the coal scuttle like a man.

.   .   .   .

There was a story of Granma Wandon's that cut deep into my memory. It was the story of the man who died cursing God, and who brought, by his cursing, the dancing of the very flames of Hell, red-licking and serrate, in a hideous cluster, like an infernal bed of flowers, just outside the window, for all around his death-bed to see!

In the fall of the next year Granma Wandon took sick. We knew it was all over for her. She faded painlessly into death. She knew she was going, said so calmly and happily. She made Millie and Granma Gregory promise they'd be good to me. I wept and wept. I kissed her leathery, leaf-like hand with utter devotion . . she could hardly lift it. Almost of itself it sought my face and flickered there for a moment.

.   .   .   .

She seemed to be listening to something far off.
"Can't you hear it, Maggie?" she asked her daughter.
"Hear what, mother?"
"Music . . that beautiful music!"
"Do you see anything, mother?"
"Yes . . heaven!"
Then the fine old pioneer soul passed on. I'll bet she still clings grimly to an astral corncob pipe somewhere in space.

.   .   .   .

A week before she died, Aunt Millie told us she was sure the end was near. For Millie had waked up in the night and had seen the old lady come into her room, reach under the bed, take the pot forth, use it,—and glide silently upstairs to her room again.
Millie spoke to the figure and received no answer. Then, frightened, she knew she had seen a "token" of Granma Wandon's approaching death.

.   .   .   .

In the parlour stood the black coffin on trestles; the door open, for we had a fear of cats getting at the body,—we could glimpse the ominous black object as we sat down to breakfast. And I laid my head on the table and wept as much because of that sight as over the loss of my old comrade and playmate.
Something vivid had gone out of my life. And for the first time I felt and knew the actuality of death. Like a universe-filling, soft, impalpable dust it slowly sifted over me, bearing me under. I saw for the first time into all the full graves of the world.

.   .   .   .

To my great-grandmother's funeral came many distant relatives I had never rested eye on before . . especially there came my Great-aunt Rachel, Granma Gregory's sister,—a woman just as sweet-natured as she, and almost her twin even to the blue rupture of a

vein in the middle of the lower lip. She, too, had a slightly pro-
trusive stomach over which she had the habit of folding her hard-
working hands restfully, when she talked . . and also there came
with her my Great-uncle Joshua, her husband . . and my second
cousins, Paul and Phoebe, their children. The other children, two
girls, were off studying in a nurses' college . . working their way
there.

After the burial Josh and Paul went on back to Halton, where
they worked in the Steel Mills. They left Aunt Rachel and Phoebe
to stay on and pay us a visit.

Paul and Josh were "puddlers"—when they worked . . in the
open furnaces that were in use in those days . . when you saw
huge, magnificent men, naked to the belt, whose muscles rippled in
coils as they toiled away in the midst of the living red of flowing
metal.

. . . .

Phoebe was wild and beautiful in a frail way. She wore a pea
green skirt and a waist of filmy, feminine texture. We instantly
took to each other. She was always up and off, skimming swallow-
like in all directions, now this way, now that, as if seeking for some
new flavour in life, some excitement that had not come to her yet.

We made expeditions together over the country. She joined me
in my imaginary battles with Indians . . my sanguinary hunts for
big game. . . It was she who first taught me to beg hand-outs at
back doors—one day when we went fishing together and found ourselves a long way off from home.

Once Phoebe fell into a millpond from a springboard . . with
all her clothes on . . we were seeing who dared "teeter" nearest
the end. . . I had difficulty in saving her. It was by the hair, with
a chance clutch, that I drew her ashore.

The picture of her, shivering forlornly before the kitchen stove!
She was beautiful, even in her long, wet, red-flannel drawers that
came down to her slim, white ankles. She was weeping over the
licking her mother had given her.

. . . .

"I'm afraid your cousin Phoebe will come to no good end some
day, if she don't watch out," said my grandmother to me, "and I
don't like you to play with her much. . . I'm going to have Aunt

Rachel take her home soon" . . after a pause, "as sure as I have
ten fingers she'll grow up to be a bad woman."

.   .   .   .

"Granma, what is a bad woman?"

.   .   .   .

Aunt Rachel and Cousin Phoebe returned home.   Uncle Josh,
that slack old vagabond with his furtive, kindly eye-glances, came
for them with a livery rig.

.   .   .   .

I think I read every dime novel published, during those years of
my childhood . . across the bridge that Elton had helped build,
the new bridge that spanned the Hickory River, and over the railroad tracks, stood a news-stand, that was run by an old, near-
sighted woman. As she sat tending counter and knitting, I bought
her books . . but for each dime laid down before her, I stole three
extra thrillers from under her very eye.

From my grandfather's library I dug up a book on the Hawaiian
Islands, written by some missionary. In it I found a story of how
the natives speared fish off the edges of reefs. Straightway I procured a pitchfork.

I searched the shallows and ripples of Hickory River for miles
. . I followed Babson's brook over the hills nearly to its source.

One day, peering through reeds into a shallow cove, I saw a
fish-fin thrust up out of the water. I crept cautiously forward.

It was a big fish that lay there. Trembling all over with excitement, I made a mad thrust. Then I yelled, and stamped on the
fish, getting all wet in doing so. I beat its head in with the haft
of the fork. It rolled over, its white belly glinting in the sun. On
picking it up, I was disappointed. It had been dead for a long
time; had probably swam in there to die . . and its gills were a
withered brown-black in colour, like a desiccated mushroom . . not
healthy red.

But I was not to be frustrated of my glory. I tore the tell-tale
gills out . . then I beat the fish's head to a pulp, and I carried my
capture home and proudly strutted in at the kitchen door.

"Look, Granma, at what a big fish I've caught."

"Oh, Millie, he's really got one," and Granma straightened up
from the wash-tub. Millie came out snickering scornfully.

"My Gawd, Ma, can't you see it's been dead a week?"

"You're a liar, it ain't!" I cried. And I began to sob because Aunt Millie was trying to push me back into ignominy as I stood at the very threshold of glory.

"Honest-to-God, it's—fresh—Granma!" I gulped, "didn't I just kill it with the pitchfork?" Then I stopped crying, absorbed entirely in the fine story I was inventing of the big fish's capture and death. I stood aside, so to speak, amazed at myself, and proud, as my tongue ran on as if of its own will.

Even Aunt Millie was charmed.

. . . . . .

But she soon came out from under the spell with, "Ma, Johnnie means well enough, but surely you ain't going to feed that fish to the boarders?"

"Yes, I am. I believe in the little fellow."

"All right, Ma . . but I won't eat a mouthful of it, and you'd better drop a note right away for Uncle Beck to drive in, so's he'll be here on time for the cases of poison that are sure to develop."

. . . . . .

Cleaned and baked, the fish looked good, dripping with sauce and basted to an appetizing brown.

As I drew my chair up to the table and a smoking portion was heaped on my plate, Aunt Millie watched me with bright, malicious eyes.

"Granma, I want another cup o' coffee," I delayed.

But the big, fine, grey-haired mill boss, our star boarder, who liked me because I always listened to his stories—he sailed into his helping nose-first. That gave me courage and I ate, too . . and we all ate.

"Say, but this fish is good! Where did it come from?"

"The kid here caught it."

"Never tasted better in my life."

None of us were ever any the worse for our rotten fish. And I was vindicated, believed in, even by Aunt Millie.

. . . . . .

Summer vacation again, after a winter and spring's weary grind in school.

Aunt Rachel wrote to Granma that they would be glad to have me come over to Halton for a visit.

Granma let me, after I had pleaded for a long while,—but it was with great reluctance, warning me of Phoebe.

.   .   .   .

Aunt Rachel, Uncle Joshua, Cousin Phoebe and cousin Paul lived in a big, square barn-like structure. Its unpainted, barren bulk sat uneasily on top of a bare hill where the clay lay so close to the top-soil that in wet weather you could hardly labour up the precipitous path that led to their house, it was so slippery.

As I floundered upward in the late spring rain, gaining the bare summit under the drizzly sky, a rush of dogs met me. They leaped and slavered and jumped and flopped and tumbled and whined all about me and over me . . ten of them . . hound dogs with flop-ears and small, red-rimmed eyes . . skinny creatures . . there was no danger from them, but they planted their mud-sticky paws everywhere in a frenzy of welcome.

"A hound ain't got no sense onless he's a-huntin'," drawled Paul, as his great boot caught them dextrously under their bellies and lifted them gently, assiduously, severally, in different directions from me. . .

Aunt Rachel's face, ineffably ignorant and ineffably sweet, lit up with a smile of welcome. She met me in the doorway, kissed me.

And she made me a great batch of pancakes to eat, with bacon dripping and New Orleans molasses . . but first——

"Josh, where on earth is them carpet slippers o' yourn?"

Josh yawned. He knocked the tobacco out of his pipe leisurely . . then, silent, he began scraping the black, foul inside of the bowl . . then at last he drawled.

"Don't know, Ma!"

But Phoebe knew, and soon, a mile too wide, the carpet slippers hung on my feet, while my shoes were drying in the oven and sending out that peculiar, close smell that wet leather emanates when subjected to heat. Also, I put on Phoebe's pea-green cotton skirt, while my knee britches hung behind the stove, drying. The men chaffed me.

.   .   .   .

In the industrial Middle West of those days, when the steel kings' fortunes were in bloom of growth, these distantly related kinsfolk of mine still lived the precarious life of pioneer days. Through the bare boards of the uneven floor whistled the wind. Here and there lay a sparse, grey, homemade rag rug. And here and there a window pane, broken, had not been replaced. And an old pair of pants, a ragged shirt, a worn out skirt stuffed in, kept out the draft,—of which everybody but Phoebe seemed mortally afraid. Incidentally these window-stuffings kept out much of the daylight.

Aunt Rachel, near-sighted, with her rather pathetic stoop, was ceaselessly sewing, knitting, scrubbing, washing, and cooking. She took care of her "two men" as she phrased it proudly—her husband and her great-bodied son—as if they were helpless children.

.   .   .   .

"We're going a-huntin' to-day, Johnny,—wan' ter come along?"
"Sure!"
"Wall, git ready, then!"
But first Paul fed the hounds out in the yard . . huge slabs of white bread spread generously with lard. This was all they ever got, except the scraps from the table, which were few. They made a loud, slathering noise, gulping and bolting their food.

.   .   .   .

But we started off without the hounds.
"Ain't you going to take the dogs along?"
"Nope."
"Why not—ain't we going to hunt rabbits?"
"Yep."
"Then why not take them?"
"Put your hand in my right hand pocket an' find out!"
I stuck my hand down, and it was given a vicious bite by a white, pink-eyed ferret Paul was carrying there. I yelled with pain and surprise. I pulled my hand up in the air, the ferret hanging to a finger. The ferret dropped to the ground. Paul stooped and picked it up, guffawing. It didn't bite him. It knew and feared him. That was his idea of a joke, the trick he played on me!

"Yew might git blood-pisen from that bite!" teased Josh, to scare me. But I remained unscared. I sucked the blood from the tiny punctures, feeling secure, after I had done it. I remembered how Queen Eleanore had saved the life of Richard Cœur de Lion in the Holy Land, when he had been bitten by an adder, by sucking out the venom. I enjoyed the thrill of a repeated historic act.

"If we got ketched we'd be put in jail fer this!" remarked Josh with that sly, slow smile of his; "it ain't the proper season to hunt rabbits in, an' it's agin the law, in season or out, to hunt 'em with ferrets," and he chuckled with relish over the outlawry of it.

We came to a hole under a hollow tree. Paul let the ferret go down, giving him a preliminary smack.

"Mind you, Jim,—God damn you,—don't you stay down that hole too long."

"Think he understands you?"

"In course he does: jest the same es you do."

"And why would Jim stay down?"

"He might corner the rabbit, kill him, an' stay to suck his blood .. but Jim knows me. . . I've given him many 's the ungodly whipping for playing me that trick .. but he's always so greedy and hongry that sometimes the little beggar fergits."

"And then how do you get him out again?"

"Jest set an' wait till he comes out .. which he must do, sometime .. an' then you kin jest bet I *give* it to him."

We waited a long time.

"Damn Jim, he's up to his old tricks again, I'll bet," swore Josh, shifting his face-deforming quid of tobacco from one protuberant cheek to the other, meditatively. . .

The ferret appeared, or, rather, a big grey rabbit .. squealing with terror .. coming up backward .. the ferret clinging angrily to his nose .. and tugging like a playing pup.

Paul took Jim off and put him back in his pocket .. he had to smack him smartly to make him let go— "hongry little devil!" he remarked fondly.

A crack of the hand, brought down edgewise, broke the rabbit's neck, and he was thrust into a bag which Josh carried slung over his shoulder.

We caught fifteen rabbits that afternoon.

We had a big rabbit stew for supper. Afterward the two men sat about in their socks, chairs tilted back, sucking their teeth and picking them with broom straws .. and they told yarns of dogs, and hunting, and fishing, till bed-time.

.   .   .   .

The morning sun shone brightly over me through three panes of glass in the window, the fourth of which was stopped up with an old petticoat.

I woke with Phoebe's warm kiss on my mouth. We had slept

together, for the older folks considered us too young for it to make
any difference. We lay side by side all night . . and like a little
man and woman we lay together, talking, in the morning.

We could smell the cooking of eggs and bacon below . . an early
breakfast for Paul, for he had been taken by a whim that he must
work in the mine over the hill for a few weeks in order to earn some
money . . for he was a miner, as well as a puddler in the mills . . he
worked in coal mines privately run, not yet taken into the trust.
He often had to lie on his side in a shallow place, working the coal
loose with his pick—where the roof was so close he couldn't sit up
straight. . .

.   .   .   .

"What shall we do to-day?" asked Phoebe of me, as we lay there,
side by side, "I say let's go swimming?"

"You and me together?" I demurred.

"In course!"

"And you a girl?"

"Can't I swim jest as well as you can?"

"Phoebe, git up, you lazy-bones," called Aunt Rachel, from the
bottom of the stairs.

"All right, Ma!"

"Johnnie, you git up, too!"

"Coming down right now, Aunt Rachel!"

"Hurry up, or your breakfast'll git cold . . the idea of you children
laying in bed like this . . what on earth are you doing up there,
talking and talking? I kin hear you buzzing away clear down here!"

I had been rapt in telling Phoebe how, when I grew to be a man,
I was going to become a great adventurer, traveller, explorer.

Phoebe sat up on the edge of the bed, lazily stretching for a
moment, as a pretty bird stretches its leg along its wing. Then,
her slim, nubile body outlined sharply in the brilliant day, she stood
up, slipped off her flannel nightgown with a natural, unaffected
movement, and stood naked before me.

.   .   .   .   .   '   .

It was a custom of mine to swing my feet as I ate; "just like a
little calf wags its tail when it sucks its mother's tit," my grandmother would say. I swung my feet vigorously that morning, but did
not eat noisily, as my uncles, all my male relatives, in fact, did. I
never made a noise when I ate. I handled my food delicately by

instinct. If I found a fly in anything it generally made me sick
to my stomach.

Feeling warm, I suppose, in her heart toward me, because I
was different in my ways, and frail-looking, and spoke a sort of
book-English and not the *lingua franca* that obtained as speech in
the Middle West, my Aunt Rachel heaped my plate with griddle
cakes, which she made specially for me.

"You're goin' to be diff'rent from the rest, the way you read
books and newspapers," she remarked half-reverentially.

.   .   .   .

A foamy bend in a racing brook where an elbow of rock made
a swirling pool about four-foot deep. Phoebe took me there.

We undressed.

How smooth-bodied she was, how different from me! I studied
her with abashed, veiled glances. The way she wound her hair on
the top of her head, to put it out of the way, made her look like
a woman in miniature.

She dove first, like a water-rat. I followed on her heels.

We both shot to the surface immediately. For all the warmth
of the day, the water was deceptively icy. We crawled out. We
lay on the bank, in the good sun, gasping. . .

.   .   .   .

As we lay there, I spoke to her of her difference . . a thing which
was for the first time brought home to me in clear eyesight.

Phoebe proceeded to blaze her way into my imagination with
quaint, direct, explanatory talk . . things she had picked up God
knows where . . grotesque details . . Rabelaisan concentrations on
seldom-expressed particulars. . .

I learned many things at once from Phoebe . . twisted and
childish, but at least more fundamental than the silly stories about
storks and rabbits that brought babies down chimneys, or hid them
in hollow stumps . . about benevolent doctors, who, when desired
by the mothers and fathers, brought additions to the family, from
nowhere! . .

The house-cat . . kittens and the way they came . . surely I knew,
but had not lifted the analogy up the scale. . .

A furtive hand touched mine, interwove itself, finger with thrilling
finger . . close together, we laughed into each other's eyes, over-joyed
that we knew more than our elders thought we knew. . .

Girls, just at the gate of adolescence, possess a directness of purpose which, afterwards, is looked upon as a distinct, masculine prerogative. . .

Phoebe drew closer to me, pressing against me . . but a fierce, battling reluctance rose in my breast. . .

.   .   .   .

She was astonished, stunned by my negation.

Silently I dressed,—she, with a sullen pout on her fresh, childish mouth.

"You fool! I hate you! You're no damn good!" she cried passionately.

With a cruel pleasure in the action, I beat her on the back. She began to sob.

Then we walked on a space. And we sat down together on the crest of a hill. My mood changed, and I held her close to me, with one arm flung about her, till she quietened down from her sobbing. I was full of a power I had never known before.

.   .   .   .

I have told of the big, double house my grandmother had for renting, and how she might have made a good living renting it out, if she had used a little business sense . . but now she let the whole of it to a caravan of gypsies for their winter quarters,—who, instead of paying rent, actually held her and Millie in *their* debt by reading their palms, sometimes twice a day . . I think it was my Uncle Joe who at last ousted them. . .

.   .   .   .

When I came back from Aunt Rachel's I found a voluble, fat, dirty, old, yellow-haired tramp established in the ground floor of the same house. He had, in the first place, come to our back door to beg a hand-out. And, sitting on the doorstep and eating, and drinking coffee, he had persuaded my grandmother that if she would give him a place to locate on credit he knew a way to clear a whole lot of money. His project for making money was the selling of home-made hominy to the restaurants up in town.

.   .   .   .

I found him squatted on the bare floor, with no furniture in the room. He had a couple of dingy wash-boilers which he had picked up from the big garbage-dump near the race-track.

Day in, day out, I spent my time with this tramp, listening to his stories of the pleasures and adventures of tramp-life.

I see him still, wiping his nose on his ragged coat-sleeve as he vociferates. . .

When one day he disappeared, leaving boilers, hominy and all, behind, I missed his yarns as much as my grandmother missed her unpaid rent.

.   .   .   .

It appears that at this time my grandfather had a manufacturing plant for the terra cotta invention he had stolen from his comrade-in-arms, in Virginia somewhere, and that, during all these years, he had had Landon working with him,—and now word had come to us that Landon was leaving for Mornington again.

My grandmother was mad about him, her youngest . . always spoke of him as "her baby" . . informed me again and again that he was the most accomplished, the handsomest man the Gregory family had ever produced.

.   .   .   .

Landon arrived. He walked up to the front porch from the road. He came in with a long, free stride . . he gave an eager, boyish laugh . . he plumped down his big, bulged-to-bursting grip with a bang.

"Hello, Ma! . . hello, Millie! . . well, well, so this is Duncan's kid? . . how big he's grown!"

Landon's fine, even, white teeth gleamed a smile at me.

Granma couldn't say a word . . she just looked at him . . and looked at him . . and looked at him . . after a long while she began saying his name over and over again. . .

"Landon, Landon, Landon,"—holding him close.

Landon began living with us regularly as one of the family. He went to work in the steel mills, and was energetic and tireless when he worked, which he did, enough to pay his way and not be a burden on others. He performed the hardest kinds of labour in the mills.

But often he laid off for long stretches at a time and travelled about with a wild gang of young men and women, attending dances, drinking, gambling.

Nothing seemed to hurt him, he was so strong.

At most of the drinking bouts, where the object was to see who could take down the most beer, Landon would win by drinking all he could hold, then stepping outside on another pretext . . where he would push his finger down his throat and spout out all he had drunk. Then he would go back and drink more.

Sunday afternoons were the big gambling and card-playing times in our semi-rural neighbourhood.

The "boys" spent the day till dusk in the woods back of Babson's Hill. They drank and played cards. Landon taught me every card game there was.

He could play the mouth-organ famously, too . . and the guitar and banjo. And he had a good strong voice with a rollick in it. And he was also a great mimic . . one of his stunts he called "the barnyard," in which he imitated with astonishing likeness the sounds every farm-animal or bird makes . . and by drumming on his guitar as he played, and by the energetic use of his mouth-organ at the same time, he could also make you think a circus band was swinging up the street, with clowns and camels and elephants.

. . . .

His great fault was that he must have someone to bully and domineer. And he began picking on me, trying to force me to model my life on his pattern of what he thought it should be.

One day I saw him eating raw steak with vinegar. I told him it made me sick to see it.

"Well, you'll have to eat some, too, for saying that." And he chased me around and 'round the table and room till he caught me. He held me, while I kicked and protested. He compelled me, by forcing his finger and thumb painfully against my jaws, to open my mouth and eat. He struck me to make me swallow.

Everything I didn't want to do he made me do . . he took to beating me on every pretext. When my grandmother protested, he said he was only educating me the way I should go . . that I had been let run wild too long without a mastering hand, and with only women in the house. He must make a man out of me. . .

My reading meant more to me than anything else. I was never so happy as when I was sitting humped up over a book, in some obscure corner of the house, where Uncle Landon, now grown the incarnate demon of my life, could not find me.

It was a trick of his, when he surprised me stooping over a book, to hit me a terrific thwack between the shoulder-blades, a blow that made my backbone tingle with pain.

"Set up straight! Do you want to be a hump-back when you grow big?"

His pursuit drove me from corner to corner, till I lost my mischievous boldness and began to act timid and fearful.

Whenever I failed to obey Granma, that was his opportunity. (Millie would cry triumphantly, "*Now* you have someone to make you be good!") The veins on his handsome, curly forehead would swell with delight, as he caught me and whipped me . . till Granma would step in and make him stop . . but often he would over-rule her, and keep it up till his right arm was actually tired. And he would leave me to crawl off, sobbing dry sobs, incapable of more tears.

A black hatred of him began to gnaw at my heart . . I dreamed still of what I would do when I had grown to be a man . . but now it was not any more to be a great traveller or explorer, but to grow into a strong man and kill my uncle, first putting him to some savage form of torture . . torture that would last a long, long while.

He would often see it in my eyes.

"Don't you look at me that way!" with a swipe of the hand.

.   .   .   .

Out in the woods I caught a dozen big yellow spiders, the kind that make pretty silver traceries, like handwriting with a flourish—on their morning webs.

I brought these spiders home in a tin can and transferred them to some empty fruit jars in the cellar, keeping them for some boyish reason or other, in pairs, and putting in flies for them.

Aunt Millie came upon them and set up a scream that brought Uncle "Lan," as we called him, down to see what was the matter. . .

I took my beating in silence. I would no longer beg and plead for mercy. After he had finished, I lay across the sloping cellar door, lumpish and still, inwardly a shaking jelly of horror.

I was wanting to die . . these successive humiliations seemed too great to live through.

.   .   .   .

The grey light of morning filtering in.

Lan stood over my bed.

"—want to go hunting with me to-day? . . shootin' blackbirds?"

"Yes, Uncle Lan," I assented, my mind divided between fear of him and eagerness to go.

In the kitchen we ate some fried eggs and drank our coffee in silence. Then we trudged on through the dew-wet fields, drenched to the knees as if having waded through a brook.

Lan bore his double-barrelled shotgun over his shoulder. He shot into a tree-top full of bickering blackbirds and brought three down, torn, flopping, bleeding. He thrust them into his sack, which reddened through, and we went on . . still in silence. The silence began to make me tremble but I was glad, anyhow, that I had gone with him. I conjectured that he had brought me a-field to give me a final whipping—"to teach me to mind Granma."

"—had to bring you out here . . the women are too chicken-hearted—they stop me too soon. . .

"—Pity your pa's away . . don't do to leave a kid alone with women folks . . they don't make him walk the chalk enough!"

It was about an hour after sunrise. We had come to an open field among trees. Lan set down his gun against a tree-trunk.

"—needn't make to run. . . I can catch you, no matter how fast you go."

He cut a heavy stick from a hickory.

"Come on and take your medicine. . . I'm goin' away to-morrow to Halton, and I want to leave you something to remember me by— so that you'll obey Ma and Millie while I'm gone. If you don't, when I come back, you'll catch it all over again."

My heart was going like a steam engine. At the last moment I started to run, my legs sinking beneath me. He was upon me with my first few steps, and had me by the scruff of the neck, and brought down the cudgel over me.

Then an amazing thing happened inside me. It seemed that the blows were descending on someone else, not me. The pain of them was a dull, far-away thing. Weak, fragile child that I was (known among the other children as "Skinny Gregory" and "Spider-Legs") a man's slow fury was kindling in me . . let Lan beat me for a year. It didn't matter. When I grew up I would kill him for this.

I began to curse boldly at him, calling him by all the obscene terms I had ever learned or heard. This, and the astounding fact that I no longer squirmed nor cried out, but physically yielded to him, as limp as an empty sack, brought him to a puzzled stop. But he sent me an extra blow for good measure as he flung me aside. That blow rattled about my head, missing my shoulders at which it had been aimed. I saw a shower of hot sparks soaring upward into a black void.

I woke with water trickling down my face and all over me. I heard, far off, my uncle's voice calling, cajoling, coaxing, with great fright sounding through it. . .

"Johnnie, Johnnie . . I'm so sorry . . Johnnie, only speak to me!" He was behaving exactly like Aunt Millie when she had St. Vitus' dance.

He began tending me gently like a woman. He built a fire and made some coffee over it—he had brought coffee and some lunch. I crouched white and still, saying not a word.

Landon squatted with his back turned, watching the coffee. His shotgun, leaning against the tree-trunk, caught my eye. I crept toward that shotgun. I trembled with anticipatory pleasure. God, but now I would pay him back! . . .

But it was too heavy. I had struggled and brought it up, however, half to my shoulder, when that uncanny instinct that sometimes comes to people in mortal danger, came to Uncle Lan. He looked about.

He went as pale as a sheet of paper.

"—God, Johnnie!" he almost screamed my name.

I dropped the gun in the grass, sullenly, never speaking.

"Johnnie, were you—were you?" he faltered, unnerved.

"Yes, I was going to give you both barrels . . and I'm sorry I didn't."

All his desire to whip me had gone up like smoke.

"Yes, and I'll tell you what, you big, dirty ——, I'll kill you yet, when I grow big."

.   .   .   .

That night I fainted at supper. When Granma put me to bed she saw how bruised and wealed I was all over . . for the first time she went after Uncle Lan—turned into a furious thing.

.   .   .   .

Shortly after, I was taken sick with typhoid fever. They used the starvation cure for it, in those days. When they began to give me solid food, I chased single grains of rice that fell out of the plate, about the quilt, just as a jeweller would pearls, if a necklace of them broke.

. . . .

With my recovery came news, after many days, of my father.

The Hunkies were pushing out the Irish from the mills—cheaper labour. My grandmother could not afford to board the Hunkies, they lived so cheaply. Renewed poverty was breaking our household up.

My grandmother was about to begin her living about from house to house with her married sons and daughters.

My father was sending for me to come East. He had a good job there in the Composite Works at Haberford. He was at last able to take care of his son—his only child.

. . . .

My grandmother and my aunt Millie took me to the railroad station. I tried to be brave and not cry. I succeeded, till the train began to pull out. Then I cried very much.

The face of my grandmother pulled awry with grief and flowing tears. Aunt Millie wept, too.

No, I wouldn't leave them. I would stay with them, work till I was rich and prosperous, never marry, give all my life to taking care of them, to saving them from the bitter grinding poverty we had shared together.

I ran into the vestibule. But the train was gathering speed so rapidly that I did not dare jump off.

I took my seat again. Soon my tears dried.

The trees flapped by. The telegraph poles danced off in irregular lines. I became acquainted with my fellow passengers. I was happy.

I made romance out of every red and green lamp in the railroad yards we passed through, out of the dingy little restaurants in which I ate. . .

The mysterious swaying to and fro of the curtains in the sleeper thrilled me, as I looked out from my narrow berth.

In the smoker I listened till late to the talk of the drummers who clenched big black cigars between their teeth, or slender Pittsburgh stogies, expertly flicking off the grey ash with their little fingers, as they yarned.

I wore a tag on my coat lapel with my name and destination written on it. My grandmother had put it there in a painful, scrawling hand.

.   .   .   .

The swing out over wide, salt-bitten marshes, the Jersey marshes grey and smoky before dawn! . . then, far off, on the horizon line, New York, serrate, mountainous, going upward great and shining in the still dawn!

.   .   .   .

Beneath a high, vast, clamorous roof of glass. . .
As I stepped down to the platform my father met me.
I knew him instantly though it had been years since I had seen him.

.   .   .   .

My father whisked me once more across the long Jersey marshes. To Haberford. There, on the edge of the town, composed of a multitude of stone-built, separate, tin-roofed houses, stood the Composite Works. My father was foreman of the drying department, in which the highly inflammable sheets of composite were hung to dry. . .
My father rented a large, front room, with a closet for clothes, of a commuting feed merchant named Jenkins . . whose house stood three or four blocks distant from the works.
So we, my father and I, lived in that one room. But I had it to myself most of the time, excepting at night, when we shared the big double bed.

.   .   .   .

Still only a child, I was affectionate toward him. And, till he discouraged me, I kissed him good night every night. I liked the smell of the cigars he smoked.
I wanted my father to be more affectionate to me, to notice me more. I thought that a father should be something intuitively understanding and sympathetic. And mine was offish . . of a different species . . wearing his trousers always neatly pressed . . and his neckties—he had them hanging in a neat, perfect row, never disarranged. The ends of them were always pulled even over the smooth stick on which they hung.
I can see my father yet, as he stands before the mirror, painstakingly adjusting the tie he had chosen for the day's wear.

I was not at all like him. Where I took my knee britches off, there I dropped them. They sprawled, as if half-alive, on the floor . . my shirt, clinging with one arm over a chair, as if to keep from falling to the floor . . my cap, flung hurriedly into a corner.

.   .   .   .

"Christ, Johnnie, won't you ever learn to be neat or civilised? What kind of a boy are you, anyhow?"

He thought I was stubborn, was determined not to obey him, for again and again I flung things about in the same disorder for which I was rebuked. But a grey chaos was settling over me. I trembled often like a person under a strange seizure. My mind did not readily respond to questions. It went here and there in a welter. Day dreams chased through my mind one after another in hurried heaps of confusion. I was lost . . groping . . in a curious new world of growing emotions leavened with grievous, shapeless thoughts.

Strange involuntary rhythms swung through my spirit and body. Fantastic imaginations took possession of me.

And I prayed at night, kneeling, great waves of religious emotion going over me. And when my father saw me praying by the bed-side, I felt awkwardly, shamefully happy that he saw me. And I took to posing a childishness, an innocence toward him.

Jenkins, the little stringy feed merchant, had two daughters, one thirteen, Alva, and another Silvia, who was fifteen or sixteen . . and a son, Jimmy, about seven. . .

It was over Alva and Silvia that my father and Jenkins used to come together, teasing me. And, though the girls drew me with an enchanting curiosity, I would protest that I didn't like girls . . that when I became full-grown I would never marry, but would study books and mind my business, single. . .

After this close, crafty, lascivious joking between them, my father would end proudly with—

"Johnnie's a strange boy, he really doesn't care about such things. All he cares about is books."

So I succeeded in completely fooling my father as to the changes going on within me.

.   .   .   .

Though I had not an atom of belief left in orthodox Christianity (or thought I had not) I still possessed this all-pervasive need to pray to God. A need as strong as physical hunger.

Torn with these curious, new, sweet tumults, I turned to Him. And I prayed to be pure . . like Sir Galahad, or any of the old knights who wore their lady's favour in chastity, a male maiden,—and yet achieved great quests and were manly in their deeds. . .

. . . .

The crying and singing of the multitudinous life of insects and animals in the spring marshes under the stars almost made me weep, as I roamed about, distracted yet exalted, alone, at night.

I was studying the stars, locating the constellations with a little book of star-maps I possessed.

I wanted, was in search of, something . . something . . maybe other worlds could give this something to me . . what vistas of infinite imagination I saw about me in the wide-stretching, star-sprinkled sky!

Dreaming of other worlds swinging around other suns, seething with strange millions of inhabitants, through all space, I took to reading books on astronomy . . Newcomb . . Proctor's *Other Worlds* . . Camille Flammarion . . Garret Serviss as he wrote in the daily papers . . and novels and romances dealing with life on the moon, on Mars, on Venus. . .

During my night-rovings I lay down in dark hollows, sometimes, and prayed to God as fervently as if the next moment I might expect His shining face to look down at me out of the velvet, far-reaching blackness of night:

"O God, make me pure, and wonderful . . let me do great things for humanity . . make me handsome, too, O God, so that girls and women will love me, and wonder at me, in awe, while I pass by unperturbed—till one day, having kept myself wholly for *her* as she has kept herself for me,—give me then the one wonderful and beautiful white maiden who will be mine . . mine . . all and alone and altogether, as I shall be all and alone and altogether hers. And let me do things to be wondered at by watching multitudes, while bands play and people applaud."

Such was my mad, adolescent prayer, while the stars seemed to answer in sympathetic silence. And I would both laugh and weep, thrilled to the core with ineffable, enormous joy because of things

I could not understand . . and I would want to shout and dance
extravagantly.

.   .   .   .

The Jenkins girls were curious about me, and while they, together
with the rest of the feed merchant's family, thought me slightly
"touched," still they liked the unusual things I said about the stars
. . and about great men whose biographies I was reading . . and
about Steele's Zoology I was studying, committing all the Latin
nomenclature of classification to heart, with a curious hunger for
even the husks and impedimenta of learning. . .

Silvia was a rose, half-opened . . an exquisite young creature.
Alva was gawky and younger. She was callow and moulting, flat-
footed and long-shanked. Her face was sallow and full of freckles.

In the long Winter evenings we sat together by the warmth of
the kitchen stove, alone, studying our lessons,—the place given over
entirely to us for our school work.

A touch of the hand with either of them, but with Silvia especially, was a superb intoxication, an ecstasy I have never since
known. When all my power of feeling fluttered into my fingers . .
and when we kissed, each night, good-night (the girls kissed me
because I pretended to be embarrassed, to object to it) our home-
work somehow done,—the thought of their kisses was a memory to
lie and roll in, for hours, after going to bed.

I would pull away as far as I could from my father, and think
luxuriously, awake sometimes till dawn.

.   .   .   .

I hated school so that I ran away. For the first time in my
life, but by no means my last, I hopped a freight.

I was absent several weeks.

When I returned, weary, and dirty from riding in coal cars, my
father was so glad to see me he didn't whip me. He was, in fact, a
little proud of me. For he was always boastful of the many miles
he had travelled through the various states, as salesman, not many
years before. And after I had bathed, and had put on the new
suit which he bought me, I grew talkative about my adventures,
too.

I now informed my father that I wanted to go to work. Which
I didn't so very much. But anything, if only it was not going to
school. He was not averse to my getting a job. He took out papers

for me, and gave me work under him, in the drying department of
the Composite Works. My wage was three dollars a week. My
task, to hang the thin sheets of composite, cut from three to fifteen
hundredths of an inch in thickness, on metal clips to dry.

.   .   .   .

In the Composite Works I discovered a new world—the world of
factory life.

I liked to be sent to the other departments on errands. There
were whirling wheels and steadily recurring, ever-lapsing belts . .
and men and women working and working in thin fine dust, or among
a strong smell as of rubbed amber—the characteristic smell of composite when subjected to friction. . .

And these men and women were continually joking and jesting and
making horse-play at one another's expense, as rough people in their
social unease do.

They seemed part and adjunct to the machines, the workers!
Strong, sturdy, bared forearms flashed regularly like moving, rhythmic shafts . . deft hands clasped and reached, making only necessary movements.

Each department housed a different kind of worker. In the
grinding, squealing, squeaking, buzzing machine shop the men were
not mixed with women.

They were alert, well-muscled; their faces were streaked with
paleness and a black smutch like dancers made up for a masquerade.
Always they were seeking for a vigorous joke to play on someone.
And, if the trick were perpetrated within the code, the foreman
himself enjoyed it, laughing grimly with the "boys."

Once I was sent to the machine shop for "strap oil." I was thrown
over a greasy bench and was given it—the laying on of a heavy strap
not at all gently! I ran away, outraged, to tell my father; as I left,
the men seemed more attentive to their work than ever. They
smiled quietly to themselves.

In the comb department the throwing of chunks of composite
was the workers' chief diversion. And if you were strange there,
you were sure to be hit as you passed through.

The acid house was a gruesome place. Everything in it and for
yards around it, was covered with a yellow blight, as if the slight
beard of some pestilential fungous were sprouting . . the only people
the company could induce to work there were foreigners who knew

little of America. . . Swedes mostly . . attentive churchgoers on
Sunday,—who on week-days, and overtime at nights, laboured their
lives out among the pungent, lung-eating vats of acid. The fumes
rose in yellow clouds. Each man wore something over his nose and
mouth resembling a sponge. But many, grown careless, or through
a silly code of mistaken manliness, dispensed with this safeguard
part of the time. And whether they dispensed with it or not, the
lives of the workers in the acid house was not much more than a
matter of a few years . . big, hulking, healthy Swedes, newly
arrived, with roses in their cheeks like fair, young girls, faded per-
ceptibly from day to day, into hollow-cheeked, jaundice-coloured
death's-heads. They went about, soon, with eyes that had grey
gaunt hollows about them—pits already cavernous like the eye-
pits of a skull.

            .   .   .   .

"Well, they don't *have* to work in there unless they want to, do
they?"
"Ah, they're only a lot of foreigners anyhow."

            .   .   .   .

Three dollars a week was a lot of money for me . . a fortune,
because I had never owned anything higher than nickles and dimes
before.

And my father, for the first few weeks, allowed me to have all I
earned, to do with as I wished. Later on he made me save two
dollars a week.

Each Saturday I went down to Newark and bought books . .
very cheap, second hand ones, at Breasted's book store.

Every decisive influence in life has been a book, every vital change
in my life, I might say, has been brought about by a book.

My father owned a copy of Lord Byron in one volume. It was
the only book he cared for, outside of Shakespeare's *Hamlet*,
together with, of course, his own various books on Free Masonry
and other secret societies.

At first, oddly enough, it was my instinct for pedantry and linguistic learning that drew me to Byron. I became enamoured of
the Latin and Greek quotations with which he headed his lyrics in
Hours of Idleness, and laboriously I copied them, lying on my
belly on the floor, under the lamp light. And under these quotations
I indited boyish rhymes of my own.

Then I began to read—*Manfred, Marino Faliero, Sardanapalus* —*the Deformed Transformed. . . The Bride of Abydos, The Corsair, Lara, The Prisoner of Chillon.*

The frontispiece to the book was a portrait of Byron with flowing tie and open shirt. Much as a devout Catholic wears a gold cross around his neck to signify his belief, with a like devoutness I took to wearing my shirt open at the neck, and a loose, flowing black tie. And I ruffled my hair in the Byronic style.

"I see you're discovering Byron," my father laughed.

Then he slyly intimated that the best of the poet's works I had evidently overlooked, *Childe Harold* and *Don Juan.* And he quoted me the passage about the lifted skirt above the peeking ankle. And he reinforced his observation by grinning salaciously.

From that time on I searched with all the fever of adolescence through Byron for every passage which bore on sex, the mystery of which was beginning to devour my days.

I read and pondered, shaking with eagerness, the stories of Haidee, of Antonia and Julia—the tale of the dream of Dudu. I dwelt in a musk-scented room of imagination. Silver fountains played about me. Light forms flowed and undulated in white draperies over mosaiced pavements . . flashing dark eyes shone myteriously and amorously, starry through curtains and veils.

My every thought was alert with naïve, speculative curiosity concerning the mystery of woman.

Through Byron I learned about Moore. I procured the latter's *Lalla Rookh*, his odes of Anacreon.

From Byron and Moore I built up an adolescent ideal of woman, —exquisitely sensual and sexual, and yet an angel, superior to men: an ideal of a fellow creature who was both a living, breathing mystery and a walking sweetmeat . . a white creation moved and actuated by instinct and intuition—a perpetually inexplicable ecstasy and madness to man.

I drew more and more apart to myself. Always looked upon as queer by the good, bourgeois families that surrounded us, I was now considered madder still.

. . . .

How wonderful it would be to become a hermit on some far mountain side, wearing a grey robe, clear-browed and calmly speculative under the stars—or, maybe,—more wonderful: a singer for men, a travelling minstrel—in each case, whether minstrel or hermit, whether teaching great doctrines or singing great songs for all the world—to have come to me, as a pilgrim seeking enlightenment, the most beautiful maiden in the world, one who was innocent of what man meant. And together we would learn the mystery of life, and live in mutual purity and innocence.

.   .   .   .

The strangeness of my physical person lured me. I marvelled at, scrutinised intimately the wonder of myself. I was insatiable in my curiosities.

.   .   .   .

My discovery of my body, and my books, held me in equal bondage. I neglected my work in the drying room. My father was vexed. He'd hunt me out of the obscure corners back of the hanging sheets of composite where I hid, absorbed in myself and the book I held, and would run me back to work.

.   .   .   .

One day, in the factory, two other boys on an errand from another department, came back where I sat, in a hidden nook, reading Thompson's *Seasons*. One of them spit over my shoulder, between the leaves. I leaped to my feet, infuriated, and a fight began. The desecration of my beloved poetry gave me such angry strength that I struck out lustily and dropped both of them. . .

Rushing in on the uproar and blaming me for it, my father seized me by the collar. He booted the other boys off, who were by this time on their feet again, took me up into the water-tower, and beat me with one of the heavy sticks, with metal clips on it, that was used for hanging the composite on.

Still trembling with the fight, I shook with a superadded ague of fear. My father's chastisement brought back to me with a chill the remembrance of the beatings Uncle Landon had given me.

.   .   .   .

"By God, Johnnie, this is the only thing there's left to do with you." He flung me aside. I lay there sobbing.

"Tell me, my boy, what *is* the matter with you?" he asked, softening. Unlike Landon, he was usually gentle with me. He seldom treated me harshly.

"Father, I don't want to work any more."

"Don't want to work? . . but you quit school just to go to work, at your own wish!"

"I want to go back to school!"

"Back to school? . . you'll be behind the rest by now."

"I've been studying a lot by myself," I replied, forgetting the feel of the stick already and absorbed in the new idea.

By this time we were down the stairs again, and I was sitting by my father's desk. He took up the unlighted cigar he always carried in his mouth (for smoking was not allowed among such inflammable material as composite). He sucked at it thoughtfully from habit, as if he were smoking.

"Look here, my son, what *is* the matter with you . . won't you tell your daddy?"

"Nothing's the matter with me, Pop!"

"You're getting thin as a shadow . . are you feeling sick?"

"No, Pop!"

"You're a queer little duck."

There was a long silence.

"You're always reading . . good books too . . yet you're no more good in school than you are at work . . . I can't make you out, by the living God, I can't . . what is it you want to be?"

"I don't know, only I want to go back to school again."

"But what did you leave for?"

"I hated arithmetic."

"What do you want to study, then?"

"Languages."

"Would you like a special course in the high school?

"Principal Balling of the Keeley Heights High School might be able to work you in. He is a brother Mason of mine."

"I know some Latin and Greek and Ancient History already. I have been teaching myself."

"Well, you *are* a queer fish . . there never was anyone like you in the family, except your mother. She used to read and read, and read. And once or twice she wrote a short story . . had one accepted, even, by the *Youth's Companion* once, but never printed."

.   .   .   .   .

Though it was some months off till the Fall term began, on the strength of my desire to return to school my father let me throw up my job. . .

But we soon found out that, brother in the bond, or not, Principal Balling could not get me into high school because I was not well enough prepared. My studying and reading by myself, though it had been quite wide, had also been too desultory. The principal advised a winter in the night school where men and boys who had been delayed in their education went to learn.

I ran about that summer, with a gang of fellow adolescents; our headquarters, strange to say, being the front room and outside steps of an undertaker's establishment. This was because our leader was the undertaker's boy-of-all-work. Harry Mitchell was his name. Harry, a sort of young tramp, fat and pimply-faced, had jaunted into our town one day from New York, and had found work with the undertaker. Harry had watery blue eyes and a round, moon face. He was a whirlwind fighter but he never fought with us. It was only with the leaders of other gangs or with strangers that he fought.

Harry continued our education in the secrets and mysteries of life, in the stable-boy and gutter way,—by passing about among us books from a sort of underground library . . vile things, fluently conceived and made even more vivid and animal with obscene and unimaginable illustrations. And our minds were trailed black with slime.

And whole afternoons we stood about on the sidewalk jeering and fleering, jigging and singing, talking loud, horse-laughing, and hungrily eyeing the girls and women that passed by, who tried hard to seem, as they went, not self-conscious and stiff-stepping because of our observation . . and sometimes we whistled after them or called out to them in falsetto voices.

.   .   .   .   .

As a child my play had been strenuous and absorbing, like work that one is happy at, so that at night I fell asleep with all the pleasant fatigue of a labourer.

It is the adolescent who loafs and dawdles on street corners. For the cruel and fearful urge of sex stirs so powerfully in him, that he hardly knows what to do, and all his days and nights he writhes in the grip of terrible instincts.

.   .   .   .   .

Yet, in the midst of the turbidness of adolescence, I was still two distinct personalities. With my underground library of filth hidden

away where my father could not find it, at the same time I kept and
read my other books.   The first were for the moments of madness
and curious ecstasy I had learned how to induce.

But my better self periodically revolted.   And I took oath that
I would never again spew a filthy expression from my mouth or do
an ill thing.   I suffered all the agonies of the damned in hell.   I
believe hell to be the invention of adolescence.

Always, inevitably, I returned to my wallow and the gang.

.   .   .   .

We were not always loafing in front of the undertaker's shop.
Sometimes we were quite active.   Many windows and street lamps
were smashed.   And we derived great joy from being pursued by
the "cops"—especially by a certain fat one, for whom we made life
a continual burden.

Once we went in a body to the outskirts of the town and stoned
a greenhouse.   Its owner chased us across ploughed fields.   We
flung stones back at him.   One hit him with a dull thud and made
him cry out with pain, and he left off pursuing us.   It was so dark
we could not be identified.

One of our favourite diversions was to follow mature lovers as
they strolled a-field, hoping to catch them in the midst of intimate
endearments.

.   .   .   .

My father received a raise of a few dollars in salary.   As it was
they paid him too little, because he was easy-going.   The additional
weekly money warranted our leaving the Jenkinses and renting four
rooms all our own, over the main street.   This meant that I was to
have a whole room to myself, and I was glad . . a whole room
where I could stand a small writing desk and set up my books in
rows.   With an extreme effort I burned my underground books.

.   .   .   .

All the women liked my father.   He dressed neatly and well.   His
trousers were never without their fresh crease.   He was very vain
of his neat appearance, even to the wearing of a fresh-cut flower
in his buttonhole.   This vanity made him also wear his derby indoors
and out, because of his entirely bald head.

Every time he could devise an excuse for going to the departments where the women worked, he would do so, and flirt with them.
He, for this reason I am sure, made special friends with Schlegel,

foreman of the collar department. I never saw a man derive a keener pleasure out of just standing and talking with women.

Though, like most men, he enjoyed a smutty story, yet I never heard him say a really gross thing about any woman. And his language was always in good English, with few curses and oaths in it.

.   .   .   .

Our new place was a bit of heaven to me. I procured a copy of Whitman's *Leaves of Grass*, of Darwin's *Origin of Species* and *Descent of Man*. Laboriously I delved through these last two books, my knowledge of elementary zoology helping me to the explication of their meaning.

The theory of evolution came as a natural thing to me. It seemed that I knew it all, before,—as I did, because, in my own way, I had thought out the problem of the growth of the varying forms of animal life, exactly to the Darwinian conclusion.

Whitman's *Leaves of Grass* became my Bible.

.   .   .   .

It was at this time that I made the harrowing discovery that I had been working evil on myself . . through an advertisement of a quack in a daily paper.

And now I became an anchorite battling to save myself from the newly discovered monstrosity of the flesh. . . For several days I would be the victor, but the thing I hugged to my bosom would finally win. Then would follow a terror beyond comprehension, a horror of remorse and degradation that human nature seemed too frail to bear. I grew thinner still. I fell into a hacking cough.

And, at the same time, I became more perverse in my affectation of innocence and purity—saying always to my father that I never could care for girls, and that what people married for was beyond my comprehension. Thus I threw his alarmed inquisitiveness off the track. . .

I procured books about sexual life. My most cherished volume was an old family medical book with charred covers, smelling of smoke and water, that I had dug out of the ruins of a neighbouring fire.

In the book was a picture of a nude woman, entitled *The Female Form Divine*. I tore this from the body of the book and kept it under my pillow.

I would draw it forth, press it against myself, speak soft words of affection to it, caress and kiss it, fix my mind on it as if it were a living presence. Often the grey light of dawn would put its ashen hand across my sunken cheeks before dead-heavy, exhausted sleep proved kind to me. . .

Again: my imagination grew to be all graveyards, sepulchral urns, skeletons. How beautiful it would be to die young and a poet, to die like the young English poet, Henry Kirke White, whose works I was so enamoured of. The wan consumptive glamour of his career led me, as he had done, to stay up all night, night after night, studying. . .

After the surging and mounting of that in me which I could not resist, several hours of strange, abnormal calm would ensue and for that space I would swing calm and detached from myself, like a luminous, disembodied entity. And then it was that I would write and write. The verses would come rushing from my pen. I must hurry with them before my early death overtook me.

There were two visions I saw continually in my sleep:
One was of myself walking with a proud step down a vast hall, the usual wreath of fame on my head. I wore a sort of toga. And of course a great concourse of people stood apart in silent reverence on either side, gazing at me admiringly. With the thunder of their hand-clapping I would wake.
The other dream was of being buried alive.
I lay there, smelling the dark earth, and not being able to stir so much as the last joint of my little finger. Yet every nerve of me ached with sentience . . and I woke gasping, my face bathed with tears and the moisture of terror.

From head to foot hot flushes swept over me. And I was stung with the pricking of a million needles going in sharply at every pore! . . was bathed in cold sweats. And I hoped I was dying.

"Johnnie, what are you doing to yourself?" And my father fixed his eyes on me.
"Nothing, Father!"

"If you weren't such a good boy, I'd—" and he halted, to continue, "as it is, you're a clean boy, and I'm proud of you."

I struggled hard to speak with him, to make a confidant of him, but I could not.

"I wonder," he added with alarm in his voice, "I wonder if you're catching consumption, the disease your mother died of . . you must be careful of yourself."

I told him I would be careful. . .

"I think I'll send you back home to visit the folks this fall."

.   .   .   .

There was a restaurant just around the corner from where we lived in our second story flat—a restaurant which bore the legend stuck up in the window, "Home Cooking." The sign itself was of a dull, dirty, fly-specked white which ought to have been a sufficient warning to the nice palate.

The place was run by a family of three . . there was Mister Brown, the man, a huge-built, blotch-faced, retired stone-mason, his meagre little wife, Mrs. Brown, and their grass-widow daughter, Flora . . . Flora did but little work, except to lean familiarly and with an air of unspoken intimacy, over the tables of the men, as she slouched up with their food . . and she liked to sit outside in the back yard when there was sunshine . . in the hammock for more comfort . . shelling peas or languidly peeling potatoes.

Flora's vibrant, little, wasplike mother whose nose was so sharp and red that it made me think of Paul's ferret—she bustled and buzzed about, doing most of the work.

.   .   .   .

Looking out from our back window, I could see Flora lolling, and I would read or write a little and then the unrest would become too strong and I would go down to her. Soon two potato knives would be working.

"Come and sit by me in the hammock."

I liked that invitation . . she was plump to heaviness and sitting in the hammock crushed us pleasantly together.

This almost daily propinquity goaded my adolescent hunger into an infatuation for her,—I thought I was in love with her,—though I never quite reconciled myself to the cowlikeness with which she chewed gum.

She was as free and frank of herself as I was curious and timid.

"Johnnie, what small feet and little hands you have . . you're a regular aristocrat."

   •   •   •   •   •   •   •

A pause.

I give her a poem written to her. She reads it, letting her knife stick in a half-peeled potato. She looks up at me out of heavy-lidded eyes.

   •   •   •   •   •   •   •

"I believe you're falling in love with me."

I trembled, answered nothing, was silent.

"Kiss me!"

Seeing me so a-tremble, she obeyed her own injunction. With slow deliberation she crushed her lips, full and voluptuous, into mine. The warmth of them seemed to catch hold of something deep down in me, and, with exquisite painfulness, draw it out. Blinded with emotion, I clutched close to her. She laughed. I put one hand over her full breast as infants do. She pushed me back.

"There, that's enough for one day—a promise of sweets to come!" and she laughed again, with a hearty purr like a cat that has a mouse at its mercy.

She rose and carried in the pan of potatoes we had just finished peeling. And I saw her sturdy, but not unshapely ankles going from me as she went up the steps from the yard, her legs gleaming white through her half-silk hose (that were always coming down, and that she was always twisting up, just under her knees, before my abashed eyes). She wore shoes much too little for her plump feet . . and, when not abroad, let them yawn open unbuttoned. And her plump body was alive and bursting through her careless, half-fastened clothes.

She sang with a deep sultriness of voice as she walked away with the pan of potatoes.

   •   •   •   •   •   •   •

"You ought to see my Florrie read books!" exclaimed the mother.

Flora did read a lot . . but chiefly the erotic near-society novels that Belford used to print. . .

"Yes, she's a smart girl, she is."

And the father. . .

"I won't work till the unions get better conditions for a man. I won't be no slave to no man."

.   .   .   .

One sultry afternoon I went into the restaurant and found Flora away. Poignantly disappointed, I asked where she was.

"—Gone on a trip!" her mother explained, without explaining.

From time to time Flora went on "trips."

.   .   .   .   .   .

And one morning, several mornings, Flora was not there to serve at the breakfast table . . and I was hurt when I learned that she had gone back to Newark to live, and had left no word for me. Her father told me she "had gone back to George," meaning her never-seen husband from whom she evidently enjoyed intervals of separation and grass-widowhood.

I was puzzled and hurt indeed, because she had not even said good-bye to me. But soon came this brief note from her:

"Dearest Boy:—

Do come up to Newark and see me some afternoon. And come more than once. Bring your Tennyson that you was reading aloud to me. I love to hear you read poetry. I think you are a dear and want to see more of you. But I suppose you have already forgotten

Your loving

FLORA.

In the absurd and pitiful folly of youth I lifted the letter to my lips and kissed it. I trembled with eagerness till the paper rattled as I read it again and again. It seemed like some precious holy script.

I bolted my lunch nervously and it stuck half way down in a hard lump. I would go to her that very afternoon.

.   .   .   .

The car on which I rode was subject to too frequent stoppage for me. I leaped out and walked along with brisk strides. But the car sailed forth ahead of me now on a long stretch of roadway and I ran after it to catch it again. The conductor looked back at me in derisive scorn and made a significant whirling motion near

his temple with his index finger, indicating that I had wheels
there. . .

At last I found the street where Flora lived. I trailed from door
to door till the number she had given me met my eye. It made my
heart jump and my knees give in, to be so near the quarry. For
the first time I was to be alone with a woman I desired.

At the bell, it took me a long time to gain courage to pull. But
at last I reached out my hand. I had to stand my ground. I
couldn't run away now. The bell made a tinkling sound far within.

·   ·   ·   ·   ·   ·   ·

The door opened cautiously. A head of touseled black hair crept
out.

"Johnnie, dear! *You!* . . . you *are* a surprise!"

Did I really detect an echo of disappointment in her deep, con-
tralto voice?

Frightened in my heart like a trapped animal, I went in. Down
a long, dusk, musty-smelling corridor and into a back-apartment
on the first floor; she led me into a room which was bed-and-sitting
room combined. In one part of it stood several upholstered chairs
with covers on, cluttered about a plain table. In the other part
stood a bureau heaped with promiscuous toilette articles, and a huge,
brass-knobbed bed with a spread of lace over its great, semi-upright
pillows.

"Shall I let in a little more light, dear?"

"Do."

For the blinds were two-thirds down.

"I like to sit and think in the dark," she explained, and her one
dimple broke in a rich, brown-faced animal smile.

"Yes, but I—I want to see your lovely face," I stuttered, with
much effort at gallantry. . .

·   ·   ·   ·   ·   ·   ·

"He's not at home . . he's off at Wilmington, on a job" (meaning her husband, though I had not asked about him). "But what
made you come so soon? You must of just got my letter!"

"I—I wanted you," I blurted . . in the next moment I was at her
feet in approved romantic fashion, following up my declaration of
desire. Calmly she let me kneel there. . . I put my arms about her
plump legs . . I was almost fainting. . .

After a while she took me by the hair with both hands. She

slowly bent my head back as I knelt. Leaning over, she kissed deliberately, deeply into my mouth . . then, gazing into my eyes with a puzzled expression, as I relaxed to her—almost like something inanimate. . .

"Why, you dear boy, I believe you're innocent like a child. And yet you know so much about books . . and you're so wise, too!"

As she spoke she pushed back my mad hands from their clutching and reaching. She held both of them in hers, and closed them in against her half-uncovered, full breasts, pressing them there.

"Do you mean to tell me that you've never gone out with the boys for a good time? . . how old are you?"

I told her I was just sixteen.

"Do you think I'm . . I'm too young?" I asked.

"I feel as if I was your mother . . and I'm not much over twenty . . but do sit up on a chair, dear!"

She stood on her feet, shook out her dress, smiled curiously, and started out of the room. I was up and after her, my arms around her waist, desperate. She slid around in my arms, laughing quietly to herself till the back of her head was against my mouth. I kissed and kissed the top of her head. Then she turned slowly to face me, pressing all the contours of her body into me . . she crushed her bosom to mine. Already I was quite tall; and she was stocky and short . . she lifted her face up to me, a curious kindling light in her eyes . . of a phosphorescent, greenish lustre, like those chance gleams in a cat's eyes you catch at night. . .

She took my little finger and deliberately bit it . . then she leaned away from my seeking mouth, my convulsive arms. . .

"You want too much, all at once," she said, and, whirling about broke away. . .

With the table between me and her. . .

"Wouldn't you like a little beer, and some sandwiches? I have some in the ice box . . *Do* let's have some beer and sandwiches."

I assented, though hating the bitter taste of beer, and hungry for her instead of sandwiches. And soon we were sitting down calmly at the table, or rather, she was sitting down calmly . . baffled, I pretended to be calm.

As she rose for something or other, I sprang around the table and caught her close to me once more, marvelling, at the same time,

at my loss of shyness, my new-found audacity. Again she snuggled
in close to me, her flesh like a warm, palpitating cushion.

"Flora, my darling . . help me!" I cried, half-sobbing.

"What do you mean?" laughing.

"I love you!"

"I know all *you* want!"

"But I do love you . . see. . . "

And I prostrated myself, in a frenzy, at her feet.

"Say, you're the queerest kid I've ever known."

And she walked out of the room abruptly, while I rose to my feet
and sat in a chair, dejected. She came in again, a twinkle in her
eye.

"Don't torture me, Flora!" I pleaded, "either send me away,
or——"

"Stop pestering me . . let's talk . . read me some of that Tennyson you gave me . . " and I began reading aloud, for there was
nothing else she would for the moment, have me do. . .

.   .   .   .

"You're a poet," whimsically, "I want you to write some letters
to me because I know you must write beautiful."

"——if you will only let me love you!"

"Well, ain't I lettin' you love me?"

A perverse look came into her face, a thought, an idea that
pleased her——

"I've lots and lots of letters from men," she began, "men that
have been in love with me."

"Oh!" I exclaimed weakly . . she had just expressed a desire to
add some of mine to the pack . . the next thing that she followed
up with gave me a start——

"Your father——"

"My father?——" I echoed.

"He's written me the best letters of all . . wait a minute. . . I'll
read a little here and there to you." And, gloating and triumphant,
and either not seeing or, in her vulgarity, not caring what effect
the reading of my father's love letters would have on me, she began
reading ardent passages aloud. "See!" She showed me a page
to prove that it was in his handwriting. The letters told a tale
easy to understand. She was so eager in her vanity that she read

on and on without seeing in my face what, seen, would have made
her stop.

A frightful trembling seized me, a loathing, a horror. This was
my father's woman . . and . . I!. . .

I sat on, dumbfounded, paralysed. I remembered his stories of
trips to T— and other places on supposed lodge business . . un-
luckily, I also remembered that several times Flora had been off
on trips at the same time.

"Just listen to this, will you!" and she began at another passage.

She was so absorbed in her reading that she did not see how I was
on my feet . . . had seized my hat . . . was going.

"I'm sorry, Flora, but I've got to go!"

"What?" looking up and surprised, "—got to go?"

"Yes . . Yes . . I must—must go!" my lips trembled.

"Why, we're just getting acquainted . . I didn't mean for you to
go yet."

She rose, dropping the letters all in a heap.

She was the aggressive one now. She drew me to her quickly,
"Stay . . and I'll promise to be good to you!"

I pushed back, loathing . . loathing her and myself, but myself
more, because in spite of all my disgust, my pulses leaped quick
again to hers.

"Sit down again."

I did not listen, but stood.

"I was thinking that you would stay for supper and then we
could go to some show and after come back here and I would give
you a good time."

.   .   .   .   .   .

I staggered out, shocked beyond belief, the last animal flush had
died out of me. All my body was ice-cold.

"Promise me you'll come again this day next week," she called
after me persistently.

She drew the door softly shut and left me reeling down the dark
corridor.

.   .   .   .

I could hardly speak to my father that night. I avoided him.

.   .   .   .   .   .

At the creeping edge of dawn I woke from a dream with a jerk
as I slid down an endless black abyss. The abyss was my bed's

edge and I found myself on the floor. When I went to rise again, I had to clutch things to stand up. I was so weak I sat on the bed breathing heavily. I tumbled backward into bed again and lay in a daze during which dream-objects mixed with reality and my room walked full of people from all the books I had read—all to evaporate as my father's face grew, from a cluster of white foreheads and myriads of eyes, into *him*.

"Johnnie, wake up . . are you sick?"

"Please go away from me and let me alone." I turned my face to the wall in loathing.

"I'll call a doctor."

.   .   .   .

The doctor came. He felt my pulse. Put something under my tongue. Whispered my father in a room, apart. Left.

My father returned, dejected, yet trying to act light and merry.

"What did the doctor say?" I forced myself to ask of him.

"To be frank, Johnnie . . you're old enough to learn the truth . . . he thinks you're taken down with consumption."

"That's what my mother died of."

My father shuddered and put his face down in his hands. I felt a little sorry for him, then.

"Well you've got to go West now . . and work on a farm . . or something."

.   .   .   .

I began to get ready for my trip West. Surely enough, I had consumption, if symptoms counted . . pains under the shoulder blades . . spitting of blood . . night-sweats. . .

But my mind was quickened: I read Morley's *History of English Literature*. . . Chaucer all through . . Spenser . . even Gower's *Confessio Amantis* and Lydgate's ballads . . my recent discovery of Chatterton having made me Old English-mad.

As I read the life of young Chatterton I envied him, his fame and his early death and more than ever, I too desired to die young.

.   .   .   .

The week before I was to set out my father calmly discovered to me that he intended I should work on a farm as a hand for the next four years, when I reached Ohio . . was even willing to pay the farmer something to employ me. This is what the doctor had prescribed as the only thing that would save my life—work in the

open air. My father had written Uncle Beck to see that this pro-
gram was inaugurated.

"I won't become a clod-hopper," I exclaimed, seeing the dreary,
endless monotony of such a life.

"But it will do you good. It will be a fine experience for you."

"If it's such a fine experience why don't you go and do it?"

"I won't stand any nonsense."

"I'd rather die . . I'm going to die anyhow."

"Yes, if you don't do what I tell you."

"I won't."

"We'll see."

"Very well, father, we *will* see."

"If you weren't such a sick kid I'd trounce you."

.   .   .   .

You could approach Antonville by surrey, buggy or foot . .
along a winding length of dusty road . . or muddy . . according to
rain or shine.

My Uncle Beck drove me out in a buggy.

Aunt Alice, so patient-faced and pretty and sweet-eyed in her
neat poverty—greeted me with a warm kiss.

"Well, you'll soon be well now."

"But I won't work on a farm."

"Never mind, dear . . don't worry about that just yet."

.   .   .   .

That afternoon I sat with Aunt Alice in the kitchen, watching
her make bread. Everyone else was out: Uncle Beck, on a case . .
Cousin Anders, over helping with the harvest on a neighbouring
farm. . . Cousin Anna was also with the harvesters, helping cook
for the hands . . for the Doctor's family needed all the outside
money they could earn.

For Uncle Beck was a dreamer. He thought more of his variorum
Shakespeare than he did of his medical practice. And he was slow-
going and slow-speaking and so conscientious that he told patients
the truth . . all which did not help him toward success and solid
emolument. He would take eggs in payment for his visits . . or
jars of preserves . . or fresh meat, if the farmer happened to be
slaughtering.

.   .   .   .

"Where's Granma?" I asked Aunt Alice, as she shoved a batch of bread in the oven.

"She's out Halton way . . she'll go crazy with joy when she gets word you're back home. She'll start for here right off as soon as she hears the news. She's visiting with Lan and his folks."

When I heard Lan mentioned I couldn't help giving a savage look.

Aunt Alice misinterpreted.

"What, Johnnie—won't you be glad to see her! . . you ought to . . she's said over and over again that she loved you more than she did any of her own children."

"It isn't that—I hate Landon. I wish he was dead or someone would kill him for me."

"Johnnie, you ought to forgive and forget. It ain't Christian."

"I don't care. I'm not a Christian."

"O Johnnie!" shocked . . then, after a pause of reproach which I enjoyed— "your Uncle Lan's toned down a lot since then . . married . . has four children . . one every year." And Alice laughed whimsically.

"—and he's stopped gambling and drinking, and he's got a good job as master-mechanic in a factory. . .

He was young . . he was only a boy in the days when he whipped you."

"Yes, and I suppose I was old? . . I tell you, Aunt Alice, it's something I can't forget . . the dirty coward," and I swore violently, forgetting myself.

At that moment Uncle Beck appeared suddenly at the door, back from a case.

"Here, here, that won't do! I don't allow that kind of language in my household." And he gave me a severe and admonishing look before going off on another and more urgent call that waited him.

.   .   .   .

"And how's Granma been getting on?"

"—aging rapidly . ." a pause, ". . hasn't got either of the two houses on Mansion Avenue now . . sold them and divided the money among her children . . gave us some . . and Millie . . and Lan . . wouldn't hear of 'no' . ." parenthetically, "Uncle Joe didn't need any; he's always prospered since the early days, you know."

"And what's Granma up to these days?" For she was always doing sweet, ignorant, childish, impractical things.

"—spirit-rapping is it? or palmistry? or magnetic healing? or what?"

"You'll laugh!"

"Tell me!"

"She's got a beau."

"What? a beau? and she eighty if a day!"

"Yes, we—all her children—think it's absurd. And we're all trying to advise her against it . . but she vows she's going to get married to him anyhow."

"And who is her "fellow"?

"—a one-legged Civil War veteran . . a Pennsylvania Dutchman named Snyder . . owns a house near Beaver Falls . . draws a pension . . he's a jolly old apple-cheeked fellow . . there's no doubt they love each other . . only—only it seems rather horrible for two people as old as they are to go and get married like two young things . . and really fall in love, too!"

I was silent . . amused . . interested . . then—"well, Granma'll tell me all about it when she comes . . and I can judge for myself, and," I added whimsically, "I suppose if they love each other it ought to be all right."

And we both laughed.

.   .   .   .

When Granma heard I was West she couldn't reach Antonville fast enough. She was the same dear childlike woman, only incredibly older-looking. Age seemed to have fallen on her like an invading army, all at once. Her hair was, every shred of it, not only grey, but almost white. There shone the same patient, sweet, ignorant, too-trusting eyes . . there was the blue burst of vein on her lower lip.

After she had kissed and kissed me, stroked and stroked my head and face in speechless love, I looked at her intently and lied to please her:

"Why, Granma, you don't look a day older."

"But I am, Johnnie, I am. I've been working hard since you left." As if she had not worked hard *before* I left . . she informed me that, giving away to her children what she had received for the sale of her two houses (that never brought her anything because of her simplicity, while they were in her possession) she had grown tired of "being a burden to them," as she phrased it, and had hired herself out here and there as scrubwoman, washerwoman, housekeeper, and what not. . .

Later I learned that nothing could be done with her, she was so obstinate. She had broken away despite the solicitude of all her children—who all loved her and wanted her to stay with them.

At last she had answered an advertisement for a housekeeper . . that appeared in a farm journal . . and so she had met her old cork-legged veteran, whom she now had her mind set on marrying.

"But Granma, to get married at your age?"

"I'd like to ask why not?" she answered sweetly, "I feel as young as ever when it comes to men . . and the man . . you wait till you see him . . you'll like him . . he's such a good provider, Johnnie; he draws a steady pension of sixty dollars a month from the Government, and he'll give me a good home."

"But any of my aunts and uncles would do the same."

"Yes, Johnnie, but it ain't the same as having a man of your own around . . there's nothing like that, Johnnie, for a woman."

"But your own children welcome you and treat you well?"

"Oh, yes, Johnnie, my little boy, but in spite of that, I feel in the way. And, no matter how much they love me, it's better for me to have a home of my own and a man of my own."

"Besides, Billy loves me so much," she continued, wistfully, "and even though he's seventy whereas I'm eighty past, he says his being younger don't make no difference . . and he's always so jolly . . always laughing and joking."

.   .   .   .

"We must begin to allow for Granma," Aunt Alice told me, "she's coming into her second childhood."

.   .   .   .

Granma believed thoroughly in my aspirations to become a poet. With great delight she retailed incidents of my childhood, reminding me of a thousand youthful escapades of which she constituted me the hero, drawing therefrom auguries of my future greatness.

One of the incidents which alone sticks in my memory:

"Do you 'mind,' " she would say, "how you used to follow Millie about when she papered the pantry shelves with newspapers with scalloped edges? and how you would turn the papers and read them, right after her, as she laid them down, and make her frantic?"

"Yes," I would respond, highly gratified with the anecdote, "and you would say, Oh, Millie, don't get mad at the little codger, some day he might turn out to be a great man!' "

.   .   .   .

Uncle Beck had a fine collection of American Letters. I found a complete set of Hawthorne and straightway became a moody and sombre Puritan .. and I wrote in Hawthornian prose, quaint essays and stories. And I lived in a world of old lace and lavender, of crinoline and brocade.

And then I discovered my uncle's books on gynecology and obstetrics .. full of guilty fevers I waited until he had gone out on a call and then slunk into his office to read. ..

One afternoon my doctor-uncle came suddenly upon me, taking me unaware.

.   .   .   .

"Johnnie, what are you up to?"

"—was just reading your medical books."

"Come over here," already seated at his desk, on his swivel-chair, he motioned me to a seat.

"Sit down!"

I obeyed him in humiliated silence.

He rose and closed the door, hanging the sign "Busy" outside.

.   .   .   .

At last I learned about myself and about life.

.   .   .   .

The harvesting over, Anders began to chum with me. We took long walks together, talking of many things .. but, chiefly, of course, of those things that take up the minds of adolescents .. of the mysteries of creation, of life at its source .. of why men and women are so .. and I took it for granted, after he confessed that he had fallen into the same mistakes as I, suffering similar agonies, that he had been set right by his father, the doctor, as I just had. I was surprised to find he had not. So I shared with him the recent knowledge I had acquired.

.   .   .   .

And you mean to tell me that Uncle Beck has said nothing to you?"

"Not a single word .. never."

"But why didn't you ask him then .. him being a doctor?"

"How can a fellow talk with his father about such things?"

"It's funny to me he didn't inform you, anyhow."

"I was his son, you see!"

.   .   .   .

Anders had a girl, he told me, confidingly. She was off on a visit to Mornington, at present . . a mighty pretty little girl and the best there was. . .

.   .   .   .

"By the way, Anders, do you know second cousin Phoebe at all?"

"Sure thing I know her . . the last time I heard of her . . which was almost a year ago—she was wilder than ever."

"How do you mean, Anders?"

"Her folks couldn't keep her in of nights . . a gang of boys and girls would come and whistle for her, and she'd get out, sooner or later, and join them."

"I tell you what," I began, in an unpremeditated burst of invention, which I straightway believed, it so appealed to my imagination, "I've never told anybody before, but all these years I've been desperately in love with Phoebe."

Anders scrutinised me quizzically, then the enthusiasm of the actor in my face made him believe me. . .

"Well, no matter how bad she is, she certainly was a beaut, the last time I saw her."

"I'm going," I continued "(you mustn't tell anybody), I'm going down to Aunt Rachel's, after I leave here, and *get* Phoebe." And eagerly and naïvely we discussed the possibilities as we walked homeward. . .

.   .   .   .

After my talk with Uncle Beck all my morbidity began to melt away, and, growing better in mind, my body grew stronger . . he wrote to my father that it was not consumption . . so now I was turning my coming West into a passing visit, instead of a long enforced sojourn there for the good of my health.

.   .   .   .

I found different household arrangements on revisiting Aunt Rachel and her household.

For one thing, the family had moved into town . . Newcastle . . and they had a fine house to live in, neat and comfortable. Gone was that atmosphere of picturesque, pioneer poverty. Though, to

be sure, there sat Josh close up against the kitchen stove, as of old.
For the first sharp days of fall were come . . he was spitting
streams of tobacco, as usual.

"I hate cities," was his first greeting to me. He squirted a brown
parabola of tobacco juice, parenthetically, into the wood-box behind
the stove, right on top of the cat that had some kittens in there.

Aunt Rachel caught him at it.

"Josh, how often have I told you you mustn't spit on that cat."

" 'Scuse me, Ma, I'm kind o' absint-minded."

The incident seemed to me so funny that I laughed hard. Aunt
Rachel gave me a quiet smile.

"Drat the boy, he's allus findin' somethin' funny about things!"

This made me laugh more. But I had brought Uncle Josh a big
plug of tobacco, and he was placated, ripping off a huge chew as
soon as he held it in his hands.

The great change I have just spoken of came over the family
because Phoebe's two sisters, Jessie and Mona—who had been off
studying to be nurses, now had come back, and, taking cases in
town, they were making a good living both for themselves and the
two old folks. . .

I had learned from Uncle Beck, as he drove me in to Mornington,
that, the last he heard of Phoebe, she was working out as a maid
to "some swells," in that city.

.   .   .   .

"Damme, ef I don't hate cities an' big towns," ejaculated Uncle
Josh, breaking out of a long, meditative silence, "you kain't keep
no dogs there . . onless they're muzzled . . and no ferrets, neither . .
and what 'ud be the use if you could? . . there ain't nothin' to hunt
anyhow . . wisht we lived back on thet old muddy hilltop agin."

.   .   .   .

Supper almost ready . . the appetizing smell of frying ham—
there's nothing, being cooked, smells better. . .

Paul came in from work . . was working steady in the mills now,
Aunt Rachel had informed me.

Paul came in without a word, his face a mask of such empty
hopelessness that I was moved by it deeply.

"Paul, you mustn't take on so. It ain't right nor religious,"
said Uncle Josh, knocking the ashes out of his pipe . . he smoked
and chewed in relays. Paul replied nothing.

"Come on, folks," put in Rachel, "supper's ready . . draw your chairs up to the table."

We ate our supper under a quiet, grey mood. An air of tragedy seemed to hang over us . . for the life of me I couldn't understand what had become of Paul's good-natured, rude jocosity. Why he had grown into a silent, sorrowful man. . .

.   .   .   .   .   .

"You kin bunk up with Paul to-night, Johnnie," announced Rachel, when it came bedtime.

Paul had already slunk off to bed right after supper. It was dark in the room when I got there.

"Paul, where's the light?"

"—put it out . . like to lie in the dark an' think," answered a deep, sepulchral voice.

"Whatever *is* the matter with you, Paul?"

"Ain't you heered? Ain't Ma told you?"

"No!"

Paul struck a match and lit the lamp. I sat on the side of the bed and talked with him.

"Ain't you heered how I been married?" he began.

"So that's it, is it?" I anticipated prematurely, "and you weren't happy . . and she went off and left you!"

"Yes, she's left me all right, Johnnie, but not that way . . she's dead!"

And Paul stopped with a sob in his throat. I didn't know what to say to his sudden declaration, so I just repeated foolishly, "why, I never knew you got married!" twice.

"Christ, Johnnie, she was the best little woman in the world—such a little creature, Johnnie . . her head didn't more'n come up to under my armpits."

There followed a long silence, to me an awkward one; I didn't know what to do or say. Then I perceived the best thing was to let him ease his hurt by just talking on . . and he talked . . on and on . . in his slow, drawling monotone . . and ever so often came the refrain, "Christ, but she was a good woman, Johnnie. . I wish you'd 'a' knowed her."

At last I ventured, "and how—how did she come to die?"

"—baby killed her, she was that small . . she was like a little girl . . she oughtn't to of had no baby at all, doctor said. . ."

"I killed her, Johnnie," he cried in agony, "and that's the God's truth of it."

Another long silence.

The lamp guttered but didn't go out. A moth had flown down its chimney, was sizzling, charring, inside . . Paul lifted off the globe. Burnt his hands, but said nothing . . flicked the wingless, blackened body to the floor. . .

"But the baby?—it lived?"

"Yes, it lived . . a girl . . if it hadn't of lived . . if it had gone, too, I wouldn't of wanted to live, either! . . .

"That's why I'm workin' so hard, these days, with no lay-offs fer huntin' or fishin' or anything."

.　　.　　.　　.　　.　　.　　.

The next day I learned more from Rachel of how Paul had agonized over the death of his tiny wife . . "she was that small you had a'most to shake out the sheets to find her," as Josh useter say," said Rachel gravely and unhumorously . . and she told how the bereaved husband savagely fought off all his womenfolk and insisted on mothering, for a year, the baby whose birth had killed its mother.

"At last he's gittin' a little cheer in his face. But every so often the gloomy fit comes over him like it did last night at supper. I keep tellin' him it ain't Christian, with her dead two years a'ready—but he won't listen . . he's got to have his fit out each time."

.　　.　　.　　.　　.　　.　　.

As if this had not been enough of the tragic, the next day when I asked about Phoebe, Aunt Rachel started crying.

"Phoebe's gone, too," she sobbed.

"O, Aunt Rachel, I'm so sorry . . but I didn't know . . nobody told me."

"That's all right, Johnnie. Somehow it relieves me to talk about Phoebe." She rose from her rocker, laid down her darning, and went to a dresser in the next room. She came out again, holding forth to me a picture . . Phoebe's picture. . .

A shy, small, oval, half-wild face like that of a dryad's. Her chin lifted as if she were some wood-creature listening to the approaching tread of the hunter and ready on the instant to spring forth and run along the wind. . .

An outdoor picture, a mere snapshot, but an accidental work of art.

Voluminous leafage blew behind and above her head, splashed with the white of sunlight and the gloom of swaying shadow.

"Why, she's—she's beautiful!"

"Yes—got prettier and prettier every time you looked at her. . ."

"But," and Aunt Rachel sighed, "I couldn't do nothin' with her at all. An' scoldin' an' whippin' done no good, neither. Josh useter whip her till he was blue in the face, an' she wouldn't budge. Only made her more sot and stubborner. . .

"—guess she was born the way she was . . she never could stay still a minute . . always fidgettin' . . when she was a little girl, even—I used to say, 'Now, look here, Phoebe,' I'd say, 'your ma 'ull give you a whole dime all at once if you'll set still jest for five minutes in that chair.' An' she'd try . . and, before sixty seconds was ticked off she'd be on her feet, sayin', 'Ma, I guess you kin keep that dime.'

"When she took to runnin' out at nights," my great-aunt continued, in a low voice, "yes, an' swearin' back at her pa when he gave her a bit of his mind, it nigh broke my heart . . and sometimes she'd see me cryin', and that would make her feel bad an' she'd quiet down fer a few days . . an' she'd say, 'Ma, I'm goin' to be a good girl now,' an' fer maybe two or three nights she'd help clean up the supper-things—an' then—" with a breaking voice, "an' then all at once she'd scare me by clappin' both hands to that pretty brown head o' hers, in sech a crazy way, an' sayin', 'Honest, Ma, I can't stand it any longer . . this life's too slow. . . I've gotta go out where there's some life n' fun!'

"It was only toward the last that she took to sneakin' out after she pretended to go to bed . . gangs of boys an' girls, mixed, would come an' whistle soft fer her, under the window . . an' strange men would sometimes hang aroun' the house . . till Josh went out an' licked a couple.

"It drove Josh nigh crazy.

"One evenin', after this had gone on a long time, Josh ups an' says, 'Ma, Phoebe's run complete out o' hand . . she'll hafta be broke o' this right now . . when she comes back to-night I'm going to give her the lickin' of her life.'

" 'Josh, you mustn't whip her. Let's both have a long talk with

her. (I knowed Josh 'ud hurt her bad if he whipped her. He has a
bad temper when he is het up.) Maybe goin' down on our knees
with her an' prayin' might do some good.' "

" 'No, Ma, talkin' nor prayin' won't do no good . . the only
thing left 's a good whippin' to straighten her out.' "

"O Aunt Rachel," I cried, all my desire of Phoebe breaking out
into tenderness. I looked at the lovely face, crossed with sunlight,
full of such quick intelligence, such mischievousness. . .

You can catch a wild animal in a trap, but to whip it would
be sacrilege . . that might do for domesticated animals.

"Josh never laid a hand on her, though, that night . . she never
came home . . men are so awful in their pride, Johnnie . . don't
you be like that when you grow to be a man. . ."

Then Aunt Rachel said no more, as Paul came in at that moment.
Nor did she resume the subject.

.   .   .   .

Next morning I packed away to visit Uncle Lan. I might as
well go, even if I hated him. It would be too noticeable, not to go.

He was at the train, waiting for me. He proffered me his hand.
To my surprise, I took it. He seized my grip from me, put his
other hand affectionately on my shoulder.

"I've often wondered whether you'd ever forgive me for the way
I beat you. . . I've learned better since."

Before I knew it my voice played me the trick of saying yes, I
forgave him.

"That's a good boy!" and Lan gave my hand such a squeeze that
it almost made me cry out with the pain of it.

.   .   .   .

"Lan," as we walked along, "can you tell me more about
Phoebe. . . Aunt Rachel told me some, but——"

"Oh, she ended up by running away with a drummer . . she hadn't
been gone long when her ma got word from her asking her to forgive
her . . that she'd run off with a man she loved, and was to be
married to him pretty soon. . . Phoebe gave no address, but the
letter had a Pittsburgh postmark. . .

"A month . . six months went by. Then a letter came in a
strange hand. The girl that wrote it said that she was Phoebe's
'Roommate.' " Lan paused here, and gave me a significant look.
then resumed:

"Paul went down to bring the body home, and found she'd been buried already. They were too poor to have it dug up and brought home."

"It seems that the man that took Phoebe off was nothing but a pimp!"

Suicide: early one Sunday morning; early, for girls of their profession, the two girls, Phoebe and her roommate were sitting in their bedrooms in kimonos.

"What a nice Sunday," Phoebe had said, looking out at the window. "Jenny," she continued to her roommate, "I have a feeling I'd like to go to church this morning. . ."

Jenny had thought *that* was rather a queer thing for Phoebe to say. . .

Jenny went out to go to the delicatessen around the corner, to buy a snack for them to eat, private, away from the rest of the girls, it being Sunday morning. She'd bring in a Sunday paper, too.

When she returned, Phoebe didn't seem to be in the room. Jenny felt that something was wrong, had felt it all along, anyhow. . .

She heard a sort of gasping and gurgling. . .

She found Phoebe on the floor, two-thirds under the bed. Her eyes were rolled back to the whites from agony. A creamy froth was on her mouth. And all her mouth and chin and pretty white neck were burned brown with the carbolic acid she had drunk . . a whole damn bottle of it.

Jenny dropped on her knees by Phoebe and called out her name loud. . . "Phoebe, why don't you speak to me!" Took her head in her lap and it only lolled. Then she began screaming, did Jenny, and brought the whole house up. And the madame had shouted:

"Shut up, you bitch, do you want people to think someone's gettin' killed? Ain't we in bad enough already?"

"So Phoebe came to a bad end," commented Lan, "as we always thought she would."

The nearest I came to having my long-cherished revenge on Landon:

Once, in the night, during my week's stay with him, I stepped from bed, sleep-walking, moving toward the room where he and

Aunt Emily lay.   Imagining I held a knife in my left hand (I am left-handed) to stick him through the heart with.

But I bumped terrifically into a door half ajar, and received such a crash between the eyes that it not only brought me broad awake, but gave me a bump as big as a hen's egg, into the bargain.

The dream of my revenge had been so strong in my brain that still I could feel the butcher-knife in my hand . . and I looked into the empty palm to verify the sensation, still there, of clasping the handle.

"—that you, Johnnie?" called my uncle.

"Yep!"

"What's the matter? can't you sleep?"

"No! —got up to take a drink of water."

"You'll find a bucketful on the kitchen table, and the dipper floating in it . . and there's matches on the stand by your bed." A pause.   He continued: "You must of run into something.   I heard a bang."

"I did.   I bumped my head into the door."

.   .   .   .

I visited Aunt Millie last.

I found her a giantess of a woman, not fat, but raw-boned and tall.   Her cheeks were still as pitted with hollows, her breath as catarrhal as ever.   But she had become a different woman since she had married.

Her husband was a widower with three children already before he took her in marriage.   He was a railroad engineer who drove a switch engine in the yards.   He was as short as she was tall . . a diminutive man, but virile . . with a deep, hoarse voice resonant like a foghorn.   The little man had an enormous chest matted with dense, black hair.   It would almost have made a whole head of hair for an average man.   One could always see this hair because he was proud of its possession, thought it denoted virility and strength, and wore his shirt open at the neck, and several buttons lower, in order to reveal his full hirsuteness.

Millie had already given birth to two children of her own, by him.   And she toiled about the house at endless duties, day and night, happy with him, and loving his children and hers with an equal love.   And being adored in turn by them.

It was "Ma!" here and "Ma!" there . . the voices of the children ever calling for her. . . And she, running about, waiting on the youngsters, baking ovensful of bread, sewing, scrubbing, dusting . . and talking, talking, talking all the time she flew about at her ceaseless work. . .

Uncle Dick loved his joke, and the broader the better. As I sat across the table from him, at mealtimes, and looked into his amused, small twinkling eyes, I thought continually of the Miller in Chaucer's *Canterbury Tales*. . .

Millie, too, was not slow at having her joke. She was roughly affectionate of me, in memory of old days. And she continually asked me, with loud, enjoying laughter, if I remembered this, that, and the other bad (Rabelaisan) trick I had played on her back in Mornington. . .

. . . .

But I was glad to see Haberford and the East again. I was all over my desire to die a poet, and young. . . Principal Balling had me come to see him. He examined me in Latin and in English and History. He found that, from study by myself, I had prepared so that I was more than able to pass in these subjects. But when it came to mathematics I was no less than an idiot. He informed my father that he had been mistaken in me, before . . that he had given me a too cursory look-over, judging me after the usual run . . he announced that he would admit me as special student at the Keeley Heights High School.

The one thing High School gave me—my Winter there—was Shelley. In English we touched on him briefly, mainly emphasising his *Skylark*. It was his *Ode to the West Wind* that made me want more of him . . with his complete works I made myself a nuisance in class, never paying attention to what anyone said or did, but sitting there like a man in a trance, and, with Shelley, dreaming beautiful dreams of revolutionising the world.

I awoke only for English Composition. But there, inevitably, I quarrelled with the teacher over her ideas of the way English prose was to be written. She tried to make us write after the Addisonian model. I pointed out that the better style was the nervous, short-sentenced, modern one—as Kipling wrote, at his best, in his prose. We had altercation after altercation, and the little dumpy woman's eyes raged behind her glasses at me—to the laughter of the rest of the class. Who really did not care for anything but a lark, while I was all the while convinced with the belief that they sat up nights, dreaming over great books as I did.

Even yet, though now I know better, I cannot accept the fact that the vast majority find their only poetry in a good bellyful of food, as I do in the *Ode to the Nightingale* and in the *Epipsychidion*. . .

Dissatisfied and disillusioned, it was again a book that lifted me out of the stupidity in which I found myself enmeshed. Josiah Flynt's *Tramping With Tramps,*—and one other—*Two Years Before the Mast*, by Dana. And I lay back, mixing my dreams of humanity's liberation, with visions of big American cities, fields of wheat and corn, forests, little towns on river-bends.

A tramp or sailor—which?

First, the sea . . why not start out adventuring around the world and back again?

Land . . sea . . everything . . become a great adventurer like my favourite heroes in the picaresque novels of Le Sage, Defoe, Smollett and Fielding?

It took me days of talk with the gang—boasting—and nights of dreaming, to screw myself up to the right pitch.

Then, one afternoon, in high disgust over my usual quarrel with the English teacher, I returned to my room determined to leave for the New York waterfront that same afternoon. . .

I left a note for my father informing him that I had made up my mind to go to sea, and that he needn't try to find me in order to fetch me home again. I wished him good luck and good-bye.

Into my grip I cast a change of clothes, and a few books: my Cæsar and Vergil in the Latin, Young's *Night Thoughts*, and Shelley.

.   .   .   .

South Street . . here were ships . . great tall fellows, their masts dizzy things to look up at.

I came to a pier where two three-masted barks lay, one on either side. First I turned to the one on the right because I saw two men up aloft. And there was a boy passing down the deck, carrying a pot of coffee aft. I could smell the good aroma of that coffee. Ever since, the smell of coffee makes me wish to set out on a trip somewhere.

"Hey, Jimmy," I shouted to the boy.

"Hey, yourself!" he replied, coming belligerently to the side. Then, "what do ye want?"

"To go to sea. Do you need anybody aboard for the voyage?"

He looked scornfully at me, as I stood there, skinny, shadow-thin.

"You go to hell!" he cried. Then he resumed his way to the cabin, whistling.

The ship opposite, I inspected her next. It was grand with the figurehead of a long, wooden lady leaning out obliquely with ever-staring eyes, her hands crossed over her breasts.

Aboard I went, down the solitude of the deck. I stopped at the cook's galley. I had gone there because I had seen smoke coming out of the little crooked pipe that stood akimbo.

I looked in at the door. A dim figure developed within, moving about among pots and pans. It was the cook, I could tell by the white cap he wore . . an old, very old man. He wore a sleeveless shirt. His long skinny, hairy arms were bare. His long silvery-grey beard gave him an appearance like an ancient prophet. But where the beard left off there was the anomaly of an almost smooth, ruddy face, and very young, straight-seeing, blue eyes.

When I told the old cook what I wanted, he invited me in to the galley and reached me a stool to sit on.

"The captain isn't up yet. He was ashore on a jamboree last night. You'll see him walking up and down the poop when he's hopped out of his bunk and eaten his breakfast."

The cook talked about himself, while I waited there. I helped him peel a pail of potatoes. . .

Though I heard much of strange lands and far-away ports, he talked mostly of the women who had been in love with him . . slews of them . . "and even yet, sixty-five years old, I can make a good impression when I want to . . I had a girl not yet twenty down in Buenos Ayres. She was crazy about me . . that was only two years ago."

He showed me pictures of the various women, in all parts of the world, that had "gone mad about him" . . obviously, they were all prostitutes. He brought out a batch of obscene photographs, chuckling over them.

It was a German ship—the *Valkyrie.* But the cook spoke excellent English, as did, I later found out, the captain, both the mates, and all but one or two of the crew.

Before the captain came up from below the cook changed the subject from women to history. In senile fashion, to show off, he recited the names of the Roman emperors, in chronological sequence. And, drawing a curtain aside from a shelf he himself had built over his bunk, he showed me Momsen's complete history of Rome, in a row of formidable volumes.

.   .   .   .   .   °   .

"There's the captain now!"

A great hulk of a man was lounging over the rail of the poop-deck, looking down over the dock.

I started aft.

"Hist!" the cook motioned me back mysteriously. "Be sure you say 'Sir' to him frequently."

.   .   .   .

"Beg pardon, sir. But are you Captain Schantze, sir?" (the cook had told me the captain's name).

"Yes. What do you want?"

"I've heard you needed a cabin boy."

"Are you of German descent?"

"No, sir."

"What nationality are you, then?"

"American, sir."

"That means nothing, what were your people?"

"Straight English on my mother's side . . Pennsylvania Dutch on my father's."

"What a mixture!"

He began walking up and down in seaman fashion. After spending several minutes in silence I ventured to speak to him again.

"Do you think you could use me, sir?"

He swung on me abruptly.

"In what capacity?"

"As anything . . I'm willing to go as able seaman before the mast, if necessary."

He stopped and looked me over and laughed explosively.

"Able seaman! you're so thin you have to stand twice in one place to make a shadow . . you've got the romantic boy's idea of

the sea . . but, are you willing to do hard work from four o'clock
in the morning till nine or ten at night?"

"Anything, to get to sea, sir!"

"—sure you haven't run away from home?"

"No-no, sir!"

"Then why in the devil do you want to go to sea? isn't the land
good enough?"

I took a chance and told the captain all about my romantic
notions of sea-life, travel, and adventure.

"You talk just like one of our German poets."

"I *am* a poet," I ventured further.

The captain gave an amused whistle. But I could see that he
liked me.

"To-morrow morning at four o'clock . . come back, then, and
Karl, the cabin boy, will start you in at his job. I'll promote him
to boy before the mast."

.   .   .   .

I spent the night at Uncle Jim's house . . he was the uncle that
had come east, years before. He was married . . a head-book-
keeper . . lived in a flat in the Bronx.

He thought it was queer that I was over in New York, alone . .
when he came home from work, that evening. . .

I could keep my adventure to myself no longer. I told him all
about my going to sea. But did Duncan (my father) approve of
it? Yes, I replied. But when I refused to locate the ship I was
sailing on, at first Jim tried to bully me into telling. I didn't want
my father to learn where I was, in case he came over to find me . .
and went up to Uncle Jim's. . .

Then he began laughing at me.

"You've always been known for your big imagination and the
things you make up . . I suppose this is one of them."

"Let the boy alone," my aunt put in, a little dark woman of
French and English ancestry, "you ought to thank God that he
has enough imagination to make up stories . . he might be a great
writer some day."

.   .   .   .

"Imagination's all right. I'm not quarrelling with Johnnie for
that. But you can't be all balloon and no ballast."

They made me up a bed on a sofa in the parlour . . among all the bizarre chairs and tables that Uncle Jim had made from spools . . Aunt Lottie still made dresses now and again . . before she married Jim she had run a dressmaking establishment.

Uncle Jim set a Big Ben alarm clock down on one of the spool tables for me.

"I've set the clock for half-past three. That will give you half an hour to make your hypothetical ship in . . you'll have to jump up and stop the clock, anyhow. It'll keep on ringing till you do."

. . . .

My first morning on shipboard was spent scrubbing cabin floors, washing down the walls, washing dishes, waiting on the captain and mates' mess . . the afternoon, polishing brass on the poop and officers' bridge, under the supervision of Karl, the former cabin boy.

"Well, how do you like it?" asked the cook, as he stirred something in a pot, with a big wooden ladle.

"Fine! but when are we sailing?"

"In about three days we drop down to Bayonne for a cargo of White Rose oil and then we make a clean jump for Sydney, Australia."

"Around Cape Horn?" I asked, stirred romantically at the thought.

"No. Around the Cape of Good Hope."

. . . .

Early in the afternoon of the day before we left the dock, as I was polishing brass on deck, my father appeared before me, as abruptly as a spirit.

"Well, here he is, as big as life!"

"Hello, Pop!"

I straightened up to ease a kink in my back.

"You had no need to hide this from me, son; I envy you, that's all, I wish I wasn't too old to do it, myself . . this beats travelling about the country, selling goods as a salesman. It knocks my dream of having a chicken farm all hollow, too. . ."

He drew in a deep breath of the good, sunny harbour air. Sailors were up aloft, they were singing. The cook was in his galley, singing too. There were gulls glinting about in the sun.

"Of course you know I almost made West Point once . . had

the appointment . . if it hadn't been for a slight touch of rheumatism in the joints . ." he trailed off wistfully.

"We've never really got to know each other, Johnnie."

I looked at him. "No, we haven't."

"I'm going to start you out right. Will the captain let you off for a while?"

"The cook's my boss . . as far as my time is concerned. I'm cabin boy."

My father gave the cook a couple of big, black cigars. I was allowed shore leave till four o'clock that afternoon. . .

"—you need a little outfitting," explained my father, as we walked along the dock to the street. . .

"I've saved up a couple of hundred dollars, which I drew out before I came over."

"But, Father. . ."

"You need a lot of things. I'm going to start you off right. While you were up in the cabin getting ready to go ashore I had a talk with the cook. . . I sort o' left you in his charge——"

"But I don't want to be left in anyone's charge."

"—found out from him just what you'd need and now we're going to do a little shopping."

I accompanied my father to a seamen's outfitting place, and he spent a good part of his two hundred buying needful things for me . . shirts of strong material . . heavy underwear . . oilskins . . boots . . strong thread and needles . . and a dunnage bag to pack it all away in. . .

.   .   .   .

We stood together on the after-deck again, my father and I.

"Now I must be going," he remarked, trying to be casual. He put a ten dollar bill in my hand.

"—to give the boys a treat with," he explained . . "there's nothing like standing in good with an outfit you're to travel with . . and here," he was rummaging in his inside pocket . . "put these in your pocket and keep them there . . a bunch of Masonic cards of the lodge your daddy belongs to . . if you ever get into straits, you'll stand a better chance of being helped, as son of a Mason."

"No, Father," I replied, seriously and unhumorously, "I can't keep them."

"I'd like to know why not?"

"I want to belong to the brotherhood of man, not the brotherhood of the Masons."

He looked puzzled for a moment, then his countenance cleared.

"That's all right, Son . . you just keep those cards. They might come in handy if you find yourself stranded anywhere."

When my father turned his back, with a thought almost prayerful to the spirit of Shelley, I flung the Masonic cards overboard.

. . . .

After dusk, the crew poured *en masse* to the nearest waterfront saloon with me. The ten dollars didn't last long.

. . . .

"His old man has lots of money."

. . . .

Our last night at the pier was a night of a million stars.

The sailmaker, with whom I had become well acquainted, waddled up to me. He was bow-legged. He waddled instead of walked. We sat talking on the foreward hatch. . .

"I'm glad we're getting off to-morrow," I remarked.

"—we might not. We lack a man for the crew yet."

"—thought we had the full number?"

"We did. But one of the boys in your party strayed away . . went to another saloon and had a few more drinks . . and someone stuck him with a knife in the short ribs . . he's in the hospital."

"But can't Captain Schantze pick up another man right away?"

"The consulate's closed till ten to-morrow morning. We're to sail at five . . so he can't sign on a new sailor before . . of course he might shanghai someone . . but the law's too severe these days . . and the Sailors' Aid Society is always on the job . . it isn't like it used to be."

. . . .

But in spite of what the sailmaker had told me, the captain decided to take his chance, rather than delay the time of putting forth to sea. Around ten o'clock, in the full of the moon, a night-hawk cab drew up alongside the ship where she lay docked, and out of it jumped the first mate and the captain with a lad who was so drunk or drugged, or both, that his legs went down under him when they tried to set him on his feet.

They tumbled him aboard, where he lay in an insensate heap, drooling spit and making incoherent, bubbling noises.

Without lifting an eyebrow in surprise, the sailmaker stepped forward and joined the mate in jerking the man to his feet. The captain went aft as if it was all in the day's work.

The mate and the sailmaker jerked the shanghaied man forward and bundled him into a locker where bits of rope and nautical odds and ends were piled, just forward of the galley .

.   .   .   .

In the sharp but misty dawn we cast our moorings loose. A busy little tug nuzzled up to take us in tow for open sea.

We were all intent on putting forth, when a cry came from the port side. The shanghaied man had broken out, and came running aft . . he stopped a moment, like a trapped animal, to survey the distance between the dock and the side . . measuring the possibilities of a successful leap.

By this time the first and second mates were after him, with some of the men . . he ran forward again, doubled in his tracks like a schoolboy playing tag . . we laughed at that, it was so funny the way he went under the mate's arm . . the look of surprise on the mate's face was funny. . . Then the man who was pursued, in a flash, did a hazardous thing . . he flung himself in the air, over the starboard side, and took a long headlong tumble into the tugboat. . .

.   .   .   .

He was tied like a hog, and hauled up by a couple of ropes, the sailmaker singing a humorous chantey that made the boys laugh, as they pulled away.

.   .   .   .

This delayed the sailing anyhow. The mist had lifted like magic, and we were not far toward Staten Island before we knew a fine, blowing, clear day, presided over, in the still, upper spaces, by great, leaning cumulus clouds. They toppled huge over the great-clustered buildings as we trod outward toward the harbour mouth. . .

The pilot swung aboard. The voyage was begun.

The coast of America now looked more like a low-lying fringe of insubstantial cloud than solid land.

My heart sank. I had committed myself definitely to a three-months' sea-trip . . there was no backing out, it was too far to swim ashore.

"What's wrong, Johann," asked the captain, "are you sea-sick already?" He had noticed my expression as he walked by.

"No, sir!"

"If you are, it isn't anything to be ashamed of. I've known old sea-captains who got sea-sick every time they put out of port."

.   .   .   .

There was a running forward. The shanghaied man hove in sight, on the rampage again. He came racing aft. "I must speak with the captain."

There was a scuffle. He broke away. Again the two mates were close upon him. Suddenly he flung himself down and both the mates tripped over him and went headlong.

The captain couldn't help laughing. Then he began to swear . . "that fellow's going to give us a lot of trouble," he prophesied.

Several sailors, grinning, had joined in the chase. They had caught the fellow and were dragging him forward by the back and scruff of the neck, while he deliberately hung limp and let his feet drag as if paralysed from the waist down.

The captain stood over the group, that had come to a halt below. The captain was in good humour.

"Bring him up here."

The shanghaied man stood facing Schantze, with all the deference of a sailor, yet subtly defiant.

The captain began to talk in German.

"I don't speak German," responded the sailor stubbornly.

Yet it was in German that he had called out he must see the captain.

This did not make the captain angry. Instead, like a vain boy, he began in French. . .

"I don't speak French . ." again objected the sailor, still in English.

"Very well, we'll speak in English, then . . bring him down into the cabin . ." to the men and mates. . . . To the sailor again, "Come on, Englishman! (in derision), and we'll sign you on in the ship's articles."

They haled him below. The captain dismissed the sailors. The captain, the two mates and I, were alone with the mutineer. . . I stepped into the pantry, pretending to be busy with the dishes. I didn't want to miss anything.

"Now," explained the captain, "what's happened has happened . . it's up to you to make the best of it . . we had to shanghai you," and he explained the case in full . . and if he would behave and do his share of the work with the rest of the crew, he would be treated decently and be paid . . and let go, if he wished, when the *Valkyrie* reached Sydney. . .

"Now sign," commanded the mate, "I never heard of a man in your fix ever being treated so good before."

"But I won't sign."

"Damme, but you will," returned Miller, the first mate, who, though German, spoke English in real English fashion—a result, he later told me, of fifteen years' service on English boats. . .

"Take hold of him, Stanger," this to the second mate, a lithe, sun-browned, handsome lad who knew English but hated to speak it.

They wrestled about the cabin at a great rate . . finally they succeeded in forcing a pen into the mutineer's hand. . .

Then the man calmed down, apparently whipped.

"Very well, where shall I sign?"

"Da," pointed the captain triumphantly, pointing the line out, with his great, hairy forefinger . . and, with victory near, relapsing into German.

But, just as it reached the designated spot, the fellow gave a violent swish with the pen. The mates made a grab for his hand, but too late. He tore a great, ink-smeared rent through the paper. . .

Whang! Captain Schantze caught him with the full force of his big, open right hand on the left side of his face. . . *Whish!* Captain Schantze caught him with the full force of his open left, on the other cheek!

The shanghaied man stiffened. He trembled violently.

"Do it a thousand times, my dear captain. I won't sign till you kill me."

"Take him forward. He'll work, and work hard, without signing on. . . No, wait . . tie him up to the rail on the poop . . twenty-four hours of that, my man, since you must speak English—will make you change your mind."

He was tied, with his hands behind him.

The captain paced up and down beside him.

Then Franz (as I afterward learned his name) boldly began chaffing the "old man" . . first in English.

"I don't understand," replied Schantze; he was playful now, as a cat is with a mouse . . or rather, like a big boy with a smaller boy whom he can bully.

After all, Schantze was only a big, good-natured "kid" of thirty.

Then Franz ran through one language after another . . Spanish, Italian, French. . .

The captain noticed me out of the tail of his eye. His big, broad face kindled into a grin.

"What are you doing here on deck, you rascal!" He gave me an affectionate, rough pull of the ear.

"Polishing the brass, sir!"

"And taking everything in at the same time, eh? so you can write a poem about it?"

His vanity flattered, Schantze began answering Franz back, and, to and fro they shuttled their tongues, each showing off to the other—and to me, a mere cabin boy. And Franz, for the moment, seemed to have forgotten how he had been dragged aboard . . and the captain—that Franz was a mutineer, tied to the taffrail for insubordination!

. . . .

Sea-sickness never came near me. Only it was queer to feel the footing beneath my feet rhythmically rising and falling . . for that's the way it seemed to my land-legs. But then I never was very sturdy on my legs . . which were then like brittle pipestems. . . I sprawled about, spreading and sliding, as I went to and from the galley, bringing, in the huge basket, the breakfast, dinner and supper for the cabin. . .

The sailors called me "Albatross" (from the way an albatross acts when sprawling on shipdeck). They laughed and poked fun at me.

. . . .

"Look here, you Yankee rascal," said the captain, when I told him I never drank. . . "I think it would do you good if you got a little smear of beer-froth on your mouth once in a while . . you'd stop looking leathery like a mummy . . you've already got some wrinkles on your face . . a few good drinks would plump you out, make a man of you.

"In Germany mothers give their babies a sip from their steins before they are weaned . . that's what makes us such a great nation."

. . . .

If I didn't drink, at least the two mates and the sailmaker made up for me . . we had on board many cases of beer stowed away down in the afterhold, where the sails were stored. And next to the dining room there was the space where provisions were kept—together with kegs of kümmel, and French and Rhine wines and claret. . .

And before we had been to sea three days I detected a conspiracy on the part of the first and second mates, the cook, and the sailmaker—the object of the conspiracy being, apparently, to drink half the liquor out of each receptacle, then fill the depleted cask with hot water, shaking it up thoroughly, and so mixing it.

As far as I could judge, the old, bow-legged sailmaker had taken out a monopoly on the cases of beer aft. Never were sails kept in better condition. He was always down there, singing and sewing.

Several times I saw him coming up whistling softly with a lush air of subdued and happy reminiscence.

. . . .

Several mornings out . . and I couldn't believe my ears. . . I heard a sound of music. It sounded like a grind-organ on a city street. . .

The Sunshine of Paradise Alley.

And the captain's voice was booming along with the melody.

I peeked into Schantze's cabin to announce breakfast.

He had a huge music box there. And he was singing to its playing, and dancing clumsily about like a happy young mammoth.

"Spying on the 'old man,' eh?"

He came over and caught me by an ear roughly but playfully.

"No, Captain, I was only saying breakfast is ready."

"You're a sly one . . do you like that tune? *The Sunshine of Paradise Alley?* It's my favorite Yankee hymn."

And it must have been; every morning for eighty-nine days the gaudy music box faithfully played the tune over and over again.

. . . .

The ship drifted slowly through the Sargasso Sea—that dead, sweltering area of smooth waters and endless leagues of drifting seaweed. . . Or we lifted and sank on great, smooth swells . . the last disturbance of a storm far off where there were honest winds that blew.

.   .   .   .

The prickly heat assailed us . . hundreds of little red, biting pimples on our bodies . . the cook's fresh-baked bread grew fuzz in twenty-four hours after baking . . the forecastle and cabin jangled and snarled irritably, like tortured animals. . .

.   .   .   .

It was with a shout, one day, that we welcomed a good wind, and shot clear of this dead sea of vegetable matter.

.   .   .   .

As we crossed the equator Father Neptune came on board . . a curious sea-ceremony that must hark back to the Greeks and Romans. . .

The bow-legged sailmaker played Neptune.

He combed out a beard of rope, wrapped a sheet around his shoulders, procured a trident of wood. . .

"Come," shouted one of the sailors to me, running up like a happy boy, "come, see Neptune climbing on board."

The sail-maker pretended to mount up out of the sea, climbing over the forecastle head—just as if he had left his car of enormous, pearl-tinted sea-shell, with the spouting dolphins still hitched to it, waiting for him, while he paid his respects to our captain.

Captain Schantze, First Mate Miller, Second Mate Stange, stood waiting the ceremonial on the officers' bridge, an amused smile playing over their faces.

A big, boy-faced sailor named Klaus, and the ship's blacksmith, a grey-eyed, sandy-haired fellow named Klumpf, followed the sail-maker close behind, as he swept along in his regalia, solemnly and majestically. And Klaus beat a triangle. And Klumpf played an accordion.

"Sailmaker" (the only name he was called by on the ship) made a grandiose speech to the Captain.

Schantze replied in the same vein, beginning,

"Euer Majestät——"

.   .   .   .

The sailors marched forward again, to their music, like pleased children. For custom was that they should have plum duff this day, and plenty of hot grog. . .

Before I was aware, I was caught up by several arms.

For I had never before crossed the line. So I must be initiated.

They set me on a board, over a great barrel of sea-water.

Klumpf gave me a mock-shave with a vile mixture of tar and soap. He used a great wooden razor about three feet long. The officers shouted and laughed, looking on from the bridge.

"What's your name, my boy?" asked Father Neptune.

"John Greg—" Before I could articulate fully the blacksmith thrust a gob of the vile lather into my mouth. As I spluttered and spit everyone gave shouts of laughter. One or two sailors rolled on the deck, laughing, as savages are said to do when overtaken with humour.

The board on which I sat was jerked from under me. Once, two times, three times, I was pushed, almost bent double, far down into the barrel of sea-water. It was warm, at least.

Then a hue and cry went up for Franz. He was caught. He swore that he had crossed the line before, as doubtless he had. But there was now a sort of quiet feud between him and the rest aboard. So in a tumbling heap, they at last bore him over. He fought and shrieked. And because he did not submit and take the ceremony good-naturedly, he was treated rather roughly.

.   .   .   .

My certificate of initiation was handed me formally and solemnly. It was a semi-legal florid document, sealed with a bit of rope and tar. It certified that I had crossed the line. The witnesses were "The Mainmast," "The Mizzen Mast," and other inanimate ship's parts and objects. . .

"Keep this," said Sailmaker, as he handed it to me, "as evidence that you have already crossed the line, and you will never be shaved with tar and a wooden razor again. You are now a full-fledged son of Neptune."

.   .   .   .

On a ship at sea where the work to do never ends, it is a serious matter if one of the crew does not know his work, or fails to hold up his end. That means that there is so much more work to be done by the others.

Franz deliberately shirked. And, as far as I could see, he purposely got in bad with the mates, under whom he had approximately sixty days more of pulling and hauling, going up aloft, scrubbing, and chipping to do. I was puzzled at the steadfast, deliberate malingering of the man. The crew all hated him, too. I have seen the man at the wheel deliberately deflect the ship from its course, in order to bring the wind against the mutineer's belly, hoping to have him blown overboard while he was running aloft. . .

And one night, in the forecastle, someone hurled a shoe at him. A blow so savagely well-aimed, that when he came running aft, howling with pain (for, for all his obstinacy, he seemed to lack courage)—to complain of the outrage, to Schantze—his eye popped out so far that it seemed as if leaping out of its socket! It was ghastly and bloody like a butchered heart.

Later, I asked the sailors why this had been done to Franz. And Klumpf said—

"We had a scuffle over something. We were all taking it friendly . . and Franz bit Klaus through the hand, almost . . then someone threw a shoe and hit him in the eye". . .

.   .   .   .

In about a week, after his eye had healed just a little, I drew Franz apart. We sat down together on the main hatch. I was worried about him. I did not understand him. I was sorry for him.

"Look here, Franz . . don't you know you might get put clean out of business if you keep this mutiny of one up much longer? You can't whip a whole ship's crew."

"I don't want to whip a whole ship's crew."

"The captain had to have another man in a hurry, you know . . but he's really willing to give you decent treatment."

"Did the captain send you to tell me this?"

"Of course not . . only I'm sorry for you."

Franz gave me a broad, inexplicable wink. He smiled grotesquely—from swollen lips made more grotesque because of a recent punch in the mouth "Sailmaker" had fetched him. . .

"Don't trouble yourself about me. I know what I'm doing, my boy."

"What do you mean?"

"I mean that, as soon as I came out of my drunk, and found

myself shanghaied, I *wanted* them to ill-treat me . . there's a Sailors' Aid Society at Sydney, you know!"

"What good will the Sailors' Aid Society do you?"

"You just wait and see what good it will do me!"

"Nonsense, Franz! The captain's willing to pay you off at Sydney."

"Pay me off, eh? Yes, and the old boy will pay me handsome damages, too! . . the sentimental old ladies that have nothing else to do but befriend the poor abused sailor, will see to it that I find justice in the courts there."

"You have a good case against the captain as it is, then. Why don't you turn to and behave and be treated decently?"

"No," he replied, with a curious note of strength in his voice, "the worse I'm treated the more damages I can collect. I'm going to make it a real case of brutal treatment before I leave this old tub."

"But they—they'll—they might kill you!"

"Not much . . those days are about gone . . for a man who knows how to handle himself, as I do. . .

"Well, let us thank God," he finished, "for the Sailors' Aid Society and the dear old maids at Sydney!"

I walked off, thinking. Franz had sworn me not to tell. Yet I was tempted to. It would get me in right with Captain Schantze.

.   .   .   .

We shaped to the Cape of Good Hope with great, southern jumps. We were striking far south for the strong, steady winds.

.   .   .   .

"There was a damned English ship, the *Lord Summerville*, that left New York about the same time we did . . she's a sky-sailer . . we mustn't let her beat us into Sydney."

"Why not, Captain?"

"An Englishman beat a German!" the captain spat, "fui! We're going to beat England yet at everything . . already we're taking their world-trade away from them . . and some day we'll beat them at sea and on land, both."

"In a war, sir?"

"Yes, in a war . . in a great, big war! It will have to come to that, Johann, my boy."

.   .   .   .

The cook's opinion on the same subject was illuminating.

He told me many anecdotes which tended to prove that even England's colonies were growing tired of her arrogance: he related droll stories told him by Colonials about the Queen . . obscene and nasty they were, too.

"Catch a German talking that way about the Kaiserin!"

The old cook couldn't realize a peculiarity of the Anglo-Saxon temperament—that those they rail against and jibe at they love the most!

.   .   .   .   .   .

Off the Tristan da Cunha Islands we ran head-on into a terrific storm . . one that lasted forty-eight hours or more, with rushing, screaming winds, and steady, stinging blasts of sleet that came thick in successions of driving, grey cloud.

It was then that we lost overboard a fine, handsome young Saxon, one Gottlieb Kampke:

Five men aloft . . only four came down . . Kampke was blown overboard off the footrope that ran under the yard, as he stood there hauling in on the sail. For he was like a young bull in strength; and, scorning, in his strength, the tearing wind, he used to heave in with both hands . . not holding fast at all, no matter how hard the wind tore.

.   .   .   .

It was all that the ship herself could do, to live. Already two lifeboats had been bashed in. And the compass stanchioned on the bridge had gone along with a wave, stanchions and all.

.   .   .   .   .   .

There was no use trying to rescue Gottlieb Kampke. Besides, he would be dead as soon as he reached the water, in such a boiling sea, the captain said to me.

The melancholy cry, "Man overboard!" . . .

I took oath that if I ever reached home alive, I would never go to sea again. If I just got home, alive, I would be willing even to tie up brown parcels in grocery cord, for the rest of my life, to sweep out a store day after day, regularly and monotonously, in safety! . . .

The captain saw me trembling with a nausea of fear. And, with the winds booming from all sides, the deck as slippery as the body of a live eel, he gave me a shove far out on the slant of the poop. I sped in the grey drive of sleet clear to the rail. The ship dipped under as a huge wave smashed over, all fury and foam, overwhelming the helmsman and bearing down on me. . .

It was miraculous that I was not swept overboard.

After that, strangely, I no longer feared, but enjoyed a quickening of pulse. And I gladly took in the turns in the rope as the men sang and heaved away . . waves would heap up over us. We would hold tight till we emerged again. Then again we would shout and haul away.

. . . .

"It's all according to what you grow used to," commented the captain.

. . . .

By the time I was beginning to look into the face of danger as into a mother's face, the weather wore down. The ocean was still heavy with running seas, but we rode high and dry.

. . . .

Unlucky Kampke!

His shipmates bore his dunnage aft, for the captain to take in charge. And, just as in melodramas and popular novels, a picture of a fair-haired girl was found at the bottom of his sea-chest, together with one of his mother . . his sweetheart and his mother. . .

Depositions were taken down from his forecastle mates, as to his going overboard, and duly entered into the log . . and the captain wrote a letter to his mother, to be mailed to her from Sydney.

. . . .

For a day we were sad. An imminent sense of mortality hung over us.

But there broke, the next morning, a clear sky of sunshine and an open though still yesty sea—and we sang, and became thoughtless and gay again.

. . . .

"Yes," sighed the cook, "I wish it had been Franz instead of Gottlieb. Gottlieb was such a fine fellow, and Franz is such a son of a ——."

. . . .

. . . I have left something out.

At the beginning of the voyage Captain Schantze housed a flock of two dozen chickens in a coop under the forecastle . . in order to insure himself of fresh eggs during the voyage. . .

And for fresh meat, he had a huge sow hauled aboard—to be killed later on. . .

.   .   .   .

One morning, when I went forward to fetch the captain's and mates' breakfast, I found the cook all white and ghastly. . .

"What's the matter, Cook?"

"To-day's the day I've got to butcher the sow," he complained, "and I'd give anything to have someone else do it. . . I've made such a pet of her during the voyage . . and she's so intelligent and affectionate . . she's decenter than lots of human beings I've met."

I kept to the cabin while the butchering was going on.

The cook, the next day, with tears streaming down his face, told me how trusting the sow had been to the last moment. . .

"I'll never forget the look in her eyes when she realised what I had done to her when I cut her throat."

"And I'll never be able to eat any of her. I'd throw it up as fast as it went down . . much as I do like good, fresh pork."

.   .   .   .

The ship-boys, Karl and Albert, always stole the eggs, the captain was sure, as soon as they were laid, though he was never able to catch them at it.

"Run," he would shout hurriedly to me, "there! I hear the hens cackling. They've laid an egg."

I'd run. But there'd be no egg. Someone would have reached the nest, from the forecastle, before I did.

Because the eggs were always stolen as soon as laid, the captain decreed the slaughter of the hens, too . . not a rooster among them . . the hens were frankly unhappy, because of this. . .

.   .   .   .

The last hen was to be slain. Pursued, she flew far out over the still ocean. Further and further she flew, keeping up her heavy body as if by an effort of will.

"Come back! Don't be such a damn fool!" I shouted in my excitement.

Everybody was watching when the chicken would light . . how long it could keep up. . .

As soon as I shouted "come back!" the bird, as if giving heed to my exhortation, slowly veered, and turned toward the ship again. Everybody had laughed till they nearly sank on deck, at my naïve words.

Now a spontaneous cheer went up, as the hen slowly tacked and started back. . .

It was still weather, but the ship was moving ahead. . .

"She won't make it!"

"She will!"

Another great shout. She lit astern, right by the wheel. Straightway she began running forward, wings spread in genuine triumph.

"Catch her!" shouted the mate.

Nobody obeyed him; they stood by laughing and cheering, till the hen made safety beneath the forecastle head.

.   .   .   .

She was spared for three days.

.   .   .   .

"If you ever tell the captain on us," First Mate Miller threatened, as he and the second mate stood over a barrel of Kümmel, mixing hot water with it, to fill up for what they had stolen, "if you ever tell, I'll see that you go overboard—by accident . . when we clear for Iqueque, after we unload at Sydney."

"Why should I tell? It's none of my business!"

I had come upon them, as they were at work. The cook had sent me into the store-room for some potatoes.

.   .   .   .

Miller, the first mate, was quite fat and bleary-eyed. He used to go about sweating clear through his clothes on warm days. At such times I could detect the faint reek of alcohol coming through his pores. It's a wonder Schantze didn't notice it, as I did.

.   .   .   .

Sometimes, at meals, the captain would swear and say, sniffing at the edge of his glass, "What's the matter with this damned brandy . . it tastes more like water than a good drink of liquor."

As he set his glass down in disgust, the mates would solemnly and hypocritically go through the same operation, and express their wonder with the captain's.

Finally one of the latter would remark sagely, "they always try to palm off bad stuff on ships."

In spite of my fear of the mates, I once had to stuff a dirty dish-rag down my mouth to keep from laughing outright. The greasy rag made me gag and almost vomit.

"And what's the matter with you?" inquired Schantze, glaring into the pantry at me, while the two mates also glowered, for a different reason.

. . . .

"You skinny Yankee," said the captain, taking me by the ear, rather painfully, several days after that incident, "I'm sure some-one's drinking my booze. Could it be you, in spite of all your talk about not drinking? You Anglo-Saxons are such dirty hypocrites."

"Indeed, no, sir,—it isn't me."

"Well, this cabin's in your care, and so is the storeroom. You keep a watch-out and find out for me who it is. . . I don't think its Miller or the second mate . . it must be either the cook or that old rogue of a sailmaker. . .

"Or it might be some of the crew," he further speculated, "but anyhow, it's your job to take care of the cabin, as I said be-fore. . .

"Remember this—all sailors are thieves, aboard ship, if the chance to take anything good to eat or drink comes their way."

I promised to keep a good look-out.

On the other hand. . .

"Mind you keep your mouth shut . . and don't find things so damned funny, neither," this from the first mate, early one morn-ing, as I scrubbed the floors. He stirred my posteriors heavily with a booted foot, in emphasis.

. . . .

The sea kicked backward in long, speedy trails of foam, lacing the surface of a grey-green waste of waves. . .

. . . . . .

When I had any spare time, I used to lie in the net under the bowsprit, and read. From there I could look back on the entire ship as it sailed ahead, every sail spread, a magnificent sight.

One day, as I lay there, reading Shelley, or was it my Vergil that I was puzzling out line by line, with occasional glances at the great ship seeming to sail into me—myself poised outward in space——

There came a great surge of water. I leaped up in the net,

bouncing like a circus acrobat.   My book fell out of my hand into
the sea.

I looked up, and saw fully half the crew grinning down at me.
The mate stood over me.   A bucket that still dripped water in his
hand showed me where the water had come from.

"Come up out of there!   The captain's been bawling for you
for half an hour . . we thought you'd gone overboard."

I came along the net, drenched and forlorn.

"What in hell were you doing down there?"

"I—I was thinking," I stammered.

"He was thinking," echoed the mate scornfully.   "Well, thinking
will never make a sailor of you."

Boisterous laughter.

"After this do your thinking where we can find you when you're
wanted."

As I walked aft, the mate went with me pace for pace, poking more
fun at me.   To which I dared not answer, as I was impelled, because
he was strong and I was very frail . . and always, when on the
verge of danger, or a physical encounter, the memory of my Uncle
Lan's beatings would now crash into my memory like an earthquake,
and render my resolution and sinews all a-tremble and unstrung.

I was of a mind to tell the captain *who* was drinking his liquor
—but here again I feared, and cursed myself for fearing.

When the mate told him of where he had found me, at last—what
he had done—what I had said—Schantze laughed. . .

But, later on, he sympathised with me and unexpectedly remarked:

"Johann, how can you expect a heavy-minded numbskull like
Miller to understand!"

Then, laughing, he seized me by the ear—his usual gesture of
fondness for me——

"Remember me if you ever write a book about this voyage, and
don't give me too black a name!   I'm not so bad, am I, eh?"

.   .   .   .

The Australian coast had lain blue across the horizon for several
days. ·

"Watch me to-morrow!" whispered Franz cryptically to me as
he strolled lazily by. . .

.   .   .   .

Next day, around noon, I heard a big rumpus on the main deck. I hurried up from the cabin.

There lay Franz, sprawled on his back like a huge, lazy dog, and the mate was shaking his belly with his foot on top of it, just as one plays with a dog . . but to show he was not playing, he delivered the prostrate form of the sailor a swift succession of kicks in the ribs. . .

"You won't work any longer, you say?"

"No."

"I'll kick your guts out."

"Very well."

"Stand on your feet like a man."

"What for? You'll only knock me down again!" and Franz grinned comically and grotesquely upward, through the gap in his mouth where two of his teeth had been punched out earlier in the voyage.

It was easy to see that Franz's curious attitude of non-resistance had the mate puzzled what to do next. All the sailors indulged in furtive laughter. None of them had a very deep-rooted love for Miller, and, for the first time, they rather sympathised with the man who had been shanghaied . . some of them even snickered audibly . . and straightway grew intent on their work. . .

Miller turned irritably on them. "And what's the matter with *you!*" . .

"Bring him up here!" shouted Captain Schantze.

Four sailors picked Franz up and carried him, unresisting, bumping his back on the steps as he sagged like a sack half full of flour. . .

"Here! I've had about enough of this!" cried the captain, furious, "tie him to the rail again! . ."

"Now, we'll leave you there, on bread and water, till you say you'll work."

"What does it matter what you do," sauced Franz; "we'll be in port in four days . . and then you'll see what I'll do!"

.   .   .   .

"What's that?" cried the captain. Then catching an inkling of Franz's scheme, he hit the man a quick, hard blow in the mouth with his clenched fist.

"Give him another!" urged the mate.

But the captain's rage was over, though Franz sent him a bold, mocking laugh, even as the blood trickled down in a tiny red stream from where his mouth had been struck.

I never saw such courage of its kind.

They left him there for ten hours. But he stood without a sign of exhaustion or giving in. And they untied him. And let him loose.

And, till we hove to at Dalghety's Wharf, in Sydney Harbour, unnoticed, Franz, the Alsace-Lorrainer, roamed the boat at will, like a passenger.

"Wait till I get on shore . . this little shanghaiing party of the captain's will cost him a lot of hard money," he said, in a low voice, to me,—standing idly by, his hands in his pockets, while I was bending over the brass on the bridge railing, polishing away.

"But they've nearly killed you, Franz . . will it be worth it?"

"All I can say is I wish they'd use me rougher."

"You know, Franz, I'm not a bit sorry for you now . . I was at first."

"That so? . . I don't need anybody to be sorry for me. In a week or so, when I have won my suit against the captain through the Sailors' Aid Society, I'll be rolling in money . . then you can be sorry for the captain."

    .   .   .   .

Sydney Harbour . . the air alive with sunlight and white flutterings of sea gulls a-wing . . alive with pleasure boats that leaned here and yon on white sails.

    .   .   .   .

Now that we were safe in harbour, I hesitated whether to run away or continue with the ship. For I had signed on to complete the voyage, via Iqueque, on the West Coast of South America, to Hamburg. . . I hesitated, I say, because, on shipboard, you're at least sure of food and a place to sleep. . .

Karl and I had been set to work at giving the cabin a thorough overhauling. We fooled away much of our time looking into the captain's collections of erotic pictures and photographs . . and his obscene books in every language.

And we discovered under the sofa-seat that was built against the side, a great quantity of French syrups and soda waters. So we spent quite a little of our time in mixing temperance drinks for ourselves.

Cautiously I spoke to the cook about what Karl and I were doing. For he knew, of course, that I knew of his marauding . . and of the mates' and sailmaker's . . so it was safe to tell him.

"You'd better be careful," the cook admonished me.

"But what could Captain Schantze want with so many bottles of syrup and soda water aboard?"

"The English custom's officer who comes aboard here is an old friend of Schantze's, and a teetotaler . . so the captain always treats him to soda water."

"But Karl and I have drunk it all up already," I confessed slowly.

"You'll both catch a good hiding then when he calls for it and finds there is none."

The next day the customs man came aboard.

"Have a drink, Mr. Wollaston?" Schantze asked him.

"Yes, but nothing strong," for probably the tenth occasion came the answer.

Then offhandedly, the captain—as if he had not, perhaps, said the same thing for ten previous voyages: "I have some fine French soda water and syrup in my private locker, perhaps you'd like some of that, Mr. Wollaston?"

Mr. Wollaston, whose face and nose was so ruddy and pimply anyone would take him for a toper, answers: "Yes, a little of that won't do any harm, Captain!"

"Karl!—Johann!" We had been listening, frightened, to the colloquy. We came out, trembling.

"Look under the cushions in my cabin . . bring out some of the syrup and soda water you find there."

"Very well, sir!"

We both hurried in . . stood facing each other, too scared to laugh at the situation. The captain had a heavy hand—and carried a heavy cane when he went ashore. He had the cane with him now.

After a long time: "You tell him there is none," whispered Karl.

"Well, what's wrong in there?" cried Schantze impatiently.

"We can't find a single bottle, sir!" I repeated, louder.

"What? Come out here! Speak louder! What did you say?" ,

"We can't find a single bottle, sir!" I murmured, almost inaudibly.

Then Karl, stammering, reinforced me with, "There are a lot of empty bottles here, sir!"

"What does this mean? Every voyage for years I have had soda and French syrup in my locker for Mr. Wollaston."

"Oh, don't mind me," deprecated the little customs man, at the same time as furious as his host.

Karl had already began to blubber in anticipation of the whipping due. The captain laid his heavy cane on everywhere. The boy fell at his feet, bawling louder, less from fear than from the knowledge that his abjectness would please the captain's vanity and induce him to let up sooner.

"Now *you* come here!" Schantze beckoned me.

He raised the cane at me. But, to my own surprise, something brave and strange entered into me. I would not be humiliated before a countryman of my mother's, that was what it was!

I looked the captain straight in the eye.

"Sir, I did not do it, and I won't be whipped!"

"Wha-at!" ejaculated Schantze, astonished at my novel behaviour.

"I didn't touch the syrup." Karl looked at me, astonished and incredulous at my audacity, through his tear-stained face.

The captain stepped back from me.

I must be telling the truth to be behaving so differently.

"Get to your bunk then!" he commanded.

I obeyed.

"Who is he?" . . I heard the little customs man ask the skipper; "he doesn't talk like an Englishman."

"He isn't. He just a damn-fool Yankee boy I picked up in New York."

.　　　.　　　.　　　.　　　.　　　.　　　.

They had rounded Franz up and locked him away. The captain was determined to frustrate his little scheme for reimbursement, which he had by this time guessed.

I lie. I must tell the truth in these memoirs.

I had told on him.

But my motive was only an itch to see what would then take place. But when I saw that the issue would be an obvious one: that he would merely be spirited forth to sea again, and this time, *forced* to work, I felt a little sorry for the man. At the same time,

I admit I wanted to observe the dénouement myself, of his case . . and as I now intended to desert the ship, it would have to take place in Sydney.

So, on the second night of Franz's incarceration, when nearly everybody was away on shore-leave, I took the captain's bunch of keys, and I let the shanghaied man, the mutineer, the man from Alsace-Lorraine—out!

It was not a very dark night. Franz stole along like a rat till he reached the centre of the dock. There he gave a great shout of defiance . . why, I learned later. . .

The *Lord Summerville,* which had, after all, beat us in by two days, despite Captain Schantze's boast, was lying on the other side of our dock. And her mate and several sailors thus became witnesses of what happened.

The shout brought, of course, our few men who remained on watch, on deck, and over on the dock after Franz . . who allowed himself to be caught . . the dock was English ground . . the ship was German . . a good point legally, as the canny Franz had foreseen.

His clothes were almost torn from his body.

Miller accidentally showed up, coming back from shore. And he joined in.

"Come back with us, you verfluchte *Alsatz*-Lothringer."

The Englishmen from the *Lord Summerville* now began calling out, "Let him alone!" and "I say, give the lad fair play!"

Some of them leaped down on the dock in a trice.

"Who the hell let him out?" roared the mate.

I stood on deck, holding my breath, and ready to bolt in case Franz betrayed me. But nevertheless my blood was running high and happy over the excitement I had caused by unlocking the door.

"No one let me out. I picked the lock. Will that suit you?" lied Franz, protecting me.

"What's the lad been and done?" asked the mate of the *Lord Summerville.*

"I was shanghaied in New York," put in Franz swiftly, "and I demand English justice."

"And you shall get it, my man!" answered the mate proudly, "for you have been assaulted on English ground, as I'll stand witness."

A whistle was blown. Men came running. Soon Franz was outside the jurisdiction of Germany.

.   .   .   .

The next day Captain Schantze stalked about, hardly speaking to Miller. He was angry and laid the blame at the latter's door.

"Miller, why in the name of God didn't you guard that fellow better? An English court . . you know what *they'll* do to us!"

Miller spread his hands outward, shrugged his shoulders expressively, remained in silence. The two mates and the captain ate the rest of their supper in a silence that bristled.

The ship was detained for ten days more after its cargo had been unloaded.

At the trial, during which the "old maids" and The Sailors' Aid Society came to the fore, Captain Schantze roared his indignant best—so much so that the judge warned him that he was not on his ship but on English ground. . .

Franz got a handsome verdict in his favour, of course.

And for several days he was seen, rolling drunk about the streets, by our boys, who now looked on him as a pretty clever person.

.   .   .   .

It was my time to run away—if I ever intended to. Within the next day or so we were to take on coal for the West Coast. We were to load down so heavily, the mate, who had conceived a hatred of me, informed me, that even in fair weather the scuppers would be a-wash. Significantly he added there would be much danger for a man who was not liked aboard a certain ship . . by the mates . . much danger of such a person's being washed overboard. For the waves, you know, washed over the deck of so heavily loaded a ship at will.

.   .   .   .   .   .

On the *Lord Summerville* was a mad Pennsylvania boy who had, like myself, gone to sea for the first time . . but he had had no uncle to beat timidity into him . . and he had dared ship as able seaman on the big sky-sailed lime-juicer, and had gloriously acquitted himself.

He was a tall, rangy young bullock of a lad. He could split any door with his fist. He liked to drink and fight. And he liked women in the grog-house sense.

One of his chief exploits had been the punching of the **second**

mate in the jaw when both were high a-loft. Then he had caught
him about the waist, and held him till he came to, to keep him
from falling. The mate had used bad language at him.

Hoppner had worked from the first as if he had been born to
the sea.

He and I met in a saloon. The plump little barmaid had made
him what she called, "A man's drink," while me she had served
contemptuously with a ginger ale.

Hoppner boasted of his exploits. I, of mine.

"I tell you what, Gregory, since we're both jumping ship here,
let's be pals for awhile and travel together."

"I'm with you, Hoppner."

"And why jump off empty-handed, since we are jumping off?"

"What is it you're driving at?"

"There ought to be a lot of loot on two boats!"

"Suppose we get caught?" I asked cautiously.

"Anybody that's worth a damn will take a chance in this world.
Aren't you game to take a chance?"

"Of course I'm game."

"Well, then, you watch your chance and I'll watch mine. I'll
hook into everything valuable that's liftable on my ship and you
tend to yours in the same fashion."

We struck hands in partnership, parted, and agreed to meet at
the wharf-gate the next night, just after dark, he with his loot, I
with mine.

.   .   .   .

I spent the morning of the following day prospecting. I had seen
the captain put the ship's money for the paying of the crew in a
drawer, and turn the key.

But first, with a curious primitive instinct, I fixed on a small
ham and a loaf of rye bread as part of the projected booty, in
spite of the fact that, if I but laid hands on the ship's money, I
would have quite a large sum.

It was the piquaresque romance of what I was about to do that
moved me. The romance of the deed, not the possession of the
objects stolen, that appealed to my imagination. I pictured my
comrade and myself going overland, our swag on our backs, eluding

pursuit . . and joining with the natives in some far hinterland. I
would be a sort of Jonathan Wilde plus a François Villon.

Before the captain returned I had surveyed everything to my
satisfaction . . after supper the captain and the two mates left
for shore again.

Now was the time. I searched the captain's old trousers and
found the ship's keys there. They were too bulky to carry around
with him.

The keys seemed to jangle like thunder as I tried them one after
the other on the drawer where I had seen him put away the gold.

I heard someone coming. I started to whistle noisily, and to
polish the captain's *carpet slippers!* . . it was only someone walking
on deck. . . The last key was, dramatically, the right one. The
drawer opened . . but it was empty! I had seen the captain—the
captain had also seen me. Now I started to take anything I could
lay my hands on.

I snatched off the wall two silver-mounted cavalry pistols, a
present from his brother to Schantze. I added a bottle of kümmel
to the ham and the rye bread. The kümmel a present for Hoppner.

Then, before leaving the *Valkyrie* forever, I sat down to think
if there were not something I might do to show my contempt for
Miller. There were many things I could do, I found.

In the first place, I took a large sail-needle and some heavy
thread and I sewed two pairs of his trousers and two of his
coats up the middle of the legs and arms, so he couldn't put them
on, at least right away. I picked up hammer and nails and nailed
his shoes and sea-boots securely to the middle of his cabin floor.
Under his pillow I found a full flask of brandy. I emptied half . .
when I replaced it, it was full again. But I had not resorted to
the brandy cask to fill it.

   ·   ·   ·   ·   ·   ·   ·

The apprehension that I might be come upon *flagrante delictu*
gave me a shiver of apprehension. But it was a pleasurable shiver.
I enjoyed the malicious wantonness of my acts, and my prospective
jump into the unknown . . all the South Seas waited for me . .
all the world!

But, though every moment's delay brought detection and danger
nearer, I found time for yet one more stroke. With a laughable

vision of Schantze smashing Miller all over the cabin, I wrote and left this note pinned on the former's pillow:

Dear Captain:—

By the time you read this letter I will be beyond your reach (then out of the instant's imagination . . I had not considered such a thing hitherto). I am going far into the interior and discover a gold mine. When I am rich I shall repay you for the cavalry pistols which I am compelled to confiscate in lieu of my wages, which I now forfeit by running away, though entitled to them.

You have been a good captain and I like you.

As for Miller, he is beneath my contempt. It was he who drank all your wines, brandies, and whiskies . . the sailmaker is to answer for your beer. The second mate has been in on this theft of your liquors, too (I left the cook out because he had been nice to me).

Good-bye, and good luck.

Your former cabin boy, and, though you may not believe me, always your well-wisher and friend,

JOHN GREGORY.

I left what I had stolen bundled up in my blanket. I walked forward nonchalantly to see if anyone was out to observe me. I discovered the sandy-haired Blacksmith, Klumpf, sitting on the main hatch. I saw that I could not pass him with my bundle without strategy. The strategy I employed was simple.

I drew him a bottle of brandy. I gave it to him. After he had drawn a long drink I told him I was running away from the ship. He laughed and took another drink. I passed him with my bundle. He shouted good-bye to me.

Before I had gone by the nose of the old ship, who should I run into but Klaus, coming back from a spree. He was pushing along on all fours like an animal, he was so drunk . . good, simple Klaus, whom I liked. I laid down my bundle, risking capture, while I helped him to the deck. He stopped a moment to pat the ship's side affectionately as if it were a living friend, or nearer, a mother.

"Gute alte *Valkyrie!* . . gute alte *Valkyrie!*" he murmured.

Safe so far. At the outside of the dock-gate Hoppner waited my arrival. He was interested in the kümmel, and in the pistols, which were pawnable.

He had been more daring than I. He had tried to pick his captain's pocket of a gold watch while the latter slept. But every time he reached for it the captain stirred uneasily. He would have snatched it anyhow, but just then his first mate stepped into the cabin . . "and I hid till the mate went out again."

"And what then?"

"I picked up a lot of silverware the captian had for show occasions . . that I found, rummaging about."

"And him there sleeping?"

"Why not?"

"I found four revolvers that belonged to the mates and captain. I put them all in one bundle and chucked them into a rowboat over the ship's side. And nōw we must go back to your boat——"

"To my boat?" I asked, amazed.

"Yes" (I had told him how nearly I had missed our ship-money). "To your boat, and ransack the cabin till we locate that coin."

"That's too risky."

"Hell, take a chance, can't you?"

That's what Hoppner was always saying as long as we travelled together: "Hell, take a chance."

But when I began telling him with convulsive laughter, of the revenge I had taken on the mate . . and also how I had thrown all the keys overboard, Hoppner, instead of joining in with my laughter, struck at me, not at all playfully, "What kind of damn jackass have I joined up with, anyhow," he exclaimed. "Now it won't be any use going back, you've thrown the keys away and we'd make too great a racket, breaking open things. . ."

He insisted, however, on going back to his own boat, sliding down to the rowboat, and rowing away with the loot he had cast into it. We had no sooner reached the prow of the *Lord Summerville* than we observed people bestirring themselves on board her more than was natural.

"Come on, *now* we'll beat it. They're after me."

Hoppner had also brought a blanket. We went "humping bluey" as swagmen, as the tramp is called in Australia.

The existence of the swagman is the happiest vagrant's life in the world. He is usually regarded as a bona fide seeker for work, and food is readily given him for the asking. Unlike the American hobo, he is given his food raw, and is expected to cook it himself. So he carries what he calls a "tucker bag" to hold his provisions; also, almost more important—his "billy can" or tea-pot. . .

Hoppner and I acquired the tea-habit as badly as the rest of the Australian swagmen. Every mile or so the swagman seems to stop, build a fire, and brew his draught of tea, which he makes strong enough to take the place of the firiest swig of whiskey. I've seen an old swagman boil his tea for an actual half-hour, till the resultant concoction was as thick and black as New Orleans molasses. With such continual draughts of tea, only the crystalline air, and the healthy dryness of the climate keeps them from drugging themselves to death.

"Tea ain't any good to drink unless you can put a stick straight up in it, and it can stand alone there," joked an old swagman, who had invited us to partake of a hospitable "billy-can" with him.

.   .   .   .

We had long, marvellous talks with different swagmen, as we slowly sauntered north to Newcastle. . .

We heard of the snakes of Australia, which workmen dug up in torpid writhing knots, in the cold weather . . of native corrobories which one old informant told us he had often attended, where he procured native women or "gins" as they called them, for a mere drink of whiskey or gin . . "that's why they calls 'em 'gins' " he explained . . (wrong, for "gin" or a word of corresponding sound is the name for "woman" in many native languages in the antipodes). . .

The azure beauty of those days! . . tramping northward with nothing in the world to do but swap stories and rest whenever we chose, about campfires of resinous, sweetly smelling wood . . drinking and drinking that villainous tea.

In Australia the law against stealing rides on freights is strictly enforced. The tramp has always to walk—to the American tramp this is at first a hardship, but you soon grow to like it . . you learn to enjoy the wine in the air, the fragrance of the strange trees that shed bark instead of leaves, the noise of scores of unseen waterfalls in the hills of New South Wales.

The morning that the little sea-port of .Newcastle lay before us, I felt as if I had been on tour through a strange world. For the first time the story-books of my youth had come true.

But Hoppner rose from the camp fire that we'd been sleeping by, stretched, and remarked, "now, thank Christ, I'll be able to find a good seat in a pub again, just like in Sydney, and all the booze I can drink. We can go to some sailors' boarding house here, tell them we want to ship out, and they'll furnish us with the proper amount of drinks and take care of us, all hunky dory, till they find us a berth on ship . . of course they'll be well paid for their trouble . . two months' advance pay handed over to them by the skipper . . but that won't bother me a bit."

From the hill on which we lay encamped we saw .all the ships in the harbour. I no longer feared the sea. Your true adventurer forgets danger and perils experienced as a woman forgets the pangs of childbirth.

    .   .   .   .

We met a sailor on the street, who, though at first a stranger, soon became our friend and, with the quick hospitality of the sea, steered us to a pub known as the Green Emerald, bought us drinks, and introduced us to Mother Conarty, the proprietress.

"I'll ship ye out all right, but where's your dunnage?"

We confessed that we had run away from our ships down at Sydney.

The old sailor had spoken of Mother Conarty as rough-mannered, but a woman with "a good, warm heart."

She proved it by taking us in to board, with no dunnage for her to hold as security.

"Oh, they're good lads, I'm sure," vouched our sailor-friend, speaking of us as if we had been forecastle mates of his for twenty voyages on end . . the way of the sea!

Now Mother Conarty was not stupid. She was a great-bodied, jolly Irishwoman, but she possessed razor-keen, hazel eyes that narrowed on us a bit when she first saw us. But the woman in her soon hushed her passing suspicions. For Hoppner was a frank-faced, handsome lad, with wide shoulders and a small waist like a girl's. It was Hoppner's good looks took her in. She gave us a room together.

    .   .   .   .   '   .   '

There was a blowsy cheeked bar-maid, Mother Conarty's daughter. She knew well how to handle with a few sharp, ironic remarks anyone who tried to "get fresh" with her . . and if she couldn't, there were plenty of husky sailormen about, hearty in their admiration for the resolute, clean girl, and ready with mauling fists.

.   .   .   .   .   .

"Mother Conarty's proud o' that kid o' hers, she is."
"And well she may be!"

.   .   .   .   .   .

"I've been thinkin' over you b'yes, an' as ye hain't no dunnage wit' ye, I'm thinkin' ye'll be workin' fer yer board an' room."
"We're willing enough, mother," I responded, with a sinking of the heart, while Hoppner grimaced to me, behind her back.
We scrubbed out rooms, and the stairs, the bar, behind the bar, the rooms back and front, where the sailors drank. We earned our board and room . . for a few days.

.   .   .   .   .   .

At the Green Emerald I met my first case of delirium tremens. And it was a townsman who had 'em, not a sailor. The townsman was well-dressed and well-behaved—at first . . but there lurked a wild stare in his eye that was almost a glaze . . and he hung on the bar and drank and drank and drank. It apparently had no effect on him, the liquor that he took.
"Say, but you're a tough one," complimented Molly.
But *it* began in the afternoon. He picked up a stray dog from the floor and began kissing it. And the dog slavered back, returning his affection. Then he dropped the dog and began picking blue monkeys off the wall . . wee things, he explained to us . . that he could hold between thumb and forefinger . . only there were so many of them . . multitudes of them . . that they rather distressed him . . they carried the man away in an ambulance.

.   .   .   .   .   .

Hoppner and I tired of the ceaseless scrubbing. One day we simply walked out of the Green Emerald and never showed up again. Hoppner stayed on in town.
I found that the *Valkyrie* had run up from Sydney to coal at Newcastle, for the West Coast. I thought that in this case a little knowledge was not a dangerous thing, but a good thing, as long as I confined that knowledge to myself. I knew that the *Valkyrie* was

there. It was not necessary that the officers of the boat should know I was there . . which I wasn't, for I turned south, my swag on my back, and made Sydney again.

.   .   .   .

In Sydney and "on the rocks," that is with nothing to eat and no place to sleep but outdoors.

Of course I couldn't keep away from the ships. I arrived at the Circular Quay. I ran into the Sailors' Mission. They were serving tea and having a prayer-meeting. I wandered in.

A thin, wisplike man, timid, in black, but very gentlemanly, made me heartily welcome. Not with that obnoxious, forced heartiness sky-pilots think the proper manner to affect in dealing with sailors, but in a human way genuinely felt.

After a service of hearty singing, he asked me if he could help me in any way.

"I suppose you can. I'm on the rocks bad."

He gave me all the cakes to eat which were left over from the tea. And a couple of shillings beside.

"I wonder if there's anything else I can do?"

"Yes, I'm a poet," I ventured, "and I'd like to get Chaucer's *Canterbury Tales* to read again." I said this as much to startle the man as really meaning it. I can go so long without reading certain poets, and after that I starve for them as the hungry starve for food. I was hungry for Chaucer.

Such a request, coming from a youth almost in rags, impressed the sky-pilot so deeply that he insisted on giving me a job pumping the organ during services and a little room to sleep in at the mission. What is more, he lent me Skeats' edition of Chaucer, complete. And all the time I was with him he proved a "good sport." He didn't take advantage of my dependence on him to bother me so very much about God.

He took it for granted that I was a Christian, since I never discussed religion with him.

.   .   .   .

It began to grow wearisome, pumping an organ for a living. And I had fed myself full on Chaucer.

I began to yawn, behind the organ, over the growing staleness of life in a sailors' mission. And also I was being pestered by a tall, frigid old maid in purples and blacks, who had fixed her eye on me as a heathen she must convert.

. . . .

"How'd you like a voyage to China?" the sky-pilot asked, one day.

Cathay . . Marco Polo . . Milton's description of the Chinese moving their wheelbarrows along the land by means of sails . . many poetic visions marched across my mind at the question.

"I'd like to, right enough."

"Then here's a chance for you," and he handed me a copy of the Bulletin, pointing out an advertisement for cattlemen on the steamboat, *South Sea King*, about to take a cargo of steers from Queensland to Taku, province of Pechi-li, Northern China.

"What are they sending cattle away up there for?"

"Supplies for troops . . The Boxer outbreak, you know . . go down to the number given in the advertisement, and I'm sure they'll sign you on as cattleman, if you want the job."

"All right. I'll go now."

"No," looking me over dubiously, "you'd better not go there or anywhere else, in your present rig . . you're too ragged to apply even for such work . . hang around till morning, and I'll go home to-night and bring you a decent coat, at least. Your coat is worse than your trousers . . though *they* are ravelled at the bottoms and coming through in the left knee . . every time you take a step I can see a glint of white through the cloth, and," walking round me in a tour of inspection, "the seat might break through at any moment." All this was said without a glint of humour in his eyes.

. . . .

Next morning the sky-pilot came down very late. It was twelve. But he had not forgotten me. "Here's the coat," and he solemnly unwrapped and trailed before my astonished gaze a coat with a long, ministerial tail. I put it on. The tail came below the bend of my knees. I laughed. The sky-pilot did not.

Finally he stepped back, cracked a solemn smile, and remarked, "You *do* look rather odd!"

The intonation of his voice, his solemn almost deprecatory smile, set me off and I laughed till the tears ran down my face.

"I say, what's so funny?"

"Me! I am! . . in your long-tailed coat."

"If I was on the rocks like you I wouldn't see anything to laugh about."

.   .   .   .

At the shipping office, the place mentioned in the advertisement, in the dimly lit, grey-paned room, there sat one lone, pasty-faced, old-youngish clerk on the traditional clerk's high stool. But he proved lively beyond his appearance.

"My God! do look who's here!" he exclaimed facetiously, and then, rapidly, without giving me room for a biting word in return, "no, there's no use now, my boy . . we took on all the cattlemen we needed by ten o'clock this morning."

I walked away, disconsolate. I bore on my back my swagman's blanket. In the blanket I carried a change of shirts the sky-pilot had given me, a razor, a toothbrush, a Tennyson, and a Westcott and Hort's Greek New Testament with glossary, that I had stolen from a bookstall in Sydney.

.   .   .   .

I found out where the dock was, nevertheless, where the men were loafing about in groups, waiting to be taken out to the *South Sea King* . . which lay in the harbour.

At the entrance to the pier I met a powerful, chunky lad who was called "Nippers," he said. He, too, was going with the *South Sea King* . . not as a cattleman, but as stowaway. He urged me to stow away along with him. And he gave me, unimaginatively, my name of "Skinny," which the rest called me during the voyage.

.   .   .   .

We strolled up to the men and joined them.

"Hello, kids!"

"Hello, fellows!   Are you the cattlemen for the *South Sea King?*"

"Right you are, my lad . . we are that!"

The men went on with their arguing. They were fighting the Boer War all over again with their mouths. Some of them had been in it. Many of them had tramped in South Africa. They shouted violently, profanely, at each other at the tops of their voices, contending with loud assertions and counter-assertions, as if about to engage in an all-round fight.

Several personal altercations sprang up, the points of the debate forgotten . . I couldn't discover what it was about, myself . . only that one man was a fool . . another, a silly ass . . another, a bloody liar!

. . . .

The launch which was to carry them to the *South Sea King* at this moment started nosing into the dock, on a turbulent zig-zag across the harbour; and the men forgot their quarrelling. It brought up at the foot of a pile and made fast.

"Come on, Skinny," Nippers urged me aggressively, "it's front seats or nothing. Act as if you owned the boat." We thrust ahead of the others and swarmed down the ladder . . heaping, swearing, horse-playing, the cattlemen filled the launch from stern to bow.

Nippers had been a professional stowaway since his tenth year. He had gone all over the world in that fashion, he had informed me. He was now sixteen. I was almost eighteen.

His six years of rough life with rough men had brought him to premature manhood, taught him to exhibit a saucy aplomb to everybody, to have at his finger-ends all the knockabout resourcefulness and impudence that the successful vagrant must acquire in order to live at all as an individual. . .

. . . .

We were the first on deck.

"Where are the cattlemen's bunks?" Nippers asked of an oiler who stood, nonchalant, somewhat contemptuous, looking over the side at the seething, vociferous cattlemen.

Not wasting a word on us, the oiler pointed aft over his shoulder, with a grimy thumb.

We found a dark entrance like the mouth to a cave, that led down below. In our hurry we lost our footing on the greasy ladder and tumbled all the way to the bottom.

We had not time to rub our bruises. We plumped down and under the lower tier of bunks . . just in time . . the men came pouring down helter-skelter . . the talking, arguing, voluble swearing, and obscenity was renewed . . all we could see, from where we lay, was a confusion of legs to the knee, moving about. . .

They settled down on the benches about the table. They slackened their talk and began smacking their lips over ship-biscuit, marmalade, and tea.

. . . .

Still we lay in silence. The screw of the propeller had not started yet. We dared not come out or we would be put ashore.

. . . .

We were hungry. We could hear their tin plates clattering and clinking as the cattlemen ate supper, and smell the smell of corn-beef and boiled potatoes. Our mouths ran from hunger.

—"wish I had something to scoff, I'm starvin'," groaned Nippers, "but we'll hafta lay low till the bloody tub pulls out or we'll get caught an' dumped ashore."

Supper done with, the men were sitting about and smoking. They were soon, however, summoned up on deck, by a voice that roared down to them, from above, filling their quarters with a gust of sound.

We were alone now, perhaps,—it was so still.

With an almost imperceptible slowness, Nippers thrust his head out, as cautiously as a turtle . . he emerged further.

He made a quick thrust of the arm for a platter of beef and potatoes, that stood, untouched, on the table . . someone coughed. We had thought we were alone. Nippers jerked back. The tin came down with a clatter, first to the bench, then to the floor. A big friendly potato rolled under to where we were. We seized on it, divided it, ate it.

Contrary to our conjecture, some of the men must have stayed below. Someone jumped out of a bunk.

"There's rats down here!"

"—mighty big rats, if you arsks me."

"It's not rats," and I could hear a fear in the voice that quavered the words forth, "I tell you, buddy, this ship is haunted."

"—haunted!" boomed the voice of a man coming down the ladder, "you stop this silly nonsense right now . . don't spread such talk as that . . it's stowaways!"

We saw a pair of legs to the knees again. We lay still, breathless. A watch chain dangled down in a parabolic loop. Then followed a round face, beef-red with stooping. It looked under apoplectically at us.

"Ah, me b'yes, c'm on out o' there!"

And out we came, dragged by the foot, one after the other, as I myself in my childhood have pulled frogs out from a hole in a brook-bank.

"I've been hearing them for hours, Mister," spoke up the little, shrivelled, leathery-skinned West Indian negro, who spoke English without a trace of dialect, "and I was sure the place was haunted."

    .   .   .   .

We stood before the captain, cap deferentially in hand.

But he looked like anything but a man in charge of a ship. He was short. In outward appearance, moreover, he was like a wax doll. He had waxen-white cheeks with daubs of pink as if they had been put there from a rouge pot. His hair was nicely scented, oiled, and patted down. His small hands were white and perfectly manicured.

Nippers began to snicker openly at him. But the sharp variety and incisiveness of the oaths he vented at us, soon disabused us of any opinion we might have held that he was sissified. . .

"What's wrong with *you*, you young —— —— —— —— you?" began the captain. The snicker died slowly from Nipper's lips, and in his face dawned an infinite, surprised respect. . .

Then, after he had subdued us:

"So you're stowaways, eh? . . and you think you're going to be given a free ride to Brisbane and let go ashore, scot free? . . not much! You'll either go to jail there or sign up here, as cattlemen for the trip to China—even though I can see that your mouths are still wet from your mothers' tits!" And he ended with a blasphemous flourish.

Nippers and I looked at each other in astonishment. Of course we wanted to sign on as cattlemen. No doubt some of the men hired at Sydney had failed to show up at the wharf.

The ship's book was pushed before us.

"Sign here!" I signed "John Gregory" with satisfaction. Nippers signed after, laboriously.

"And now get aft with you, you ——!" cursed the captain, dismissing us with a parting volley that beat about our ears.

"Gawd, but the skipper's a *right* man enough!" worshipped Nippers.

We hurried down the ladder to gobble up what was left of the cornbeef and potatoes. . . Nippers looked up at me, with a hunk of beef sticking from his mouth, which he poked in with the butt-end of his knife. . . "Say, didn't the old man cuss wonderful, and him lookin' like such a lady!"

.　　　.　　　.　　　.　　　.　　　.　　　.

There was plenty of work to do in the few days it took to reach Brisbane, where the cattle were to be taken aboard. The boat was an ordinary tramp steamer, and we had to make an improvised cattleboat out of her. Already carpenters had done much to that effect by erecting enclosures on the top deck, the main deck, by putting up stalls in the hold. Every available foot was to be packed with the living flesh of cattle.

We gave the finishing touches to the work, trying to make the boarding and scantling more solid—solid enough to withstand the plunging, lurching, and kicking of fear-stricken, wild Queensland steers unused to being cooped up on shipboard. . .

.　　　.　　　.　　　.　　　.　　　.

We had made fast to a dock down the Brisbane River, several miles out from Brisbane . . nearby stood the stockyards, with no cattle in them yet.

In a day's time of lusty heaving and running and hauling we had taken on the bales of compressed fodder that were to feed the cattle for the twenty-day trip to Taku, China.

Then the little, fiery, doll-like skipper made the tactical error of paying each man a couple of bob advance on his forthcoming wages.

In a shouting, singing mob we made for Brisbane, like schoolboys on a holiday.

Two shilling apiece wasn't much. But a vagabond can make a little silver go far. And there are more friends to be found by men in such a condition, more good times to be had—of a sort— than a world held by more proper standards can imagine.

In both brothel and pub the men found friends. There were other sailors ashore, there were many swagmen just in from the bush—some with "stakes" they had earned on the ranches out in the country . . and in their good, simple hearts they were not averse to "standing treats."

.　　　.　　　.　　　.　　　.　　　.

As if by previous appointment, one by one we drifted together, we cattlemen of the *South Sea King*—we drifted together and found each other in the fine park near the Queensland House of Parliament.

We had, all of us, already over-stayed our shore-leave by many hours. We grouped together in informal consultation as to what should be done—should we go back to the ship or not?

"We might run into a typhoon . . with all them crazy cattle on board!" voiced one. . .

.   .   .   .

Nevertheless, perhaps because it was, after all, the line of least resistance, because there regular meals awaited us, and a secure place of sleep, by twos and threes we drifted back, down the long, hot, dusty road, to where the *South Sea King* lay waiting for us . . the mate, the captain, and the cattle-boss furious at us for our over-stayed shore-leave. . .

.   .   .   .

The cattle had been there these many hours, bellowing and moving restlessly in their land-pens, the hot sun blazing down upon them.

.   .   .   .

Our cattle-boss, it seems, knew all about the handling of his animals on land. But not on sea. When, the following morning, we started early, trying to drive the cattle on board ship, they refused to walk up the runway. In vain the boss strewed earth and sod along its course, to make it seem a natural passage for them . . they rushed around and around their pens, kicking up a vast, white, choking dust,—snorting, bellowing, and throwing their rumps out gaily in sidelong gallopades . . all young Queensland steers; wild, but not vicious. Still full of the life and strength of the open range. . .

Then we scattered bits of the broken bales of their prepared food, along the runway, to lure them . . a few were led aboard thus. But the captain cried with oaths that they didn't have time to make a coaxing-party of the job. . .

At last the donkey-engine was started, forward. A small cable was run through a block, and, fastened by their halters around their horns, one after the other the steers, now bellowing in great terror, their eyes popping for fear—were hoisted up in the air, poised on high, kicking, then swung down, and on deck.

You had to keep well from under each one as he descended, or suffer the befouling consequences of his fear . . we had great laughter over several men who came within the explosive radius . . till the mate hit on the device of tying each beast's tail close before he was jerked up into the air.

What a pandemonium . . shouting . . swearing . . whistles blowing signals . . the chugging respiration of the labouring donkey-engine . . and then the attempted stampede of each trembling, fear-crazy animal as soon as he rose four-footed, on deck; after his ride through the sky. . .

. . . .

The ship was crammed as full as Noah's ark. In the holds and on the main deck stood the steers, in long rows. . .

On the upper deck, exposed to all the weather, were housed the more tractable sheep, who had, without objection, bleated their way aboard docilely up the runway—behind their black ram . . that the cattle-boss had to help on a bit, by pulling him the few first yards by his curly horns.

. . . .

As we swam by in the fading day, a pale ghost of a moon was already up. Ghostly rows of knee-ing trees stood out like live things in the river. . .

Under the night, off at sea, what with the mooing and baaing through all the ship, it seemed like an absurd farmyard that had somehow got on the ocean.

. . . .

There were two quarters for the men . . a place under the fore-castle head, forward—as well as the after-quarters. Nippers and I had been separated—he staying aft, while I took up my bunk forward.

. . . .

But the men on the boat, the few that stick in my memory as distinct personages:

There was the bloated, fat Scotch boy, whom we called just Fatty, a sheepherder by calling. He had signed on for the trip, to take care of the sheep on the upper deck;

There was a weak, pathetic cockney, who died of sun-stroke;

The ex-jockey, a bit of a man with a withered left arm—made that way from an injury received in his last race, when his mount fell on him;

There was the West Indian Negro, a woolly, ebony wisp of a creature, a great believer in ghosts (he who thought we stowaways were ghosts when we hid under the bunk). The Irish cattle-boss gave him the job of night-watchman, "to break him of his superstitious silliness";

There was the big, black Jamaica cook .. as black as if he was polished ebony .. a fine, big, polite chap, whom everyone liked. He had a white wife in Southampton (the sailors who had seen her said she was pretty .. that the cook was true to her .. that she came down to the boat the minute the *South Sea King* reached an English port, they loved each other so deeply!). . .

Then there was the giant of an Irishman .. who, working side by side with me in the hold, shovelling out cattle-ordure there with me, informed me that I looked as if I had consumption .. that I would not be able to stand the terrific heat for many days without keeling over .. but, his prediction came true of himself, not of me.

One morning, not many days out, the little West Indian watchman, bringing down the before-daylight coffee and ships-biscuits and rousing the men, as was his duty,—found the big fellow, with whom he used to crack cheery jokes, apparently sound asleep. The watchman shook him by the foot to rouse him .. found his big friend stiff and cold.

The watchman let out a scream of horror that woke us right and proper, for *that* day. . .

The next day was Sunday. It was a still, religious afternoon.

We men ranged in two rows aft. The body had been sewn up in coarse canvas, the Union Jack draped over it.

The captain, dapper in his gold-braided uniform, stood over the body as it lay on the plank from which it was to descend into the sea. In a high, clear voice he read that beautiful burial-service for the dead .. an upward tilt of the board in the hands of two brown-armed seamen, the body flashed over the side, to swing feet-down, laden with shot, for interminable days and nights, in the vast tides of the Pacific.

No one reached quickly enough. The Union Jack went off with the body, like a floral decoration flung after. . .

   .   .   .   .

We drank the coffee brought to us before dawn, in grouchy, sleepy, monosyllabic silence. Immediately after, the cattle were to water and feed .. and a hungry lot they were .. but despite their appetites, with each day, because of the excessive heat of the tropics, and the confined existence that was theirs—such an abrupt transition from the open range—they waxed thinner and thinner, acquired more of large-eyed mournfulness and an aspect of almost human suffering in their piteous, pleading faces. . .

.   .   .   .

If the big chap who succumbed to heart failure that night had lived a few days longer, he would have wondered still more at me or anyone else surviving a day's work in the hold.

For the thermometer ran up incredibly . . hotter and hotter it grew . . and down there in the hold we had to shovel out the excrement every morning after breakfast. It was too infernal for even the prudish Anglo-Saxon souls of us to wear clothes beyond a breechclout, and shoes, to protect our feet from the harder hoof.

Our eyes stung and watered from the reek of the ammonia in the cattle-urine. What with the crowding, the bad air (despite the canvas ventilators let down) and the sudden change from green pasturage to dry, baled food, most of the beasts contracted "the skitters." This mess was what we had to shovel out through the portholes . . an offensive-smelling, greenish, fluidic material, that spilled, the half of it, always, from the carefully-held scoop of the shovel.

Cursing, with the bitter sweat streaming off our bodies and into our eyes, and with an oblique eye to guard from heat-maddened, frantic steer-kicks,—each day, for several hours, we suffered through this hell . . to emerge panting, like runners after a long race; befouled . . to throw ourselves down on the upper deck, under the blue, wind-free sky and feel as if we had come into paradise. . .

.   .   .   .

"I wish I had never come back to this hell-ship, at Brisbane!"
"I wish I had never come aboard at all at Sydney!"

.   .   .   .

At such times, and at other odd ends of leisure, I brought my Westcott and Hort's Greek New Testament from my bunk, and with the nasty smell of sheep close-by, but unheeded through custom—I studied with greater pleasure than I ever did before or since.

.   .   .   .

As I said before, it was not long before these poor steers were broken-spirited things.

But there was one among them whose spirit kept its flag in the air, "The Black Devil," as the cook had named him fondly . . a steer, all glossy-black, excepting for a white spot in the center of his forehead. He behaved, from the first, more like a turbulent little bull than a gelding. The cook fed him with tid-bits from the galley.

He had evidently been someone's pet before he had been sold for live meat, to be shipped to China.

When we took him on board by the horns he showed no fear as he rode in the air. And, once on his feet again, and loose on deck, he showed us hell's own fight—out of sheer indignation—back there in Brisbane. He flashed after us, with the rapid motions of a bull-fight in the movies. Most of us climbed every available thing to get out of his reach. He smashed here and there through wooden supports as if they were of cardboard.

The agile little ex-jockey kept running in front of him, hitting him on the nose and nimbly escaping—in spite of his wing-like, wasted arm, quicker than his pursuer . . that smashed through, while he ducked and turned. . .

"I'll be God-damned," yelled the captain from the safe vantage of the bridge, "fetch me my pistol," to the cabin boy, "I'll have to shoot the beast!"

All this while the big black Jamaica cook had been calmly looking on, leaning fearlessly out over the half-door of the galley . . while the infuriated animal rushed back and forth.

The cook said nothing. He disappeared, and reappeared with a bunch of carrots which he held out toward "The Black Devil." . .

In immediate transformation, the little beast stopped, forgot his anger, stretched forth his moist, black nuzzle, sniffing . . and walked up to the cook, accepting the carrots. The cook began to stroke the animal's nose. . .

"*You* little black devil," he said, in a soft voice, "you're all right . . they don't understand you . . but we're going to be pals— us two—aren't we?"

Then he came out at the door to where the steer stood, took "The Black Devil," as we henceforth called him, gently by the under-jaw, —and led him into a standing-place right across from the galley.

.   .   .   .

As we struck further north under vast nights of stars, and days of furnace-hot sunshine, the heat, confinement, and dry, baled food told hideously on the animals . . the sheep seemed to endure better, partly because they were not halted stationary in one spot and could move about a little on the top deck. . . But they suffered hardships that came of changing weather.

.   .   .   .

Especially the cattle in the lower hold suffered, grew weak and emaciated. . . We were ever on the watch to keep them from going down . . there was danger of their sprawling over each other and breaking legs in the scramble. So when one tried to lie down, his tail was twisted till the suffering made him rise to his feet . . sometimes a steer would be too weak to regain his feet . . in such a case, in a vain effort to make the beast rise, I have seen the Irish foreman twist the tail nearly off, while the animal at first bellowed, then moaned weakly, with anguish . . a final boot at the victim in angry frustration. . .

Last, a milky glaze would settle over the beast's eyes . . and we would drag him out and up by donkey-engine, swing him over and out, and drop him, to float, a bobbing tan object, down our receding ocean-path.

.   .   .   .

The coast of Borneo hovered, far and blue, in the offing, when we struck our first, and last, typhoon. The mate avowed it was merely the tail-end of a typhoon; if that was the tail-end, it is good that the body of it did not strike down on us.

The surface of the ocean was kicked up into high, ridge-running masses. The tops of the waves were caught in the wind and whipped into a wide, level froth as if a giant egg-beater were at work . . then water, water, water came sweeping and mounting and climbing aboard, hill after bursting hill.

The deck was swept as by a mountain-torrent . . boards whirled about with an uncanny motion in them. They came forward toward you with a bound, menacing shin and midriff,—then on the motion of the ship, they paused, and washed in the opposite direction.

Here and there a steer broke loose, which had to be caught and tethered again. But in general the animals were too much frightened to do anything but stand trembling and moaning . . when they were not floundering about. . .

Down below was a suffocating inferno. For the hatches that were ordinarily kept open for more air, had to be battened **down** till the waves subsided.

.   .   .   .

At the very height of the storm, we heard a screaming of the most abject fear.

The jockey had passed, in forgetful excitement, too close to his enemy, The Black Devil—who had not forgotten, and gave him **a** horn in the side, under the withered arm.

Several sailors carried the bleeding man aft to the captain .. who dressed his wound with fair skill. The jockey was not **so** badly injured, all things considered. The thrust had slanted **and** made only a flesh wound .. which enabled the fellow to loaf on a sort of sick-leave, during the rest of the trip.

.   .   .   .

The storm over, frantically we tore off the hatches again .. to find only ten steers dead below. The rest were gasping piteously for air. It was a day's work, heaving the dead stock overboard .. including the two more which died of the after-effects. . .

When we went to look the sheep over, we found that over a third of them had been washed overboard. The rest were huddled, in frightened, bleating heaps, wondering perhaps what kind of an insane world it was that they had been harried into.

.   .   .   .

The story of this cattleboat unfolds freshly before me again, out of the records of memory .. the pitiful suffering of the cattle .. the lives and daily doings of the rowdy, likeable men, who were really still undeveloped children, and would so go down to the grave .. with their boasting and continual vanity of small and trivial things of life.

.   .   .   .

All the time I was keeping a diary of my adventures .. in a large, brown copybook, with flexible covers. I carried it, tightened away, usually, in the lining of my coat, but occasionally I left it under the mattress of my bunk.

Nippers observed me writing in it one day.

That night it was gone. I surmised who had taken it.

Seeking Nippers, I came upon him haltingly reading my diary aloud to an amused circle of cattlemen, in his quarters aft.

"Give me that book back!" I demanded.

He ignored me.

"Give him a rap in the kisser, Skinny!"

I drew back, aiming a blow at Nippers. He flung the book down and was on me like the tornado we had just run through . . he was a natural-born fighter . . in a twinkling I was on the floor, with a black eye, a bleeding mouth.

I flung myself to my feet, full of fury . . then something went in my brain like the click of a camera-shutter . . I had an hallucination of Uncle Landon, coming at me with a club. . .

I plumped into a corner, crouching. "Don't hit me any more . . please don't, Uncle Lan!"

"He's gone crazy!"

"Naw, he's only a bloody, bleedin' coward," returned another voice, in surprise and disgust.

Someone spat on me. I was let up at last . . I staggered forward to my bunk. My book had been handed back to me. It's a wonder I didn't throw myself into the sea, in disgust over the queer fit that had come over me. I lay half the night, puzzling . . was I a coward?

Not unless an unparalleled change had occurred in me. I had fought with other children, when a boy . . had whipped two lads at once, when working in the Composite factory, that time they spit into my book.

.   .   .   .

One day a fishing-junk hove into sight, just as if it had sailed out of a Maxfield Parrish illustration,—swinging there in the mouth of a blood-red sunset . . then, like magic, appeared another and another and another. . .

"Fishing-junks," ejaculated the mate, "—pretty far out, too, but a Chink'll risk his life for a few bleedin' cash . . and yet he won't fight at all . . an' if you do him an injury he's like as not likely to up an' commit suicide at your door, to get even!"

"That's a bally orful way to get even with a henemy!" exclaimed a stoker, who sat on the edge of the forward hatch.

"I should say so, too!"

Then, far and faint, were heard a crew of Chinese sailors, on the nearest junk, singing a curious, falsetto chantey as they hauled on a bamboo-braced sail. . .

"A feller wot never travelled wouldn't bloody well believe they
was such queer people in the world," further observed the philosophic coal-heaver.

.   .   .   .   .   .

Next morning the coast of China lay right against us, on the
starboard side .. we ran into the thick of a fleet of sampans, boats
fashioned flat like overgrown rowboats, propelled each by a huge
sculling oar, from the stern .. they were fishers who manned
them .. two or three to a boat .. huge, bronze-bodied, fine-muscled,
breech-clouted men .. as they sculled swiftly to give us sea-room
each one looked fit to be a sculptor's model.

Their bodies shone in the sun like bronze. Several, fearing we
might run them down, as we clove straight through their midst,
raised their arms with a shout full of pleading and fright.

"What's the matter? are they trying to murder some of these
poor chaps?" I asked.

"No .. we're just having a little fun .. what's the life of a Chink
matter?"

.   .   .   .   .   .

"I say, if the Chinks up where the Boxers are fighting are big
and strong as them duffers, here's one that don't want no shore-
leave!" commented someone, as we stood ranged by the side.

"I always thought Chinamen was runts."

"Oh, it's only city Chinks—mostly from Canton, that come to
civilized countries to run laundries .. but these are the real
Chinamen."

.   .   .   .   .   .

After the cattle had been unladen, the crew were to be taken down
to Shanghai and dumped ashore .. as it was an English Treaty
port, that would be, technically, living up to the ship's articles,
which guaranteed that the cattlemen aboard would be given passage
back to English ground. ..

But I was all excitement over the prospect of making my way
ashore to where the Allied troops were fighting. ..

.   .   .   .   .   .

Dawn .. we were anchored in Taku Bay among the warships of
the Allied nations .. grey warships gleaming in the sun like silver ..
the sound of bugles .. flags of all nations .. of as many colours as
the coat of Joseph.

"Well, here we are at last!"

.   .   .   .   .   .

Next day the work of unloading the cattle began . . hoisted again
by the horns from our boat of heavy draught to the hold of a coast-
ing steamer, that had English captain and mates, and a Chinese
crew.

Some of the steers were so weak that they died on deck . . as
they were dying, butchers cut their throats so their beef could be
called fresh.

The only one who desired to go ashore there, I made my way,
when it was dark and the last load of steers was being transferred
to shore, down below to the hold of the coaster. I stood in a corner,
behind an iron ladder, so that the cattle couldn't crush me during
the night . . for the Chinese had turned them loose, there, in a mass.

.   .   .   .

I stumbled ashore at Tongku, a station up a way on the banks of
the Pei Ho river.

My first night ashore in China was a far cry from the China of
my dreams . . the Cathay of Marco Polo, with its towers of porce-
lain. . . I crept, to escape a cold drizzle, under the huge tarpaulin
which covered a great stack of tinned goods—army supplies. A
soldier on guard over the stack, an American soldier, spotted me.

"Come, my lad," lifting up the tarpaulin, "what are you doing
there?"

"—Trying to keep from the wet!"

"—run off from one of the transports?"

"Yes," was as good an answer as any.

"You're pretty cold . . your teeth are chattering. Here, take a
swig o' this."

And the sentinel reached me a flask of whiskey from which I
drew a nip. Unaccustomed as I was to drink, it nearly strangled
me. It went all the way down like fire. Then it spread with a
pleasant warmth all through my body. . .

"Stay here to-night . . rather uncomfortable bed, but at least
it's dry. No one 'ull bother you . . in the morning Captain ——,
who is in charge of the commissariat here, might give you a job."

.   .   .   .

That next morning Captain ——— gave me a job as mate, eighty dollars Mex. and a place to sleep, along with others, in a Compound, and find my food at my own expense. . .

Mate, on a supply-launch that went in and out to and from the transports, that were continually anchoring in the bay. Our job was to keep the officers' mess in supplies. . .

"And, if you stick to your job six months," I was informed, you'll be entitled to free transportation back to San Francisco."

My captain was a neat, young Englishman, with the merest hint of a moustache of fair gold.

Our crew—two Chinamen who jested about us between themselves in a continuous splutter of Chinese. We could tell, by their grimaces and gestures . . we rather liked their harmless, human impudence . . as long as they did the work, while we lazed about, talking . . while up and down the yellow sweep of the Pei-ho the little boat tramped.

. . . .

"It's too bad you didn't arrive on the present scene a few weeks sooner," said my young captain . . "it was quite exciting here, at that time. I used to have to take the boathook and push off the Chinese corpses that caught on the prow of the boat as they floated down, thick . . they seemed to catch hold of the prow as if still alive. It was uncanny!"

. . . .

We slept, rolled up in our blankets, on the floor of a Chinese compound . . adventurers bound up and down the river, to and from Tien-Tsin and Woo-shi-Woo and Pekin . . a sort of caravanserai. . .

. . . .

Though it was the fall of the year and the nights were cold enough to make two blankets feel good, yet some days the sun blazed down intolerably on our boat, on the river. . .

When we grew thirsty the captain and myself resorted to our jug of distilled water. I had been warned against drinking the yellow, pea-soup-like water of the Pei-ho. . .

But one afternoon I found our water had run out.

So I took the gourd used by the Chinese crew, and dipped up, as they did, the river water.

The captain clutched me by the wrist.

"Don't drink that water! If you'd seen what I have, floating in it, you'd be afraid!"

"What won't hurt a Chinaman, won't hurt me," I boasted. . .

The result of my folly was a mild case of dysentery. . .

In a few days I was so weak that I went around as if I had no bones left in my body. And I wanted to leave the country. And I repaired to Captain —— who had given me the job, and asked him for my pay and my discharge. He lit into me, disgusted, upbraiding me for a worthless tramp. . .

"I might have known that you were of that ilk, from the first, just by looking at you!"

He handed me the eighty dollars in Mexican silver, that was coming to me. . . I repaid the captain the forty I had borrowed, for food.

"Sick! yes, sick of laziness!"

Captain —— was partly right. I had an uncontrollable distaste for the monotony of daily work, repeated in the same environment, surrounded by the same scenery . . but I was also quite weak and sick, and I am persuaded, that, if I had stayed on there, I might have died.

.   .   .   .

I sat on one of the wharves and played host to a crowd of romantic thoughts that moved in their pageant through my brain . . now I would go on to Pekin and see the great Forbidden City. Now I would dress in Chinese clothes and beg my way through the very heart of the Chinese Empire . . and write a book, subsequently, about my experiences and adventures . . and perhaps win a medal of some famous society for it . . and I had a dream of marrying some quaintly beautiful mandarin's daughter, of becoming a famous, revered Chinese scholar, bringing together with my influence the East and the West. . .

I reached so far, in the dream, as to buy several novels of the Chinese, printed in their characters, of an itinerant vendor. . .

The everyday world swung into my ken again.

Three junks, laden with American marines, dropping down the river from Pekin, cut across my abstracted gaze . . the boys were singing.

They marched off on the dock on which I sat. They were stationed right where they deployed from the junks. Men were put in guard over them.

At Tien Tsin they had behaved rather badly, I was told by one of them,—had gone on a Samshu jag . . a Chinese drink, worse than the worst American "rot-gut." . .

"Wisht I c'd git off the dock an' rustle up another drink somewheres."

"They wouldn't let us off this dock fer love nor money," spoke up a lithe, blue-shaven marine to me—the company's barber, I afterward learned him to be. . .

"Yah, we got ter stay here all afternoon, an' me t'roat 's es dry es san'paper."

"Where are they taking you to, from here?"

"Manila! . . the *Indiana's* waitin' out in th' bay fer us."

"—Wish I could get off with you!" I remarked.

"Wot's the matter? On th' bum here?"

"Yes."

Immediately the barber and two others, his pals, became intensely, suspiciously so, interested in my desire to sail with them. . .

"—Tell you wot," and the company barber reached into his pocket with a surreptitious glance about, "if you'll take these bills an' sneak past to that coaster lyin' along the next dock, the Chinese steward 'ull sell you three bottles o' whiskey fer these," and he handed me a bunch of bills . ." an' w'en you come back with th' booze, we'll see to it that you get took out to the transport with us, all right . . won't we, boys?"

"—betcher boots we will."

.   .   .   .

"God, but this is like heaven to me," exclaimed the barber, as he tilted up his bottle, while the two others stood about him, to keep him from being seen. The three of them drank their bottles of whiskey as if it was water.

"That saved me life. . ."

"An' mine, too. You go to Manila wit' us, all right,—kid!"

.   .   .   .

Toward dusk came the sharp command for the men to march aboard the coaster that had drawn up for them. The boys kept their word. They loaded me down with their accoutrements to

carry. I marched up the gangway with them, and we were off to
the *Indiana.*

I was the first, almost, to scamper aboard the waiting transport
in the gathering dusk . . and, to make sure of staying aboard, I
hurried down one ladder after the other, till I reached the heavy
darkness of the lowermost hold. Having nothing to do but sleep,
I stumbled over some oblong boxes, climbed onto one, and composed myself for the night, using a coil of rope for a pillow.

I woke to find a grey patch of day streaming down the ladder-
way. My eyes soon adjusted themselves to the obscurity.

And then it was that I gave a great, scared leap. And with
difficulty I held myself back from crying out.

Those curious oblong boxes among which I had passed the night—
they were hermetically sealed coffins, and there were dead soldiers
in them. Ridges of terror crept along my flesh. Stifling a panic
in me, I forced myself to go slow as I climbed the iron rungs to the
hold above . . where living soldiers lay sleeping in long rows. . .

Still undetected, I scrambled along an aisle between them and
put myself away in a sort of life-preserver closet. Not till I had
heard the familiar throb of the propeller in motion for a long
time, did I come forth.

· · · · · · ·

During the voyage of, I believe, eight days, I loafed about, lining
up for rations with the boys . . no one questioned me. My engineer's clothes that I had taken, in lieu of part of my wages, from the
slop-chest of *The South Sea King,* caused the officers of the marines
to think I belonged to the ship's crew . . and the ship-officers must
have thought I was in some way connected with the marines . .
anyhow, I was not molested, and I led a life much to my liking . .
an easy-going and loafing and tale-telling one . . mixing about and
talking and listening . . and reading back-number magazines.

· · · · · · ·

One day my friend the barber called me aside:

"Say, kid, I've been delegated to tell you that you've got lice."
I flamed indignant.

"That's a God-damned lie! and whoever told you so is a God-
damned liar, too! I never had a louse in my life."

"Easy! Easy! . . no use gittin' huffy . . if it ain't lice you got,

wot you scratchin' all the time fer? Look in the crotch of yer pants
and the seams of your shirt, an' see!"

I *had* been scratching a lot . . and wondering what was wrong . .
my breast was all red . . but I had explained it to myself that I
was wearing a coarse woolen undershirt next my skin . . that I
had picked up from the slop-chest, also.

The barber walked jauntily away, leaving me standing sullenly
alone.

I sneaked into the toilet, looking to see if anyone was about. I
turned my shirt back. To my horror, my loathing,—the soldier's
accusation was true! . . they were so thick, thanks to my ignorant
neglect, that I could see them moving in battalions . . if I had been
the victim of some filthy disease, I could scarcely have felt more
beyond the pale, more a pariah. I had not detected them before,
because I was ignorant of the thought of having them, and because
their grey colour was exactly that of the inside of my woolen shirt.

I threw the shirt away, content to shiver for a few days till we
had steamed to warmer weather . . I scrubbed and scrubbed and
scrubbed myself. . . I had, up to now, had experience with head-lice
only . . as a child, in school. . .

I look back with a shudder even yet to that experience. . During
my subsequent tramp-career I never could grow callous to vermin,
as a few others that I met, did. Once I met a tramp who advised
me not to bother about 'em . . and you would soon get used to
'em . . and not feel them biting at all . . but most tramps "boil up"—
that is, take off their clothes, a piece at a time, and boil them—whenever they find opportunity.

.   .   .   .

Manila. A brief adventure there . . a bum for a few weeks,
hanging around soldiers' barracks, blacking shoes for free meals . .
till Provost Marshal General Bell, in an effort to clear the islands
of boys who were vags and mascots of regiments, gave me and
several other rovers and stowaways free transportation back to
America. . .

.   .   .   .

A brief stop at Nagasaki to have a broken propeller shaft mended:
a long Pacific voyage . . then hilly San Francisco one golden
morning. . .

.   .   .   .

All these ocean days I peeled potatoes and helped to dish out rations to the lined-up soldiers at meal-times .. one slice of meat, one or two potatoes, to a tin plate. . .

For long hours I listened to their lying tales and boasting .. then lied and boasted, myself. . .

My most unique adventure aboard the *Thomas;* making friends with a four-times-enlisted soldier named Lang, who liked army life because, he said, outside of drills and dress parade, it was lazy and easy .. and it gave him leisure to read and re-read his Shakespeare. He was a Shakespearean scholar. . .

"It's the best life in the world .. no worries or responsibilities about food and lodging—it spoils a fellow for any other kind of life .. the officers are always decent to a fellow who respects himself as a soldier and citizen."

Lang and I became good pals. Day after day I sat listening to him, as, to the accompaniment of the rumble and pulse of the great boat a-move, he quoted and explained Shakespeare to me, nearly always without the book.

His talk was fascinating—except when he insisted on repeating to me his own wretched rhymes .. in which he showed he had learned nothing about how to write poetry from his revered Shakespeare .. it was very bad Kiplingesque stuff .. much like my own bad verse of that period. . .

Once Lang recited by heart the whole of *King Lear* to me, having me hold a copy of the play, to prove that he did not fumble a single line or miss a single word .. which he did not. . .

Lang was a prodigious drunkard. At Nagasaki I rescued him from the water-butt. Coming back drunk on rice wine, he had stuck his head down for a cool drink, as a horse does. And in he had tumbled, head-first. If I had not seen his legs wiggling futilely in the air, and drawn him forth, dripping, he would have drowned, as the butt was too solid for his struggles to dump, and he couldn't make a sound for help.

.   .   .   .

As we neared San Francisco several of the boys spoke to me of taking up a purse for my benefit. Soldiers are always generous and warm-hearted—the best men, individually, in the world.

I said no to them, that they must not take up a collection for me . . I did not really feel that way, at heart, but I liked better seeming proud and independent, American and self-reliant. . .

Later on, at the very dock, I acceded . . but now I was punished for my hypocrisy. The boys were so eager to be home again, they only threw together about five dollars for me . . when, if I hadn't been foolish, I might have had enough to loaf with, say a month, at San Francisco, and do a lot of reading in the Library, and in books of poetry that I might have picked up at second-hand book stores. . .

However, I gathered together, before I went ashore, two suits of khaki and two army blankets, and a pair of good army shoes that afterwards seemed never to wear out.

And a young chap named Simmons, who had been sergeant, had joined the army by running away from home, took me to an obscure hotel as his valet . . he wanted to "put on dog," as the Indians say.

He had parents of wealth, back in Des Moines.

I served him as his valet for the two weeks he stayed at the hotel. He had been shot through the left foot so that a tendon was severed, and he had to walk with a cane, with a foot that flopped at every step.

He gave me fifteen dollars for wages. After he had departed I rented a cheap room for a week.

.   .   .   .

Standing in front of a store on Kearney Street, one afternoon, dressed in my suit of soldier's khaki, looking at the display in the window, I got the cue that shaped my subsequent adventures in California. . .

"Poor lad," I heard one girl say to another, standing close by, "he looks so sick and thin, I'm sorry for him."

They did not notice that my soldier's uniform had cloth buttons. Simmons had made me put cloth buttons on, at the hotel, —had furnished them to me——

"I don't want you going about the other way . . you're such a nut, you might get into trouble."

Mule-drivers and others in subsidiary service were allowed khaki with cloth buttons only . . at that time. . . I don't know how it goes now.

.   .   .   .

The girls' taking me for a sick, discharged soldier made me think. I would travel in that guise.

. . . .

With a second-hand Shakespeare, in one volume, of wretched print, with a much-abused school-copy of Cæsar, in the Latin (of whose idiomatic Latin I have never tired), an extra suit of khaki, a razor, tooth-brush, and tooth-powder—and a cake of soap—all wrapped up in my army blankets, I set forth on my peregrinations as blanket-stiff or "bindle-bum."

Where I saw I could escape without awkward questioning, I played the convalescent ex-soldier . . I thrived. My shadow-thinness almost turned to fatness. It would have, had there been any disposition toward obesity in me. . .

At times I was ashamed of doing nothing . . queer spurts of American economic conscience. . .

Once I worked, plowing . . to drive the horses as far as a tall tree for shade, at the end of the third day, sneak back to the house . . and out to the highway with my bundle and my belongings, kicking up my heels ecstatically, glad to be freed from work.

I plumped down in a fence corner and did not stir till I had read a whole play of Shakespeare, and a snatch of my Cæsar.

Once or twice, sheriffs who were bent on arresting me because I had no visible means of support, let me go, because it awed them to find a tramp reading Shakespeare. . .

"It's a shame, a clever lad like you bein' a bum!"

. . . .

Tramps, though anti-social in the larger aspects of society (as, for that matter, all special classes are, from millionaires down—or up), are more than usually companionable among themselves. I never lived and moved with a better-hearted group of people.

By "jungle" camp-fires—("the jungles," any tramp rendezvous located just outside the city limits, to be beyond police jurisdiction), in jails, on freights . . I found a feeling of sincere companionship . . a companionship that without ostentation and as a matter of course, shared the last cent, the last meal . . when every cent *was* the last cent, every meal the *last* meal . . the rest depending on luck and Providence. . .

. . . .

Tramps often travel in pairs. I picked up a "buddy" . . a

short, thick-set man of young middle age, of Scandinavian descent
.. so blond that his eyebrows were white in contrast with his face,
which was ruddy with work in the sun. He, like me, was a "gaycat"
or tramp who is not above occasional work (as the word meant
then—now it means a cheap, no-account grafter). He had recently
been working picking oranges .. previous to that, he had been
employed in a Washington lumber camp.

.   .   .   .

Together we drifted along the seacoast south to San Diego ..
then back again to Santa Barbara .. for no reason but just to
drift. Then we sauntered over to San Bernardino—"San Berdu,"
as the tramps call it. . .

.   .   .   .

It struck chilly, one night. So chilly that we went into the
freightyard to put up in an empty box-car till the sun of next day
rose to warm the world.

We found a car. There were many other men already there, which
was good; the animal heat of their bodies made the interior warmer.

The interior of the car sounded like a Scotch bagpipe a-drone ..
what with snoring, breaking of wind in various ways, groaning,
and muttering thickly in dreams .. the air was sickeningly thick and
fetid. But to open a side door meant to let in the cold.

Softly my buddy and I drew off our shoes, putting them under
our heads to serve as pillows, and also to keep them from being
stolen. (Often a tramp comes along with a deft enough touch to
untie a man's shoes from his feet without waking him. I've heard
of its being done.) We wrapped our feet in newspapers, then. Our
coats we removed, to wrap them about us .. one keeps warmer that
way than by just wearing the coat. . .

.   .   .   .

The door on each side crashed back!

"Here's another nest full of 'em!"

"Come on out, boys!"

"What's the matter?" I queried.

" 'stoo cold out here. We have a nice, warm calaboose waitin'
fer ye!"

Grunting and grumbling, we dropped to the cinders, one after
the other. A posse of deputies and citizens, had, for some dark
reason, rounded us up.

One or two made a break for it, and escaped, followed by a random shot. After that, no one else cared to be chased after by a bullet.

They conducted us to what they had termed "the calaboose," a big, ramshackle, one-roomed barn-like structure. Piled in so thick that we almost had to stand up, there were so many of us—we were held there till next morning.

But we were served, then, a good breakfast, at the town's expense. The owner of the restaurant was a queer little, grey-faced, stringy fellow. He fed us all the buckwheat cakes and sausages we could hold, and won every hobo's heart, by giving all the coffee we could drink .. we held our cups with our hands about them, grateful for the warmth.

"Say, you're all right, mister!" ventured a tramp to the proprietor, as he walked by.

"Bet your God-damned life I'm all right! . . because I ain't nothin' but a bum myself .. yes, an' I'm not ashamed of it, neither .. before I struck this burg an' started this "ham-and" and made it pay, I was on the road same es all o' you!"

"Kin I have more pancakes, boss, an' another cup of coffee?"

"You sure can, bo! . . es I was sayin', I'm a bum myself, an' proud of it .. and I think these here damn bulls (policemen .. who were sitting nearby, waiting for us to finish) have mighty little to 'tend to, roundin' up you boys, now the orange-pickin' season's over with, an' puttin' you away like this .. why, if any one of them was half as decent as one o' you bums——"

"Sh! fer Christ's sake!" I admonished, "they're hearing you."

"That's jest what I want 'em to do .. I don't owe nothin' to no man, an' it's time someone told 'em somethin'."

.   .   .   .

Breakfast over, we were marched off to the courthouse. We were turned loose together in a large room. We felt so good with the sausage, cakes and coffee in our bellies, that we pushed each other about, sang, jigged, whistled.

As we had walked in, I had asked, of the cop who walked by my side—who seemed affable ..

"Say, mister, after all what's the idea?"

"We had to make an example," he returned, frankly.

"I don't quite get you!"

"Last week a bunch of bums dropped off here, at our town, and they almost ran the diggings for about twenty-four hours . . insulted women on the streets . . robbed ice-boxes . . even stole the clothes off the lines."

"In other words, you mean that a bunch of drunken yeggs dropped in on the town, gutted it, and then jumped out . . and we poor, harmless bums are the ones that have to pay."

"—guess that's about how it is."

I passed the word along the line. My companion tramps cursed the yegg and his ways. . .

"They're always raisin' hell . . an' we git the blame . . when all we want is not loot, but hand-outs and a cup o' coffee . . and a piece of change now and then."

The yegg, the tiger among tramps—the criminal tramp—despises the ordinary bum and the "gaycat." And they in turn fear him for his ruthlessness and recklessness.

He joins with them at their camp-fires . . rides with them on the road . . robs his store or house, or cracks his safe, then flies on, taking the blinds or decking on top of a "flyer." The law, missing the right quarry, descends on the slower-moving, harmless bum. And often some poor "fall-guy" gets a good "frame-up" for a job he never thought of . . and the majesty of the law stands vindicated.

The charge against us was vagrancy. We were tried by twos.

"Come on, buddy! . . you an' your pal."

My companion and I were led in before, I think, a justice of the peace. The latter was kindly-disposed toward me because I was young and looked delicate.

When I began my plea for clemency I appropriated the name, career, and antecedents of Simmons, the young soldier whose body-servant I had been, back in San Francisco. The man on the bench was impressed by my story of coming of a wealthy family . . my father was a banker, no less.

The justice waved me aside. He asked my buddy to show his hands. As the callouses on the palms gave evidence of recent hard work, he was set free along with me. We were the only two who were let off. The rest were sent up for three months each, I am told. . .

And, after all that, what did my buddy do but up and steal my blanket roll, with all in it—including my Cæsar and Shakespeare—and my extra soldier uniform—the first chance he got! . .

. . . .

An American who had married a Mexican girl gave me work sawing and chopping wood. I stayed with him long enough to earn a second-hand suit of clothes he owned, which was too small for him, but almost fitted me . . civilian clothes . . my soldier clothes were worn to tatters.

. . . .

I picked up another pal. A chunky, beefy nondescript. I was meditating a jump across "the desert." The older hoboes had warned me against it, saying it was a cruel trip . . the train crews knew no compunction against ditching a fellow anywhere out in the desert, where there would be nothing but a tank of brackish water. . .

My new chum, on the other hand, swore, that, to one who knew the ropes, it was not so hard to make the jump on the Southern Pacific . . through Arizona and New Mexico, to El Paso. He said he would show me how to wiggle into the refrigerator box of an orange car . . on either end of the orange car is a refrigerator box, if I remember correctly . . access to which is gained through the criss-cross bars that hold up a sort of trap-door at the top. It was in the cold season, so there was now no ice inside. These trap-doors are always officially sealed, when the car is loaded. To break a seal is a penitentiary offense.

I stood off and inspected the place I was supposed to go in at. The triangular opening seemed too small for a baby to slide through. I looked my chunky pal up and down and laughed.

"—think I can't make it, eh? . . well, you watch . . there's an art in this kind of thing just like there is in anything."

Inch by inch he squeezed himself in. Then he stood up inside and called to me to try . . and he would pull me the rest of the way, if I stuck. He was plump and I was skinny. It ought to be easy for me. Nevertheless, it was the hardest task I ever set myself . . I stuck half-way. My pal pulled my shirt into rags, helping me through,—I had handed my coat in, previously, or he would have ripped that to pieces, too. It seemed that all the skin went off my hips, as I shot inside with a bang. And none too soon. A "shack" (brakeman) passed over the tops of the cars at almost that very moment. We lay still. He would have handed me a merciless drubbing if he had caught me, with my nether end hanging helplessly on the outside.

. . . .

We squatted on the floor of the refrigerator box. When we reached Yuma my pal rose to his feet.

"Ain't yer goin' ta throw yer feet fer a hand-out?" he asked me.

"No, I'm going to stick in here till I reach El Paso, if I can."

"What's the fun bein' a bum, if you're goin' ter punish yerself like that!"

"I want to find a country where there's growing green things, as soon as I can."

"So long, then."

"So long . . don't you think you'd better stick till we reach Tuscon? Some of the boys told me the 'bulls' (officers) here have been 'horstile' (had it in for the tramp fraternity) . . ever since a yegg bumped off a deputy, a while back."

"Naw, I'll take my chances."

As I rode on, alone, I stood up and took in the scenery like a tourist . . there danced away, and gathered in, the shimmering, sun-flooded desert . . an endless flat expanse of silver sage and sentinel cactus. I saw bleached bones and a side-cast skull with whitened horns, poking up into the sky . . I saw a sick steer straggling alone, exactly like some melodramatic painting of Western life . . the kind we see hanging for sale in second-rate art stores.

. . . .

I stuck till Tuscon was reached. There I was all in for lack of food and water. . .

A woman gave me a good "set-down" at her kitchen table. I was as hungry for something to read as I was for something to eat. When she walked out of the kitchen, leaving me alone for a moment, I caught sight of a compact little Bible that lay on the leaf of her sewing machine. Two steps, and I had it stowed in my hip pocket, and was back innocently eating . . the taking of the Bible was providential. I believe that it served as the main instrument, later on, in saving me from ten years in the penitentiary.

. . . .

I was glad enough to hop to the cinders at El Paso. But El Paso at that time was "unhealthy" for hoboes. They were holding twenty

or thirty of us in the city jail, and mysterious word had gone down
the line in all directions, that quick telegraph by word-of-mouth
that tramps use among themselves, to avoid the town—that it was
"horstile." . .

.   .   .   .

Again rolling miles of arid country. But this time, like a soldier
on a long march, I was prepared: I had begged, from door to door,
enough "hand-outs" to last a week . . throwing away most of the
bread . . keeping the cold meats and the pie and cake. I sat in my
open box-car, on a box that I had flung in with me, reading my Bible
and eating my "hand-outs" and a millionaire had nothing on me
for enjoyment.

I was half-way to San Antonio when I fell in with as jolly a
bunch of bums as I ever hope to see in this world . . just outside a
little town, in the "jungles."

These tramps were gathered together on a definite plan, and I
was invited to join them in it: the plan was, to go, *en masse*, from
town to town, and systematically exploit it; one day one man would
go to the butcher shops, the next, another man would take them,
and the first would, let's say, beg at the baker's . . and each day a
different man would take a different section among the houses.
Then all the food so procured would be put together and shared in
common.

As usual, there was among them an individual who held them
together—the originator of the idea. He was a fat, ruddy-faced
alcoholic ex-cook, who had never held a job for long because he
loved whiskey so much.

Besides being the presiding genius of the gang, he also did all
the cooking. He loved to cook. Each day he jumbled all the mix-
able portions of the food together, and, in a big tin wash-boiler
which he had rescued from "the dump" outside of town, he stewed
up quite a palatable mess which we called "slum" or "slumgullion,"
or, more profanely, "son-of-a-b—."

For plates we used old tomato cans hammered out flat . . for
knives and forks, our fingers, pocket-knives, and chips of wood.

It was a happy life.

One afternoon mysteriously our leader and cook disappeared
—with a broad grin on his face. Soon he returned, rolling a whole
barrel of beer which he had stolen during the night from the back

of a saloon . . and had hidden it nearby in the bushes till it was time to bring it forth. . .

We held a roaring party, and had several fights. ("Slopping up" is what the tramps call a drinking jamboree.) This was the first time I got drunk in my life. It took very little to set me off. . . I burned a big hole in my coat. I woke lying in the mud near the willows . . and with a black eye . . a fellow tramp affectionately showed me his finger that I had bitten severely . . for a day we had bad nerves, and lay about grumbling. . .

We kept quite clean. The tramp is as clean as his life permits him to be . . usually . . the myth about his dirtiness is another of the myths of the newspaper and magazine world . . though I have seen ones who were extraordinarily filthy. . .

We "boiled up" regularly . . and hung our shirts and other articles of apparel on the near-by willows to dry. . .

After about ten days of scientific exploitation of them, the "natives" of the town on the verge of which we were encamping, began to evidence signs of restlessness.

So we moved on to another town by means of a local freight.

Settled there in "the jungles," we hilariously voted to crown the cook our king. We held the ceremony, presenting him with a crown made out of an old tin pan, which one of the more expert among us hammered into a circlet and scoured bright with sand . . .

. . . .

But soon I grew tired of the gang and started on alone.

"You'd better beat it on out of the South as quick as you can," an old tramp had warned me, "they're hell on a bum down here, and harder yet on a Yankee . . no, they haven't forgot *that* yet —not by a damn sight!"

I was soon to wish that I had listened to the old tramp's wisdom.

. . . .

In the chill grey dip of an early spring dawn I dropped off a freight in the yards of the town of Granton.

I drew my threadbare coat closer as I made my way up the track, on the look-out for some place to go into and warm myself. Usually, in chilly weather, each railroad station throughout the country has a stove a-glow in the waiting room . . I found the railroad station, and the stove, red-hot, was there . . it was good to be near a fire. In the South it can be at times heavily cold. There is a moisture and a rawness in the weather, there, that hurts.

I was not alone. Two negro tramps followed me; like myself, seeking warmth and shelter. Then came a white tramp.

We stood around the stove, which shone red in the early half-light of dawn. We shivered and rubbed our hands. Then we fell into tramps' gossip about the country we were in.

The two negroes soon left to catch a freight for Austin. My fellow tramp and I stretched ourselves along the benches. He yawned with a loud noise like an animal. "I'm worn-out," he said, "I've been riding the bumpers all night." I noticed immediately that he did not speak tramp argot.

"And *I* tried to sleep on the bare boards of a box car."

We had disposed ourselves comfortably to sleep for the few hours till wide day, in the station, when the station master came. He poked the fire brighter, shook it down, then turned to us. "Boys," not unkindly, "sorry, but you can't sleep here . . it's the rules."

We shuffled to our feet.

"Do you mind if we stand about the stove till the sun's high enough to take the chill off things?"

"No."

But, standing, we fell to talking . . comparing notes. . .

"I've been through here once before," remarked my companion, whom I never knew otherwise than as "Bud."

"There's a cotton seed mill up the tracks a way toward town, and we can sleep there, if you want . . to-day's Sunday, and no one will be around, working, to disturb us. In the South it's all right for a tramp to sleep among cotton seed, provided he doesn't smoke there."

"Come on, then, let's find a place. I can hardly hold my head up."

We slumped along the track. A cinder cut into my foot through the broken sole of one shoe. It made me wince and limp.

Soon we came to the cotton seed house and looked it over from the outside. It was a four-square building, each side having a door. All the doors but one were locked. That one, when pushed against, tottered over. We climbed in over the heavy sacks, seemingly full of cement, with which the unlocked door had been propped to. It also was unhinged.

It was dark inside. There were no windows.

We struck matches and explored. We found articles of heavier hardware scattered and piled about, some sacks of guano, and about a dozen wired bales of hay.

"I thought this was a cotton seed mill," commented Bud, "because I saw so many niggers working around it, when I passed by, the other time."

"Well, and what is it, then?"

"Evidently a warehouse—where they store heavier articles of hardware."

"What are you going to do?"

"Twist the wires off a couple of these bales of hay, use it for bedding, and have a good sleep anyhow."

"But—suppose we're caught in here?"

"No chance. It's Sunday morning, no one will be here to work to-day, and we'll be let alone."

With a little effort we twisted the bales apart and made comfortable beds from the hay.

It seemed I had slept but a moment when I was seized by a nightmare. I dreamed some monstrous form was bending over me, cursing, breathing flames out of its mouth, and boring a hot, sharpened implement into the centre of my forehead. I woke, to find, that, in part, my dream was true.

There straddled over me an excited man, swearing profusely to keep his courage up. He was pressing the cold muzzle-end of a "forty-four-seventy" into my forehead.

"Come on! Get up, you —— —— ——! Come on out of here, or I'll blow your —— —— —— brains out, do you hear?"

Then I caught myself saying, as if from far away, perfectly calm and composed, and in English that was almost academic— "my dear man, put up your gun and I will go with you quietly. I am only a tramp and not a desperado."

This both puzzled and at the same time reassured my captor . . and made him swear all the louder,—this time, with a note of brave certainty in his tone.

His gun poked me in the back to expedite my exit. I stepped out at the open door into streaming daylight that at first dazzled my eyes. I saw waiting on the track outside a posse of about fifteen citizens.

"Good work, McAndrews," commended one of them, deep-voiced. The others murmured gruff approval.

McAndrews, from conversation that I gathered, was night-watchman in the yards. He had one red-rimmed eye. The other was sightless but had a half-closed leer that seemed to express discreet visual powers.

"Now go on in an' fetch out the other bum," commanded the deep-voiced member of the posse, speaking with authority.

"There wasn't but only this 'un," McAndrews replied, with renewed timidity in his voice, scarcely concealed, and jerking his thumb toward me.

"But the little nigger said they was—ain't that so, nigger?"

"Yassir, boss—I done seen two o' dem go in dar!" replied a wisp of a negro boy, rolling wide eye-whites in fright, and wedged in among the hulking posse.

"Well, this 'un 's all I seen!" protested the night watchman, "an' you betcher I looked about mighty keerful . . wot time did you see 'um break in?" turning to the negro child.

"Jes' at daylight, boss!"

"An' wot was you-all a-doin' down hee-ar?"

"He was a-stealin' coal f'um the coalkiars," put in one of the posse, "in cohse!"

All laughed.

"Anyhow, I done seed two o' dem," protested the boy, comically, "wot evah else I done!"

Everybody was now hilarious.

"Whar's yoah buddy?" I was asked.

"Did unt you-all hev no buddy wit' you?"

"Yes, I did have a buddy with me, but——" trying to give Bud a chance of escape,— "but he caught a freight West, just a little bit ago."

"You're a liar," said the one in authority, who I afterward heard was the head-clerk of the company that ran the warehouse. The negro boy had run to his house and roused him. He had drawn the posse together. . .

"You're a liar! Your buddy's still in there!"

"No, I'll sweah they haint nobuddy else," protested McAndrews.

But prodded by their urging, he climbed in again over the sacks of guano, and soon brought out Bud, who had waked, heard the rumpus, and had been hiding, burrowed down under the hay as deep as he could go.

There was a burst of laughter as he stood framed in the doorway, in which I couldn't help but join. He had such a silly, absurd, surprised look in his face . . a look of stupefied incredulity, when he saw all the men drawn up to receive him. From a straggled lock of hair that fell over one eye hung several long hay-wisps. His face looked stupid and moon-fat. He rolled his big, brown eyes in a despairful manner that was unconsciously comic. For he was, instinctively, as I was not, instantly and fully aware of the seriousness of what might come upon us for our innocent few hours' sleep.

"Come on, boys. Up with your hands till we go through your pockets."

On Bud's hip they found a whiskey flask, quarter-full. In my inside pocket, a sheaf of poor verse—I had barely as yet come to grips with my art—and, in an outside pocket, the Bible I had filched from the woman's sewing machine in Tuscon.

The finding of the Bible on my person created a speechless pause. Then——

"Good Gawd! A bum with a Bible!"

Awe and respect held the crowd for a moment.

.   .   .   .

The march began.

"Where are you taking us to?"

"To the calaboose."

Down a long stretch of peaceful, Sunday street we went—small boys following in a curious horde, and Sunday worshippers with their women's gloved hands tucked in timidly under their arms as we passed by. They gave us prim, askance glances, as if we belonged to a different species of the animal kingdom.

Buck negroes with their women stepped out into the street, while, as is customary there,—the white men passed, taking us two tramps to jail. We came to a high, newly white-washed board fence. Within it stood a two-story building of red brick. On the fence was painted, in big black letters the facetious warning, "Keep out if you can." A passage in through the gate, and McAndrews first knocked at, then kicked against the door.

The sleepy-faced, small-eyed jailer finally opened to us. The wrinkled skin of the old man hung loosely from his neck. It wabbled as he talked.

"What the hell's the mattah with you folks?" protested McAndrews, the night watchman, "slep' late," yawned the jailer, "it bein' Sunday mawhnin'."

By this time the sheriff, summoned from his house, had joined us. A big swashbuckler of a man with a hard face, hard blue eyes with quizzical wrinkles around them. They seemed wrinkles of good humour till you looked closer.

"—s a damn lie . . you 'en Jimmy hev bin a-gamblin' all night," interjected the sheriff, in angry disgust.

. . . .

They marched us upstairs. The whole top floor was given over to a huge iron cage which had been built in before the putting on of the roof. A narrow free space—a sort of corridor, ran all around it, on the outside.

Eager and interested, the prisoners already in the cage pushed their faces against the bars to look at us. But at the sheriff's word of command they went into their cells, the latter built in a row within the cage itself, and obediently slammed their doors shut while a long iron bar was shot across the whole length, from without . . then the big door of the cage was opened, and we were thrust in. The bar was drawn back, liberating the others, then, from their cells.

The posse left. Our fellow prisoners crowded about us, asking us questions . . what had we done? . . and how had we been caught? . . and what part of the country were we from? . . etc. etc. . .

From the North . . yes, Yankee . . well, when a fellow was both a Yank and a tramp he was given a short shrift in the South.

They talked much about themselves . . one thing, however, we all held in common . . our innocence . . we were all innocent . . every one of us was innocent of the crime charged against us . . we were just being persecuted.

. . . .

That afternoon a negro preacher, short and squat, who, innocent, was yet being held for Grand Jury, delivered us a fearful half-chanted sermon on the Judgment Day. I never heard so moving, compelling a sermon. I saw the sky glowing like a furnace, the star-

touching conflagration of the End of Things rippling up the east
in increasing waves of fire, in place of the usual dawn . . I heard
the crying of mankind . . of sinners . . for mountains to topple
over on them and cover them from the wrath of the Lord. . .

. . . .

"In co'hse I nevah done it," explained the preacher, "I had
some hawgs of mah own. Mah hawgs had an under-bit an' an ovah-
bit in dere eahs, an' de ones I's 'cused o' stealin', dey had only an
ovah-bit. But heah dey's got me, holdin' me foh de pen."

. . . .

The little grey-faced pickpocket—caught at his trade at the
Dallas Fair, told me how easy it was to add an under-bit to an over-
bit to the ears of the two hogs stolen, "Sure that sneakin' niggah
pahson did it," he averred—but all the while he likewise averred that
he hadn't picked the pocket of the man from whom he was accused
of stealing a wallet. . .

"Yes, I'll admit Ah've done sech things. But this taime they was
sure wrong. Ef I git framed up," he added, "I mean tuh study
law . . pull foh a job in th' prison libery an' read up . . an' take
up practice when I serve my term."

Beside the hog-stealing parson and the little grey-faced pick-
pocket there were also:

A big negro youth, black as shiny coal, who was being held over
on appeal. He'd been sentenced to ninety-nine years for rape of
a negro girl . . if it had been a white girl he would have been
burned long ago, he said . . as it was, the sheriff's son, who was
handling his case, would finally procure his release—and exact, in
return, about ten years' of serfdom as payment. And there was
a young, hard-drinking quarrelsome tenant-farmer, who was charged
with having sold two bales of cotton not belonging to him, to get
money for drinking. . .

There was another negro, hanging-handed, simous-faced, who had,
in a fit of jealousy, blown two heads off by letting loose both barrels
at once of his heavily charged shotgun . . the heads were his wife's
. . and her lover's. He caught them when their faces were close
together . . and they were kissing. But he seemed a gentle creature,
tractable and harmless.

On the outside of the cage in which we were cooped like menagerie
animals, a negro girl had her cot. She slept and lived out there

by the big stove which heated the place. She was a girl of palish yellow colour. She was a trusty. She had been caught watching outside of a house while two grown-up negro women went within to rob.

. . . .

Monday morning "kangaroo court" was called . . that court which prisoners hold, mimicking the legal procedure to which they grow so accustomed during their lives. We were arraigned for trial —the charge against us, that of "Breaking Into Jail."

The cotton thief served as prosecuting attorney. The negro youth in for rape of one of his own colour,—the sergeant-at-arms; while the negro preacher in for hog-stealing defended us . . and he did it so well that we were let off with ten blows of the strap a-piece. We had no money to be mulcted of, nor were we able to procure from friends, as the custom is, funds for the buying of whiskey and tobacco.

. . . .

In a few days Bud and I had settled down into the routine of jail-life. Every morning we swept our cells, and all the prisoners took turns sweeping the corridor. The fine for spitting on the floor was ten lashes laid on hard. And each day before breakfast we soaked the seams of our clothes in vile-smelling creosote to kill off the lice and nits. We had no chance to bathe, and were given but little water to wash our face and hands.

. . . .

"I wonder what they are going to do with us?"

"Anything they please," answered Bud gloomily.

"From thirty to ninety days on the county farm, I suppose?"

"We'll be lucky if we don't get from four to ten years in the pen."

"What for?"

"Burglary—didn't we break into that warehouse?"

. . . .

Our meals were passed in to us through an open space near the level of the floor, at the upper end of the cage, where a bar had been removed for that purpose. We'd line up and the tin plates would be handed in, one after the other . . two meals a day. For breakfast a corn pone of coarse, white corn meal, and a bit of fried sow-belly. For dinner, all the water we could drink. For supper, breakfast all over again, with the addition of a dab of greens. On rare occasions the sheriff's son or the jailer went hunting . . and then we'd have rabbit. The sheriff had the contract, at so much per head, for feeding the prisoners.

Each morning I used to ask the jailer for the occasional newspaper with which he covered the basket in which he brought our food to us. One morning my eyes fell upon an interesting item:

The story of how two young desperadoes had been caught in the warehouse beside the railroad track, in the act of committing burglary . . the tale of our capture was briefly told . . the bravery of the night watchman and the posse extolled . . and the further information was conveyed, that, having waved preliminary examination (and we had, for they told us the justice was continually too drunk to examine us) we were being held over for Grand Jury . . on a charge of burglary.

Though he had predicted this, the actuality of it struck Bud all of a heap. He paced up and down the cage for the full space of an hour, hanging his ungainly head between his shoulders in abandonment to despair.

My reaction was a strange one. I wanted to sing . . whistle . . dance . . I was in the midst of adventure and romance. I was a Count of Monte Cristo, a Baron von Trenck. I dreamed of linguistic and philosophic studies in the solitude of my cell at the penitentiary till I was master of all languages, of all wisdom, or I dreamed of escape and of rising to wealth and power, afterwards, so that I would be pardoned and could come back and magnanimously shame with my forgiveness the community that had sent me up.

Bud stopped his pacing to and fro to stand in our cell-doorway. I was sitting on a stool, thinking hard.

"We can't do a thing," said Bud, "we're in for it, good and proper."

"—tell you what *I'll* do," I responded, "I'll write a letter to the owner of the warehouse and appeal to his humanity."

"You romantic jack-ass," yelled Bud, his nerves on edge. He walked away angry. He came back calmer.

"Look here, Gregory, I want you to excuse that outburst—but you *are* a fool. This is *real life* we're up against now. You're not reading about this in a book."

"We'll see what can be done," I returned.

.   .   .   .

At the extreme end of the big cage, the end furthest from the entrance door, stood two cells not occupied. The last of these I had chosen for my study, a la Monte Cristo. The sheriff's son had lent me a dozen of Opie Reid's novels, a history of the Civil War from the Southern viewpoint, an arithmetic, and an algebra. Here all day long I studied and wrote assiduously. And it was here I went to sit on my stool and write the letter to the owner of the warehouse . . a certain Mr. Womber. . .

In it I pointed out the enormity of sending to the penitentiary two young men, on a merely technical charge of burglary. For if we had gone into the place to rob, why had we so foolishly, then, gone to sleep? And what, at the final analysis, could we have stolen but bales of hay, sacks of guano, and plowshares? All of them too unwieldy to carry away unless we had other conveyance than our backs. It was absurd, on the face of it.

Furthermore, I appealed to him, as a Christian, to let us go free . . in the name of God, not to wreck our lives by throwing us, for a term of years, into contact with criminals of the hardened type— to give us one more chance to become useful citizens of our great and glorious country.

Bud laughed sneeringly when I read the letter aloud to him . . said it was a fine effort as a composition in rhetoric, but I might expect nothing of it—if the perpetually drunk jailer really brought it to its destination—except that it would be tossed unread into the wastebasket. . .

I pleaded with the jailer to deliver it for me . . told him how important it would be to our lives . . adjured him to consider our helpless and penniless state. He promised to deliver it for me.

"I have nothing to give you, now," I ended, "but, if I ever get free, I'll send you twenty-five dollars or so from up home, when I reach the North."

.   .   .   .

A prisoner's first dream is "escape." Voices outside on the street, the sight of the tops of green trees through bars, dogs barking far away, the travels of the sun as shown by moving bands of light on the walls and in the cells—all remind him of the day when he was, as he now sees it, happy and free . . he forgets entirely, in the midst of the jail's black restraints, the lesser evils of outside, daily life. Even the termagant wife is turned into a domestic angel.

.   .   .   .

Under the smoky prison lamp made of a whiskey bottle filled with oil, and a shred of shirt drawn through a cork, we planned to cut out.

"The way to do it is easy," said the little pickpocket, "in the sole of every good shoe is a steel spring. I'll take the steel from my shoe. There's already one bar removed from the chuck-hole (No use trying to reproduce the dialect). If we saw out another bar, that will give us enough room for going through. Then it will be easy to dig out the mortar between the bricks, in the jail wall. Once out, we can make for the river bottoms, and, by wading in the water, even their bloodhounds can't track us."

"And once I get over into Indian Territory or Arkansas, you'll never see me in Texas again," I muttered.

"How'll we conceal where we've been sawing?" Bud asked.

"By plugging up the grooves with corn bread blackened with soot that we can make by holding the wick of this smoky lamp against the cage-ceiling."

"And how'll we keep folks from hearing the sawing?"

"By dancing and singing while Baykins here" (alluding to a "pore white" fiddler who had almost killed a man at a dance) "while Baykins here plays 'whip the devil.'"

The very next day we began dancing and singing and taking turns at the chuckhole bar.

"Whip the Devil" is an interminable tune like the one about the "old woman chasing her son round the room with a broom." . .

The mistake was, that in our eagerness we "whipped the devil" too long at a time. Naturally, the jailer grew suspicious of such sudden and prolonged hilarity. But even at that it took almost a week for them to catch on. We knew it was all up when, one morning at breakfast, the sheriff came in with the jailer.

"Boys, all back into your cells!" he growled.

The long bar was thrown over our closed doors.

The sheriff stooped down and inspected the chuck-hole.

"Why, Jesus Christ, they'd of been through in two more nights. It's good we caught them in time or they'd of been a hell of a big jail-delivery . . do you mean to tell me," turning to the jailer, "you never noticed this before?" and with one finger he raked out the blackened corn bread.

"You see, I'm a little near-sighted, Mistah Jenkins."

"Too damned near-sighted, an' too damned stupid, too."

The big iron door of the cage was locked again, the long bar thrown off our cell doors.

"Now, you sons of b—— can come out into the cage again; but, mind you, if any of you try such a thing again, I'll take you out one by one and give you all a rawhiding."

We received the abuse in sullen silence. For three days our rations lacked cornpone, for punishment.

We decided among ourselves that the negro preacher, to stand in well with the authorities, had given us away. . .

And if he had not, panic-stricken, pleaded with the sheriff to be taken out and put in a separate cell, I believe we would have killed him.

$\bullet$ $\quad$ $\bullet$ $\quad$ $\bullet$ $\quad$ $\bullet$ $\quad$ $\bullet$ $\quad$ $\bullet$ $\quad$ $\bullet$

There was one more way. It was so simple a way that we had not thought of it before. The mulatto girl, who slept by the big stove, on a cot, just outside the cage . . a trusty and the jailer's unwilling concubine . . this slim, yellow creature was much in love with the lusty young farmer who had stolen the bales of cotton and sold them for a drunk. And it was he who suggested that, through her, we get possession of the keys. For, every day, she informed us, she passed them by where they hung on a nail, downstairs, as she swept and cleaned house for the jailer.

It was not a difficult matter to procure them. She would bring them up to us and hand them in through the chuck-hole, which the village blacksmith had repaired and once more reinforced with extra bars, "so them bastards won't even think of sawing out again," as the jailer had expressed it.

The evening she handed the keys in to us we were so excited we wanted to have "Whip the Devil" played again for our singing and dancing. But this might have once more awakened suspicion. Before, we had raised such a row as to have caused pedestrians to stop and listen in groups, wondering what made the men inside so happy. . .

There were three separate locks on the great cage door. One, two of them went back with an easy click. For the third we could

find no key. There was nothing else to do now but to have recourse
to singing and dancing again. Baykins started sawing his fiddle
furiously while the big negro in for rape hammered and hammered
on the lock to break it, with one prison stool after another, till
all were tossed aside, broken as kindling wood is broken. It was
good that the jailer was either deaf, or, like the heathen gods in
the Old Testament, away on a journey. Finally, we gave up in
despair. The big negro collapsed with a wail. The first sign of
weakness I ever detected in him.

"Now it's shore either ninety-nine yeahs in de pen foh me, or ten
yeahs for th' sheriff's son foh lawyah fees .. an' the footprints in
de flowah bed .. of the man what done de rape was two sizes biggah
dan mine."

.   .   .   .   .   .

The next day the jailer, of course, missed the keys. Panic-
stricken, the mulatto girl was afraid to slip them back to their
accustomed nail, for fear she'd be seen at it; or was it out of
vindictiveness against the jailer that she had now actually hidden
them somewhere (for, finding them of no use, we had handed them
back to her)!

That same afternoon the sheriff, with his son and the little,
shrivelled, stuttering, half-deaf jailer, came in at the door of the big
room. It was easy to see what they wanted. They wanted the keys
and they were going to make the girl confess where they were .. as
she was the only other person, beside the prison authorities, that
was in the way to come at them.

"Martha, we want them keys! Show us where they is, like a good
girl!"

" 'Deed, Ah don' know where dey is a-tall, Marse Sheriff!"

"Come on, gal, you was the only one downstairs exceptin' Jacklin
heah!" pointing to the jailer.

The jailer nodded his head asseveratingly.

"Yes, Martha, tell us whar the keys air," urged the latter, with
caressing softness and fright in his voice. He didn't want his
mistress whipped.

"If you don't, by God, I'll whup the nigger hide clean off yore
back," and the sheriff reached for the braided whip which his son
Jimmy handed him.

"I sweah Ah don' know where dey is!"

"You dirty liah," taking out a watch; "I'll give you jest five minutes t' tell, an' then——" he menaced with the up-lifted whip.

In stubborn silence the girl waited the five minutes out.

"Jimmy! . . Jacklin! . . throw her down an' hold her, rump up, over that cot." They obeyed. With a jerk the sheriff had her dress up and her bare buttocks in view.

"I'm a-goin' to whup an' whup till you confess, Martha."

Crack! Crack! Crack! the whip descended, leaving red whelts each time. The mulatto girl writhed, but did not cry quits. Beads of perspiration glistened on the jailer's face. The girl shook off his lax grip on her arms . . the sheriff's son was holding her legs. We were crowded against the bars, angry and silent. We admired the girl's hopeless pluck. We saw she was holding out just to, somehow, have vengeance on the jailer for her being held in unwilling concubinage by him, hoping he would catch it hard for having let the keys hang carelessly in open view, and so, stolen.

"Damn you, Jacklin," shouted the sheriff, "I believe you're a little soft on the gal . . come here . . you swing the whip an' I'll hold her arms."

In mute agony Jacklin obeyed . . whipping the woman of whom he was fond.

"Harder, Jacklin, harder," and the sheriff drew his gun on him to emphasise the command.

Under such impulsion, a shower of heavy blows fell. The girl screamed.

"I'll give up. . . Oh, good Lordy, I'll give up."

And she dug the keys out from under the mattress across which they had whipped her.

After they had gone she lay crying on her face for a long while. When night came she still lay crying. Nothing any of us could say would console her. Not even the little white cotton thief had power to allay her hurt. . .

At last we began cursing and railing at her. That made her stop, after a fashion. But still she occasionally gave vent to a heart-deep, dry, racking sob.

.   .   .   .

Locked in there behind bars and forced to be impotent onlookers, the whipping we had witnessed made us as restless as wild animals. That night, under the dim flare of our jail-made lamps, the boys gambled as usual, for their strips of paper,—and as eagerly as if it were real currency. I, for my part, drew away to the vacant cell at the far end of the cage to study and read and dream my dreams. . .

As I sat there I was soon possessed with a disagreeable feeling that a malignant, ill-wishing presence hovered near. I shifted in my seat uneasily. I looked up. There stood, in the doorway, the lusty young farmer who was in for stealing the bales of cotton. He wore an evil, combative leer on his face. He was "spoiling" for a quarrel—just for the mere sake of quarrelling—that I could see. But I dissembled.

"Well, Jack?" I asked gently.

"You're a nice one," he muttered, "you pale-faced Yankee son of a b—— . . think you're better 'n the rest of us, don't ye? . . readin' in yore books?"

"Nonsense, what are you picking at me for? I'm not harming anybody, am I?"

"No, but you're a God damned fool!"

"Look here, what have I ever done to you?"

"Nothin', only you're a white-livered stinker, an' I'm jest a-spoilin' foh a fight with you-all."

"But I don't want to fight with you."

"I'll make you," he replied, striding in; and fetching me a cuff on the ear . . then, in a far-away voice that did not seem myself, I heard myself pleading to be let alone . . by this time all the other boys had crowded down about the cell to see the fun.

I was humiliated, ashamed . . but, try as I would, the thought and vision of my uncle came on me like a palsy.

Bud stepped up. He had always been so meek and placid before that what he did then was a surprise to me.

"*I'll* fight!"

"What! you?" glowered the young farmer, surprised.

"Yes, I'll give you all the fighting you want, you dirty cotton thief!"

Instantly the farmer made at him. Bud ran in, fetched him two blows in the face, and clinched.

It was not going very well for the desperado. From somewhere on his person he whipped forth a knife, and, with a series of flashes through the air, began stabbing Bud again and again in the back.

I thank God for what came over me then. Too glad of soul to believe it, I experienced a warm surge of angry courage rushing through me like an electric storm. All the others were panic-stricken for the moment. But I burst through the group, rushed back to the toilet, and, with frenzied strength, tore loose a length of pipe from the exposed plumbing. I came rushing back. I brought down the soft lead-pipe across "Jack's" ear, accompanying the blow with a volley of oaths in a roaring voice.

The farmer whipped about to face his new antagonist, letting Bud drop back. Bud sank to the iron floor. The farmer was astonished almost to powerlessness to find facing him, with a length of swinging pipe in his hand, the boy who had a few minutes before been afraid.

But he rapidly recovered and came on at me, gibbering like an incensed baboon.

By this time all the humiliations I had suffered in the past, since succumbing to the fear-complex that my uncle had beaten into me—all the outrage of them was boiling in me for vengeance. I saw the blood bathing the torn ear of my antagonist. It looked beautiful. I was no longer afraid of anything. Yelling my uncle's name I came on. . . I beat the knife out of the other's hand and bloodied his knuckles with the next blow. I beat him down with rapid blows, threshing at him, shouting and yelling exultantly.

The other men thought me gone crazy. I had, for the time, gone crazy. The fellow lay at my feet, inert. I stopped for the moment.

In that moment the gang began to close in on me, half frightened themselves. I threatened them back.

"By hell, I've had enough of bullying," I shouted wildly; "I'm not afraid of anything or anybody any more . . if there's anyone else here that wants a taste of this pipe, let them step up."

"We ain't a-tryin' to fight you-all," called out the big negro who was in for rape, "we jest don' want you to kill him an' git hung foh murduh."

At the word "murder" I stepped quickly back.

"Well, don't let him come bothering me or my pal for a fight any more when we've done nothing to him."

"Don' worry, he won't no moh!" assured the fiddler. . .

I threw down the lead pipe. It had seemed to me that all the while it was my Uncle Landon who had received the blows.

The rough-neck farmer was in bad shape; he was bloodied all over like a stuck pig. The mulatto girl on the outside had for the last five minutes been occupied in calling out of the window for help. She managed to attract the attention of a passerby-by.

"What's the matter?" was called up to her. . .

"The jailer ain't downstairs . . an' de boys is killin' each other up heah!"

. . . .

By the time the angry-faced sheriff came with his son, the jailer, and a couple of doctors, we had quieted down.

Bud and the farmer were taken out; by the side of each a pail of water was placed . . they were seated on stools, stripped to the waist. The surgeons dressed their wounds as if on a battlefield. "Jack" needed ten stitches in his scalp. . . Bud had four knife wounds that demanded sewing up. Both the boys went pale like ghosts and spewed their bellies empty from weakness and loss of blood. . .

"Mind you, you chaps in there have raised 'bout enough hell . . ef I hear o' any more trouble, I'll take you all out one by one an' treat each one o' you-all to a good cowhidin', law or no law!"

. . . .

I was let alone after that. My cowardice had gone forever. I was now a man among men. I was happy. I saw what an easy thing it is to fight, to defend yourself. I saw what an exhilaration, a pleasure, the exchanging of righteous blows can be.

. . . .

Always my dream was of being a big man when I got out—some day. Always I acted as if living a famous prison romance like that of Baron Von Trenck's.

. . . .

I collected from the living voices of my fellow prisoners innumerable jail and cocaine songs, and rhymes of the criminal world. I wrote them down on pieces of wrapping paper that the jailer occasionally covered the food-basket with in lieu of newspaper.

> "Oh, coco-Marie, and coco-Marai,
>   I'se gon' ta whiff cocaine 'twill I die.
>   Ho! (sniff) Ho! (sniff) baby, take a whiff of me!"

(The sniffing sound indicating the snuffing up into the nostril of the "snow," or "happy dust," as it is called in the underworld.)

Then there was the song about lice:

> "There's a lice in jail
> As big as a rail;
> When you lie down
> They'll tickle your tail—
> Hard times in jail, poor boy! . . "

And another, more general:

> "Along come the jailer
> About 'leven o'clock,
> Bunch o' keys in his right hand,
> The jailhouse do'h was locked . .
> 'Cheer up, you pris'ners,'
> I heard that jailer say,
> 'You got to go to the cane-brakes
> Foh ninety yeahs to stay!' "

As you can guess, most of these jail songs and ballads of the underworld could only be printed in asterisks. I was hoping, in the interests of folklore, to preserve them for some learned society's private printing press.

    .   .   .   .

A fresher green came to the stray branches of the trees that crossed our barred windows. The world outside seemed to waken with bird-song. It was spring, and time for the sitting of the grand jury that was to decide whether we were, each of us, to be held over for trial by petty jury . . days of fretful eagerness and discontent . . from the windows the yellow trusty-girl said she could see lines of buggies driving in to town. It was the custom of farmers for miles around to drive in to their county seat during the court assizes . . a week or so of holidays like a continuous circus for them.

When the sheriff would have occasion to come into the room in which stood our big cage, the boys would crowd up to the bars, each one hoping for news favourable to his case . . the prevailing atmosphere was one of hope.

    .   .   .   .

The negro who had murdered his wife and her sweetheart with a shotgun had already had his trial. He was—and had been—but waiting the arrival of the prison contractor, as the latter went from county jail to county jail, gathering in his flock, and taking them away, chained together, to the penitentiary and the cane brakes . . "where only a big buck nigger can live," the little pick-pocket had told me, with fear in his voice. . .

He came . . the contractor . . to our jail at midnight. All of us leaped from our mattresses to witness the dreary procession of neck-chained and be-manacled convicted men. In the light of the swinging lanterns, a lurid spectacle. Our man was taken out and chained in with the gang. They clanked away down the stairs, leaving us who remained with heavy chains on our hope instead of on our necks and hands and legs . . because of the sight we had just seen. For the passing day or so we were so depressed that we wandered about saying nothing to each other, like dumb men.

   .   .   .   .

One after the other the men had true bills found against them, and little slips of folded paper were thrust in to them through the bars of their cells. And shyster lawyers who fatten on the misfortunes of the prison-held being, began to hold whispered conversations (and conferences) from without, mainly to find out just how much each prisoner could raise for fees for defence. . .

Bud and I were the only ones left. All the others had had true bills found against them.

   .   .   .   .

But there came an afternoon when the big, hulky sheriff, with the cruel, quizzical eyes, came to the back bars of our cell and summoned us up with a mysterious air. . .

"Well, boys," he began, pausing to squirt a long, brown stream of tobacco juice, "well, boys——" and he paused again.

My nerves were so on edge that I controlled with difficulty a mad impulse to curse at the sheriff for holding us in such needless suspense. . .

Taking another deliberate chew off his plug, he told us that after mature deliberation the grand jury had decided that there was not enough grounds for finding a true bill against us, and, as a consequence, we were to be let go free.

   .   .   .   .

The following morning I had the satisfaction of hearing from old Jacklin, the jailer, that Womber, the owner of the warehouse, had himself gone before the grand jury and informed them that he did not wish to press the charge of burglary against us. . .

Womber, Jacklin said, had received my letter and at first had tossed it aside . . even thrown it contemptuously into the waste-basket. But his wife and daughter had raked it out and read it and had, day and night, given him no peace till he had promised to "go easy on the poor boys."

This was my triumph over Bud—the triumph of romance over realism.

"I'm glad we're getting out, but there's more damn fools in the world than I thought," he remarked, with a sour smile of gratification.

. . . .

And now, with new, trembling eagerness, we two began waiting for the hour of our release. That very afternoon it would be surely, we thought . . that night . . then the next morning . . then . . the next day. . .

But until a week more had flown, the sheriff did not let us go. In order to make a little more profit on his feeding contract, averred our prisoners.

But on Saturday morning he came to turn us loose. By this time we seemed blood brothers to the others in the cage . . negro . . mulatto . . white . . criminal and vicious . . weak, and victims of circumstance . . everything sloughed away. Genuine tears stood in our eyes as with strong hand-grips we wished the poor lads good luck!

We stumbled down the jail stairway up which, three months before, we had been conducted to our long incarceration in the cage. The light of free day stormed in on our prison-inured eyes in a blinding deluge of white and gold . . we stepped out into what seemed not an ordinary world, but a madness and tumult of birds, a delirious green of trees too beautiful for any place outside the garden of Paradise.

"Come on," said Bud, "let's go on down the main street and thank Womber for not pressing the case——"

"To hell with Womber!"

"Well, then, I'm going to thank him."

"I'm grateful enough . . I might write him a letter thanking him . . but I'm not anxious to linger in this neighbourhood."

So Bud and I parted company, shaking hands good-bye; he headed west . . to China and the East, finally, he said . . I never knew his real name . . neither of us gave his right name to the town's officials. . .

As I sought the railroad tracks again, the good air and my unwonted freedom made me stagger, so that several negroes laughed at me heartily, thinking I was drunk.

.   .   .   .

I sat down on a railroad tie and tenderly and solicitously took a brown package out of my inside pocket—the brown paper on which I had inscribed with enthusiasm the curious songs of jail, cocaine, criminal, and prostitute life I had heard during my three months' sojourn behind bars.

I looked them over again. With all their smut and filth, they were yet full of naïve folk-touches and approximations to real balladry. I was as tender of the manuscript as a woman would be with her baby.

.   .   .   .   .   .

The sky grew overcast. A rain storm blew up. A heavy wind mixed with driving wet . . chilly . . I found shelter under a leaky shed . . was soggy and miserable . . even wished, in a weak moment, for the comparative comfort of my cell again. . .

The fast freight I was waiting for came rocking along. I made a run for it in the rapidly gathering dusk. I grabbed the bar on one side and made a leap for the step, but missed, like a frantic fool, with one foot—luckily caught it with the other, or I might have fallen underneath—and was aboard, my arms almost wrenched from their sockets.

Not till I had climbed in between the cars on the bumpers did I realise that my coat had been torn open and my much-valued songs jostled out.

Without hesitation I hurled myself bodily off the train. My one idea to regain the MSS. I landed on my shoulders, saw stars, rolled over and over. I groped up and down. And tears rained from my eyes when I understood those rhymes were lost forever . . .

It was midnight before I caught another freight. I climbed wearily into an empty box car while the freight was standing still.

I was seen. A brakeman came to the door and lifted up his lantern, glancing within. I was crouching, wet and forlorn, in a corner of the car, waiting for the freight to be under way.

"Come on out with you! Hit the grit!" commanded the "shack" grimly.

I rose. I came to the door. I hated him in my heart, but quite simply and movingly I recited the story of my imprisonment, ending by asking him to let me ride, in the name of God.

He crunched away down the path, his lantern bobbing as he went.

   •   •   •   •   •   •   •

All night long I rode .. bumpity-bump, bumpity-bump, bumpity-bump! All night long my head was a-ferment with dreams of the great things I would achieve, now that I was free of the shadow of imprisonment.

   •   •   •   •   •   •   •

When I walked down the streets of Haberford once more, though I was leathery and stronger-looking, my adventures had added no meat to my bones. I was amused at myself as I walked along more than usually erect, for no other reason than to keep my coat-tail well down in back in order not to show the hole in the seat of my trousers. As I came down the street on which my father and I had lived, an anticipatory pleasure of being recognised as a sort of returned Odysseus beat through my veins like a drum. But no one saw me who knew me. It hurt me to come home, unheralded.

I came to the house where I had dwelt. I pulled the bell. There was no answer. I walked around the corner to the telegraph office. I was overjoyed to see lean, lanky Phil, the telegraph operator, half sleeping, as usual, over the key of his instrument.

"Hel-lo, John Gregory!" he shouted, with glad surprise in his voice.

   •   •   •   •   •   •   •

He telephoned my father .. who came over from the works, running with gladness. I was immediately taken home. I took three baths that afternoon before I felt civilised again. . .

   •   •   •   •   •   •   •

My father had returned to the Composite Works. I was alone in my little room, with all my cherished books once more. They had been, I could plainly observe, kept orderly and free of dust, against my home-coming. I took down my favourite books, kissing each

one of them like a sweetheart. Then I read here and there in all
of them, observing all the old passages I had marked. I lay in all
attitudes. Sprawling on the floor on my back, on my belly . . on
my side . . now with my knees crossed. . .

Whitman, Shakespeare, Scott, Shelley, Byron . . Speke, Burton,
Stanley . . my real comrades! . . my real world! Rather a world
of books than a world of actuality! . .

I was so glad to be among my books again that for a month I
gave no thought to the future. I did nothing but read and study
. . except at those times when I was talking to people prodigiously
of my trip and what I had seen and been through. And naturally
and deftly I wove huge strips of imagination and sheer invention
into the woof of every tale or anecdote. . .

I captained ships, saw Chinese slaughtered by the thousands,
fought bandits on the outskirts of Manila, helped loot the palace
of the empress in the Sacred City at Pekin . . tales of peril and
adventure that I had heard others relate at camp-fires, in jail, in
the forecastle, on the transport, I unhesitatingly appropriated as
my own experiences.

All the papers printed stories about me. And I was proud
about it. And I became prouder still when I sold a story in two
parts to a New York Sunday paper. . . I liked the notoriety. . .

But as usual, the yarns I retailed struck in upon my own imagination, too . . just as had my earlier stories of killing Indians.
Particularly the tale I had related of having seen dead Chinamen
in heaps with their heads lopped off. A nightmare of this imaginary
episode began to come to me. And another dream I had—of a
huge Boxer, with a cutlass, standing over me. And he was about
to carve me piecemeal while I lay bound and helpless before him.
The dream persisted so strongly that, after I awoke, I still seemed
to see him standing in a corner of my room. And I cried aloud.
And felt foolish when it brought my father in. So I stopped making
up adventures, especially the disagreeable ones, because they
eventually had more effect on me than they did on my auditors.

.   .   .   .

My father had changed boarding places . . but, as usual, it was
not better food, but a little, dark widow that attracted him to
that boarding house.

.   .   .   .

I now devoted myself exclusively to poetry—the reading of it. I always had a book in my pocket. I read even at meals, despite my father's protests that it was bad-mannered.

　　.　　　　.　　　　.　　　　.　　　　.　　　　.　　　　.

Breasted's book store, down in Newark, was where I was nearly always to be found, in the late afternoons.

It was there, in the murky light of a dying twilight, that I came upon the book that has meant more to my life than any other book ever written. . .

For a long time I had known of John Keats, that there was such a poet. But, in the fever of my adolescence, in the ferment of my tramp-life, I had not yet procured his poetry. . .

Now, here were his complete works, right at hand, in one volume . . a damaged but typographically intact copy. . .

I had, once before, dipped into his *Endymion* and had been discouraged . . but this time I began to read him with his very first lines—his dedication to Leigh Hunt, beginning:

"Glory and loveliness have passed away."

Then I went on to a pastoral piece:

"I stood tiptoe upon a little hill."

I forgot where I was. A new world of beauty was opened to me. . . I read and read. . .

"Come, Gregory, it's time to close"—a voice at my elbow. It was Breasted's assistant, a little, curious man who reminded me of my sky-pilot at Sydney. He, also, wore a black, long-tailed coat. He was known as "the perfessor."

"You've been standing here as quiet as a crane for three hours."

"How much do you want for this book?"

"A quarter . . for you!" He always affected to make me special reductions, as an old customer. . .

A quarter was all I had. I paid for my Keats, and walked home. Walked? I went with wings on each heel. I was as genuinely converted to a new life as a sinner is converted to the Christian religion.

I lit the light in my room. All night I read and re-read, not a whit sleepy or tired.

I went for a week in a mad dream, my face shining and glowing with inner ecstasy and happiness.

　　.　　　　.　　　　.　　　　.　　　　.　　　　.

There did not seem to be time enough in the twenty-four hours of each day for reading and studying and writing. And a new thing came to me: a shame for my shadow thinness and a desire to build myself into a better physical man.

At that time *McFadden's Physical Culture Magazine* was becoming widely read. I came across a copy of it. I found in it a guide to what I was in search for. Faithfully I took up physical culture. Fanatically I kept all the windows open, wore as little clothing as possible .. adopted a certain walk on tiptoe, like a person walking on egg-shells, to develop the calves of my legs from their thinness to a more proportionate shape. And, as I walked, I filled and emptied my lungs like a bellows. I kept a small statue of Apollo Belvedere on top of my bookcase. I had a print of the Flying Mercury on the wall, at the foot of my bed. Each morning, on waking, I filled my mind full of these perfect specimens of manhood, considering that by so doing I would gradually pilot my body to physical perfection. . . I know that many things I say about myself will appeal to the "wit" as humorous. I can't help it if I am laughed at .. everybody would be, if they told the truth about themselves, like this.

.   .   .   .

I joined the Y. M. C. A. for the physical side, not for the spiritual. I found a spirit that I did not like there, a sort of mental deadness and ineffectuality. But one thing the Y. M. C. A. did for me: I found on the bulletin board one day an announcement of the summer term of Mt. Hebron Preparatory School. . . It was a school for poor boys and men .. neither age nor even previous preparation counted .. only earnestness of purpose. And, as each student had his two hours' work a day to do, the expense for each term was nominal.

I had been paid fifty dollars for my article on my adventures in the New York Sunday paper. A Newark Sunday paper bought several articles also. To the money I had saved up my father contributed as much again. I started for preparatory school.

.   .   .   .

Mt. Hebron School consisted of a series of buildings set apart on a hill. It was an evangelical school founded by a well-known revivalist—William Moreton.

Around it lay pine forests and, at its feet, the valley of the
Connecticut River.

No matter what subjects they taught, the main endeavour
of its professors, in season and out, was the conversion of every
freshman immediately to Evangelical Christianity, as soon as he
had had his quarters assigned to him. . .

Scarcely had we settled ourselves, each with his roommate, than
the two weeks' revival began. I will not enter into the details of
this revival. This was merely the opening of the summer term.
At the opening of the school year in the fall—that was when they
held the *real* revival,—and the story of the whipped-up frenzy of
that will afford a more characteristic flavour.

. 　 . 　 . 　 . 　 . 　 . 　 .

It put a singing in my heart to find myself at last a student in a
regular preparatory school, with my face set toward college.

I had passed my examinations with credit, especially the one in
the Bible. This won me immediate notice and approval among the
professors. Fortunate, indeed, I now regarded those three months
in jail . . the most fruitful and corrective period of my life. For
not only had I studied the Bible assiduously there, but I had
learned American history—especially that of the Civil War period
. . and I had studied arithmetic and algebra, so that in these
subjects I managed to slide through.

. 　 . 　 . 　 . 　 . 　 . 　 .

I was put to cleaning stalls and currying horses for my two hours'
work each day. Though I hated manual labour, I bent my back
to the tasks with a will, glad to endure for the fulfillment of my
dream.

That first summer I took Vergil and began Homer. I had studied
these poets by myself already, but found many slack ends that only
the aid and guidance of a professor could clear up. And, allowing
for their narrow religious viewpoints, real or affected, in order to
hold their positions, they were fine teachers—my teachers of Latin
and Greek—with real fire in them . . Professor Lang made Homer
and his days live for us. The old Greek warriors rose up from the
dust, and I could see the shining of their armour, hear the clash
of their swords.

Professor Dunn made of Vergil a contemporary poet. . .

Lang was of the fair Norse type, so akin to the Greek in adven-

turous spirit. Dunn was of the dark, stocky, imperial Roman type.
In a toga he would have resembled some Roman senator. . .

That summer there were long woodland walks for me, when I
would take a volume of some great English poet from the library and
roam far a-field.

.   .   .   .

After that first summer it was my father who kept me at school.
He was too poor to pay in a lump sum for my tuition, so he sent
four dollars every week from his meagre pay, to keep me going.

.   .   .   .

There was a wide, wind-swept oval for an athletic field. From
it you gazed on a beautiful vista of valleys and enfolding hills.
Here every afternoon I practiced running . . to the frequent
derision of the other athletes, who made fun of my skinny legs,
body, and arms. . .

But as I ran, and ran, every afternoon, my mile, the boys stopped
laughing, and I heard them say among themselves, "Old Gregory,
he'll get there!"

After the exercise there would be the rub-down with fragrant
witch hazel . . then supper!

A dining-room, filled to the full, every table, with five hundred
irrepressible boys . . it was a cheerful and good attendance at each
of the three meals. We joined together in saying a blessing. We
sang a lusty hymn together, accompanied on the little, wheezy,
dining-room organ. I liked the good, simple melodies sung, straight
and hearty, without trills and twirls. . .

Every night, just before "lights out," at ten, fifteen minutes
was set aside, called "silent time"—and likewise in the morning,
just before breakfast-bell—for prayer and religious meditation.

.   .   .   .   .   .

Jimmy Anderson, my little blond roommate, fair-haired and
delicate-faced as a girl (his sisters, on the contrary, not femininely
pretty, as he, but masculine and handsome)—Jimmy Anderson
read his Bible and knelt and prayed during both "silent times."

I read the Bible and prayed for the quiet, religious luxury of it.
My prayer, when I prayed, was just to "God," not Jehovah . . not
to God of any sect, religion, creed.

"Dear God," ran always my prayer, "Dear God, if you really

exist, make me a great poet. I ask for nothing else. Only let me become famous."

.   .   .   .

I was so happy in my studies,—my work, even,—my wanderings in the woods and along the country roads, with the poets under my arms. . . I read them all, from Layamon's *Brut* on. For, for me, all that existed was poetry. At this stage of my life it was my be-all and end-all.

.   .   .   .

My father was a most impractical man. He would sit in his office as foreman, read the New York *Herald*, and suck at an unlit cigar, telling anyone who listened how he would be quite happy to retire and run a little chicken farm somewhere the rest of his life.

The men all liked him . . gave him a present every Christmas . . but they never jumped up and lit into their work, when they saw him coming, as they did for the other bosses. And the management, knowing his easiness, never paid him over twenty or twenty-five dollars a week. But whenever I could cozen an extra dollar out of him, alleging extra school expenses, I would do so. It meant that I could buy some more books of poetry.

.   .   .   .

I was sent from the stable out into the fields to work . . harder and more back-breaking than currying horses. But my labour was alleviated by the fact that a little renegade ex-priest from Italy worked by my side,—and while we weeded beets or onions, or hoed potatoes, he taught me how to make Latin a living language by conversing in it with me.

.   .   .   .

There were no women on the hill but the professors' wives, and they were an unattractive lot. We were as exempt from feminine influence as a gathering of monks—excepting when permission was given any of us to go over to Fairfield, where, besides the native New England population of women and girls, was situated the girls' branch of our educational establishment. . .

.   .   .   .

The fall term . . the opening of the regular school year. The regular students began to pour in, dumping off the frequent trains at the little school station . . absurd youths dressed in the exaggerated style of college and preparatory school . . peg-top trousers

. . jaunty, postage-stamp caps . . and there was cheering and hat-waving and singing in the parlours of the dormitories on each floor.

. . . .

There were three dormitory groups on the "hill." The "villas" were the most aristocratic. There the "gentlemen" among the students, and the teachers' favourites, dwelt—with the teachers. Then there was Crosston Hall, and Oberly. Crosston was the least desirable of the halls. It was there that I lived.

We were hardly settled in our rooms when the usual fall revival began. . .

One of the founders of the school, a well-known New England manufacturer, came on his yearly pilgrimage . . a fanatic disciple of the great Moreton, he considered it his duty to see to the immediate conversion, by every form of persuasion and subtle compulsion, of every newly arrived student.

Rask was a tall, lean, ashen-faced man. He had yellow, prominent teeth and an irregular, ascetic face. In his eyes shone an undying lightning and fire of sincere fanaticism and spiritual ruthlessness that, in mediæval times, would not have stopped short of the stake and fagot to convince sinners of the error of their ways.

The evangelist's two sons also hove on the scene from across the river . . both of them were men of pleasing appearance. There was the youthful, elegant, dark, intellectual-browed John Moreton, who had doctorates of divinity from half a dozen big theological seminaries at home and abroad; and there was the business man of the two—Stephen, middle-aged before his time, staid and formal . . to the latter, the twin schools: the seminary for girls and the preparatory school for boys—and the revivalistic religion that went with them, meant a sort of exalted business functioning . . this I say not at all invidiously . . the practical business ideal was to him the highest way of men's getting together . . the *quid pro quo* basis that even God accepted.

. . . .

The first night of the opening of the term, when the boys had scarcely been herded together in their respective dormitories, the beginning of the revival was announced from the little organ that stood in the middle of the dining-room . . a compulsory meeting, of course. In newly acquainted groups, singing, whistling, talking, and laughing, as schoolboys will, the students tramped along the winding path that led to the chapel on the crest of the hill.

On the platform sat the teachers. In the most prominent chair, with its plush seat and its old-fashioned peaked back, sat the evangelist-manufacturer, Rask,—the shine of hungry fanaticism in his face like a beacon, his legs crossed, a dazzling shine on his shoes, his hands clutching a hymn book like a warrior's weapon.

Little Principal Stanton stood nearby, his eyes gleaming spectrally through his glasses, his teeth shining like those of a miniature Roosevelt.

"We will begin," he snapped decisively, "with John Moreton's favourite hymn, when he was with us in this world."

We rose and sang, "There is a green hill far away——"

Then there were prayers and hymns and more prayers, and a lengthy exhortation from Rask, who avowed that if it wasn't for God in his heart he couldn't run his business the way he did; that God was with him every hour of his life,—and oh, wouldn't every boy there before him take the decisive step and come to Christ, and find the joy and peace that passeth understanding . . he would not stop exhorting, he asserted, till every boy in the room had come to Jesus. . .

And row by row,—Rask still standing and exhorting,—each student was solicited by the seniors, who went about from bench to bench, kneeling by sinners who proved more refractory . . the professors joined in the task, led by the principal himself.

Finally they eliminated the sheep from the goats by asking all who accepted the salvation of Christ to rise. In one sweep, most of the boys rose to their feet . . some sheepishly, to run with the crowd . . but a few of us were more sincere, and did not rise . . it was at these that the true fire of the professors and seniors was levelled.

They knelt by us. They prayed. They agonised. They groaned. They adjured us, by our mothers, to come to Jesus . . all the while, over and over again, softly, was sung, "O Lamb of God, I come, I come!"

> "Just as I am, without one plea,
> But that Thy blood was shed for me!"

Weakening under the pressure, and swung by the power of herd-instinct, most of us "came."

Then there was the hypnotism of the enthusiasm which laid hold of us. It was indescribable in its power. It even made me want to rise and declare myself, to shout and sing, to join the religious and emotional debauch.

When chapel adjourned at ten o'clock many had been cajoled and bullied into the fold. Then, still insatiable for religion, at the villas and halls, the praying and hymn-singing was kept up.

In the big parlour of Crosston Hall the boys grouped in prayer and rejoicing. One after the other each one rose and told what God had done for him. One after the other, each offered up prayer.

Toward three o'clock the climax was reached, when the captain of the hall's football team jumped to a table in an extra burst of enthusiasm and shouted, "Boys, all together now,—three cheers for Jesus Christ!"

I was one of the three in our hall who resisted all efforts at conversion. The next morning a group of covertees knelt and prayed for me, in front of my door . . that God might soften the hardness of my heart and show me the Light.

For two weeks the flame of the revival burned. Some were of the opinion that from the school this time a fire would go forth and sweep the world. . .

There were prayer-meetings, prayer-meetings, prayer-meetings . . between classes, during study-periods, at every odd minute of time to be snatched.

Though, my preceding summer, my chief pastime had been to argue against the Bible, all this praying and mental pressure was bound to have an influence on my imaginative nature. . .

Besides, the temptation toward hypocrisy was enormous. The school was honeycombed with holy spies who imputed it merit to report the laxity of others. And, once you professed open belief, everything immediately grew easy and smooth—even to the winning of scholarships there, and, on graduation, in the chief colleges of the land.

So, suddenly, I took to testifying at prayer meetings, half believing I meant it, half because of the advantages being a professed Christian offered. And the leaders sang and rejoiced doubly in the Lord over the signal conversion of so hard and obdurate a sinner as I.

. . . .

One day, as I was marching in line from the chapel, a queer thing took place. . .

One of the boys whom I could not identify hissed, "Go on, you hypocrite!" at me.

 • • • • • • •

In a few weeks the pendulum swung as far to the other extreme. My hypocrisy made me sick of living in my own body with myself. I threw off the transient cloak of assumed belief. Once more I attacked the stupidity of belief in a six-day God, inventor of an impossible paradise, an equally impossible hell.

 • • • • • • •

In the early spring I left school before the term was over, impatient, restless, at odds with the faculty. . . Stanton termed it "under a cloud." I had my eyes set on another ideal.

 • • • • • • •

Down in the mosquito-infested pine woods of New Jersey Stephen Barton had located. Barton was possessed with the dream of making the men and women of the world physically perfect—a harking back to the old Greeks with their worship of the perfection of bodily beauty and health. I had long been a reader of his magazines, a follower of his cult, and, now that I heard of his planning to build a city out in the open country, where people could congregate who wished to live according to his teachings, I enrolled myself ardently as one of his first followers and disciples. . .

Barton had taken over a great barn-like, abandoned factory building that stood on the shore of an artificial lake—which, in his wife's honour, he re-named after her, Lake Emily . . his wife was a fussy Canadian woman who interfered in everyone's affairs beyond endurable measure. I was told she used to steal off the chair the old clothes Barton used to wear by preference—paddling along the winding creek in a canoe to his work each morning, his pants rolled up to the knees—and put in their stead a new, nicely creased suit!

 • • • • • • •

Barton's face was wizened and worried . . but, when we took our morning shower, after exercise, under the lifted gates of the dam, his body showed like a pyramid of perfect muscles . . though his

legs—one of the boys who had known him a long time said his
chief sorrow was that he could never develop his legs the way he
wished them to be.

.   .   .   .

We began the building of the city. We laid out the streets through
the pines . . many of us went clad in trunks . . or in nothing . . as
we surveyed, and drove stakes. The play of the sun and the wind
on the naked skin—there is nothing pleasanter, what though one
has to slap away horseflies and mosquitoes . . the vistas through the
pines were glorious. I saw in my mind's eyes a world of the
physically perfect!

As the laying out of the sites and the streets progressed, dwellers
came to join with us . . fanatics . . "nuts" of every description . .
the sick.   .

.   .   .   .

A woman, the wife of some bishop or other, came to join us early
in the season. She had cancer and came there to be cured of it by
the nature treatment. She brought with her an old-fashioned army
tent, and rented for its location the most desirable site on the lake
shore.

She had a disagreement with Barton—and left to consult
regular doctors. She turned over all rights to her tent and to
the site to me.

"And mind you, Mr. Gregory," she admonished, "this tent and the
place it stands on is as much yours as if you paid for it . . for it's
paid for till Christmas."

So, with my Shelley, my Keats, and my growing pile of manuscript,
I took possession. And with covering from the wet and weather
over my head and with plenty of mosquito netting, I felt established
for the summer.

Every morning I rose to behold the beauty of the little, mist-
wreathed lake. Every morning I plunged, naked, into the water,
and swam the quarter of a mile out to the float, and there went
through my system of calisthenics.

I lived religiously on one meal a day—a mono-diet (mostly) of
whole wheat grains, soaked in water till they burst open to the white
of the inside kernel. . .

Everybody in our rapidly increasing tent-colony enjoyed a fad
of his or her own. There was a little brown woman like the shrivelled

inside of an old walnut, who believed that you should imbibe no fluid other than that found in the eating of fruits . . when she wanted a drink she never went to the pitcher, bucket, or well . . instead she sucked oranges or ate some watermelon. There was a man from Philadelphia who ate nothing but raw meat. He had eruptions all over his body from the diet, but still persisted in it. There were several young Italian nature-folk who ate nothing but vegetables and fruits, raw. They insisted that all the ills of flesh came to humanity with the cooking of food, that the sun was enough of a chef. If appearances prove anything, theirs was the theory nearest right. They were like two fine, sleek animals. A fire of health shone in their eyes. As they swam off the dam they looked like two strong seals.

Each had his special method of exercising—bending, jumping, flexing the muscles this way or that . . lying, sitting, standing! . . those who brought children allowed them to run naked. And we older ones went naked, when we reached secluded places in the woods.

The townspeople from neighbouring small towns and other country folk used to come from miles about, Sundays, to watch us swim and exercise. The women wore men's bathing suits, the men wore just trunks. I wore only a gee-string, till Barton called me aside and informed me, that, although he didn't mind it, others objected. I donned trunks, then, like the rest of the men. . .

Behind board lean-tos,—one for the men, the other for the women, —we dressed and undressed. . .

One Sunday afternoon a Russian Jewess slipped off her clothes, in an innocent and inoffensive manner, just as if it was quite the thing,—standing up in plain view of everybody. There went up a great shout of spontaneous astonishment from both banks of the lake where the on-lookers sat. But the shout did not disturb the rather pretty, dark anarchist. Leisurely she stepped into her one-piece bathing suit.

.   .   .   .

Barton was a strange, strong-minded, ignorant man. Hardly able to compose a sentence in correct English, he employed educated, but unresourceful assistants who furnished the good grammar, while he supplied the initiative and original ideas, and increased the influence and circulation of his magazine. Also he lived strenuously up to the doctrines he taught; fasting, for instance.

Soon after I reached "Perfection City" he launched on his **two** weeks' annual fast. Up in the big house where he lived, in the next town of Andersonville (he himself would have been gladder of a mere shack or tent like the rest of us—but his wife negated any such idea) Mrs. Barton used to taunt and insult him by putting out the best food under his nose, during this time.

Mrs. Barton was a terror. She was ever inviting to her house that kind of people who know somebody "worth while" or are related to somebody who, in their turn, are, perhaps, related to—somebody else! . .

In their presence she would patronise Barton by calling him "Stevie!" in her drawling, patronising manner. . .

When the woman came in among the tents and shacks of our "city" she would, in speaking with any of us, imply all sorts of mean, insinuating things about her reformer-husband. . .

Barton, they said, met her while on one of his lecture tours. . .

Their baby . . a little, red object like a boiled lobster . . the anonymous, undistinguished creatures all babies are at that time— the mother used to bring it in among us and coo and coo over it so ridiculously that we made her behaviour a joke among us.

.   .   .   .

Barton's secretary was a beautiful, gentle, large-eyed girl . . wholly feminine . . soft-voiced . . as a reaction from the nagging of his wife, from her blatancy and utter lack of sympathy with any of his projects, he insensibly drifted into a relationship closer and closer, with this girl . . they used to take long walks into the pines together . . and be observed coming back slowly out of the sunset . . hand in hand . . to drop each other's hands, when they considered that the observing line of vision had been reached.

.   .   .   .

Lying under my huge army tent, by the shore of pretty little Lake Emily, I dreamed long and often, in the hush of starry midnight, of reconstructing the life of the whole world—especially the love-life between men and women.

Shelley was my God, not Christ. Shelley's notes to *Queen Mab* were my creed, as his poetry and Whitman's furnished me my Bible. Through them I would reform the world!

I had not realised then (as Shelley did not till his death), the terrific inertia of people, their content, even, with the cramping and conventional ideas and beliefs that hold them in unconscious slavery. . .

I think that summer I learned Shelley and Whitman by heart. And Keats was more than my creed. He comprised my life!

Day by day I took care of my body, gaining in weight, filling out the hollows in my face, till I had grown into a presentable young man. For the first time in my life I knew the meaning of perfect health. Every atom of my blood tingled with natural happiness as I have felt it in later days, under the stimulation of good wine.

No coffee, no tea, no beefsteak, no alcohol. . .

On that summer's ideal living I built the foundation of the health and strength, that, long after, I finally acquired as a permanent possession.

    ·   ·   ·   ·   ·   ·   ·

Stephen Barton and I had many interesting talks together. With the cultural background of Europe he might have been a Rousseau or a Phalanisterian. As it was, he ran a "natural life" magazine which, though crude, benefited hundreds of people. What though it showed pictures of stupid men and women revealing, in poses rivalling the contortionist, their physical development acquired through his methods.

    ·   ·   ·   ·   ·   ·   ·

We would collect many people about us, to serve as a nucleus from which the future society of men and women would expand . . we would all live together as nearly naked as possible, because that was, after all, the only pure thing . . as Art showed, in its painting and sculpture. We would make our livings by the manufacture of all sorts of exercising apparatus and health-foods. . .

And so the world would be leavened with the new idea . . and men and women and little children would wander forth from the great, unclean, insanitary cities and live in clusters of pretty cottages . . naked, in good weather,—in bad, clothed for warmth and comfort, but not for shame. And the human body would become holy.

    ·   ·   ·   ·   ·   ·   ·

Meanwhile the petty, local fight had started which was to disrupt this hope of Barton's, and thwart its fulfillment forever.

The town of Andersonville became jealous of the town of Cottswold because the latter handled most of the mail of our city and thereby had achieved the position of third or fourth class post-office—I don't know exactly which.

The struggle commenced when the two lone policemen of Andersonville began to arrest us—men and women—when we walked into their town for provisions, clad in our bathing suits . . later on, we were forbidden to run for exercise, in our bathing suits, on the fine, macadamised road that passed not far from our dwellings . . it shocked the motorists.

Yet people came from far and near, just to be shocked. That seems to be the chief, most delightful, and only lawfully indulged emotion of the Puritan.

Barton summoned us to a meeting, one night, and we held a long palaver over the situation. We decided to become more cautious, in spite of a few hotheads who advised defiance to the hilt. . .

And the beautiful girl that possessed such fine breasts could no longer row about on our little lake, naked to the waist. And we were requested to go far in among the trees for our nude sun-baths.

The more radical of us moved entirely into the woods, despite the sand flies. . .

Then the affair simmered down to quietness—till the New York *World* and the New York *Journal* sent out their reporters. . . After that, what with the lurid and insinuating stories printed, the state authorities began to look into the matter—and found no harm in us.

But the Andersonville officials were out for blood. Cottswold was growing too fast for their injured civic pride and vanity.

"Can't you divide your mail between the two towns, and make them both third or fourth class or whatever-it-is postoffice towns?" I asked Barton, after he had given me the simple explanation of the whole affair.

"No—for if I took anything away from Cottswold and added it to Andersonville, then the Cottswold authorities would become my adversaries, too . . the only thing I can do," he added, "is what I meant to do all along,—as soon as our 'city' has grown important enough—have 'Perfection City' made a postoffice."

"And then make enemies of both towns at once?"

He threw up his hands in despair and walked away.

.   .   .   .

Having quit work with the gang that was laying out the streets of the future city through the pines, I was entirely out of the few dollars my several weeks' work had enabled me to save . . though but little was needed to exist by, in that community of simple livers . . my procuring my tent free had rendered me quite independent. . .

One afternoon Barton met me on the dam-head.

"Come on in swimming with me . . I have something to talk with you about," he said.

We swam around and talked, as nonchalantly as two other men would have done, sitting in their club.

"How would you like to work for me again?"

"What is it you want me to work at?"

"I need a cook for my nature restaurant . . can you cook?"

I thought. I knew his present cook, MacGregor, the Scot, and I didn't want to do him out of a job. Besides, I didn't know how to cook.

The first objection Barton read in my face.

"MacGregor is quitting . . I'm not firing him."

"All right . . I'll take the job."

Our conference over, we had climbed out to the top of the dam, slid over, and were now standing beneath. The water galloped down in a snowy cataract of foam, as we topped off our swim with the heavy "shower-bath" that was like a massage in its pummelling.

. . . .

MacGregor good-naturedly stayed an extra week, saying he'd show me the run of things. Secretly he tried to teach me how to cook. . .

As the cooking was not all of the "nature" order, but involved preparing food for a horde of people we called "outsiders" who were employed in Barton's publishing plant, I would have to prepare meat and bake bread and make tea and coffee. . .

Barton confessed to me that a food-compromise was distasteful to him. But he could not coerce. While lecturing about the country it was often, even with him, "eat beefsteaks or starve!"

MacGregor was a professional Scotchman, just as there are professional Irishmen, Englishmen and professional Southern Gentlemen . . every Scotchman is a professional Scotchman . . but there is always something pleasant and poetic about his being so . . it is not as it is with the others—whose "professionalism" generally bears an unpleasant reek.

MacGregor had sandy, scanty hair, a tiny white shadow of a moustache, kindly, weak eyes, a forehead prematurely wrinkled with minute, horizontal lines. Burns . . of course . . he knew and quoted every line to me. And *Sentimental Tommy* and *Tommy and Grizel.*

. . . .

In a week I was left in full possession of the nature restaurant.

Barton had been rendered slightly paring and mean, in matters of money,—by smooth individuals who came to him, glowing with words of what they could effect for him, in this or that project—individuals who soon decamped, leaving Barton the poorer, except in experience.

In return he had to retrench. But the retrenchments fell in the place where the penny, not the dollar, lay.

He practised economy on me. He gave me only ten dollars a week, board and room free, as cook; and also I was to wait on the diners, as well as prepare the meals.

Nevertheless the fault for having two jobs at once thrust on me, rested partly with me: when he asked me if I was able to do both, I fell into a foolish, boasting mood and said "yes."

MacGregor figured out my menu for me a week ahead, the day he left: "Anyhow, you'll only last a week," he joked.

The night before the first breakfast I lay awake all night, worrying . . hadn't I better just sneak away with daylight? . . no, I must return to Mt. Hebron in the fall. Though all I wanted to return for was to show the school, that, in spite of my spindly legs, I could win my "H" in track athletics.

I must make good at this job, and save . . my grandmother, who had sent me money the previous year, I must not call on her again. And I did not count on my father . . for he was strenuously in the saddle to a grass widow, the one who had lured him to change boarding houses, and she was devouring his meagre substance like the Scriptural locust.

. . . .

That first breakfast was a nightmare. I "practised breakfast" from three o'clock till six . . by six I had started another breakfast, and by seven, after having spoiled and burned much food, I was tolerably ready for customers . . who seemed, at that hour, to storm the place.

.   .   .   .

It is not necessary to go into detail.   In three days I was through. And I had my first fight with Barton.

.   .   .   .

I was back in my army tent once more, free, with my Shelley, my Keats, my manuscript. . .

In despair of ever returning to Hebron, once more I lay under starry nights, dreaming poetry and comparing myself to all the Great Dead. . .

With the top of the tent pulled back to let the stars in, I lay beneath the gigantic, marching constellations overhead—under my mosquito netting—and wrote poems under stress of great inspiration . . at times it seemed that Shelley was with me in my tent— a slight, grey form . . and little, valiant, stocky Keats, too.

.   .   .   .

After my quarrel with Barton, he tried to oust me from that desirable site the Bishop's wife had turned over to me . . indeed, he tried to persuade me to leave the colony.   But I would not stir.

There was a young fellow in the "City" named Vinton. . . Vinton was the strong man of the place.   He spent three hours every morning exercising, in minute detail, every muscle of his body . . and he had developed beautiful muscles, each one of which stood out, like a turn in a rope, of itself.

Vinton was sent to oust me, by force if need be.

I really was afraid of him when he strode up to me, as I lay there reading the *Revolt of Islam* again.

With a big voice he began to hint, mysteriously, that it would be wise for me to clear out.   I showed him that I held a clear title and right to sojourn there till Christmas, if I chose to, as the bishop's wife had paid for the site till that time, and had then transferred the use of the location to me.   I showed him her letter . . with the Tallahassee postmark.

His only answer was, that he knew nothing about that . . that Barton wanted the place, and, that if I wouldn't vacate peaceably —and he looked me in the eyes like some great, calm animal.

Though my heart was pounding painfully, against, it seemed, the very roof of my mouth, I compelled my eyes not to waver, but to look fiercely into his. . .

"Are you going to start packing?"

"No, I am not going to start packing."

"I can break your neck with one twist," and he illustrated that feat with a turn of one large hand in the air.

He came slowly in, head down, as if to pick me up and throw me down.

I waited till he was close, then gave him an upward rip with all my might, a blow on the forehead that made the blood flow, and staggered him with consternation. To keep myself still at white heat, I showered blows on him. To my surprise, he fell back.

"Wait—wait," he protested in a small voice, "I—I was just fooling."

.   .   .   .

After Vinton left, my blood still pouring through my veins in a triumphant glow, I sat on the ground by the side of my tent-floor and composed a poem. . .

That afternoon Barton's office boy was sent to me, as an emissary of peace.

"The boss wants to see you in his office."

"Tell your boss that my office is down here. If he wants to see me he can come here."

The boy scurried away. I was now looked upon as a desperate man.

.   .   .   .   .   .

And I was happy. I sang at the top of my voice, an old ballad about Captain John Smith, so that Barton could hear it through the open window of his office. . .

"And the little papooses dig holes in the sand. . .
Vive le Capitaine John! . . ."

I leaped into the lake, without even my gee-string on, and swam far out, singing. . .

.   .   .   .   .   .

Late that evening, Barton came to my tent . . very gently and sweetly . . he no longer called me John or Johnnie . . I was now Mr. Gregory. He asked me, if he rented the plot back from me, would I go in peace? I replied, no, I meant to stay there till the middle of September, when the fall term opened at Mt. Hebron.

Then he asked me, would I just join forces with him,—since we must put the movement above personalities. . .

We had a long talk about life and "Nature" ideals. The man showed all his soul, all his struggles, to me. And I saw his real greatness and was moved greatly. And I informed him I would antagonise him no longer, that, though I would not give up the desirable site, otherwise, I would help him all I could.

Then he said he would be glad to have me stay, and we shook hands warmly, the moisture of feeling shining in our eyes.

· · · · · · ·

As the time for my return to school drew near, I was in fine physical condition, better than ever before in my life. I was still somewhat thin, but now it could be called slenderness, not thinness. And I was surprised at the laughing, healthy, sun-browned look of my face.

I felt a confidence in myself I had never known before. . .

· · · · · · ·

I had a flirtation with a pretty, freckle-faced girl. She worked in Barton's "factory," and she used to come down to my tent where I sat reading, with only my trunks on,—during the noon hour,— and ask me to read poetry aloud to her. And I read Shelley. She would draw shyly closer to me, sending me into a visible tremour that made me ashamed of myself.

At times, as we read, her fair, fine hair would brush my cheek and send a shiver of fire through me. But I still knew nothing about women. I never even offered to kiss her.

But when she was away from me, at night specially, I would go into long, luxurious, amorous imaginations over her and the possession of her, and I would dream of loving her, and of having a little cottage and children. . .

But words and elegant, burning phrases are never enough for a woman.

In a week I noticed her going by on the arm of a mill-hand.

· · · · · · ·

And, broke again, I wrote to my grandmother that I must have fifty dollars to get back to school on. And, somehow, she scraped it together and sent it to me. My first impulse was to be ashamed

of myself and start to return it. Then I kept it. For, after all,
it was for poetry's sake.

·   ·   ·   ·   ·   ·   ·

On the train to Hebron, as I walked up the car to my seat, health
shining in my smooth, clear face and skin, the women and girls
gave me approving, friendly glances, and I was happy.

A summer of control from unhealthy habits had done this for
me, a summer of life, naked, in the open air, plus exercise. I had
learned a great lesson. To Barton I owe it that I am still alive,
vigorously alive, not crawlingly . . but I suffered several slumps
before I attained and held my present physique. For the world and
life afford complications not found in "Perfection City."

·   ·   ·   ·   ·   ·   ·

The school hill lay before my eyes again. From it spread on
all sides the wonderful Connecticut valley. Up and down the paths
to the dining hall, the buildings in which classes were held, the
Chapel crowning the topmost crest, wandered groups of boys in
their absurd, postage-stamp caps, their peg-top trousers, their
wide, floppy raglan coats.

I was a senior now. At first my change in bodily build and bet-
tered health rendered me hardly recognisable to my friends.

The very first day I reached Hebron again I was out on the wide,
oval field, lacing around the track. In a month would come the
big track-meet and I was determined this time, to win enough
points to earn me my "H."

·   ·   ·   ·   ·   ·   ·

Principal Stanton sent for me, the second day after my arrival.

"I wanted to have a long talk with you before you got settled,
Gregory."

His steely, blue eyes gleamed through his gold-rimmed eye-
glasses.

"Sit down."

And we had a talk lasting over an hour . . about religion mainly.
He was surprised to learn that I knew a lot about the early Church
fathers, had read Newman, and understood the Oxford contro-
versy . . had read many of the early English divines. . .

"Gregory," he cried, putting his hand on my knee, "what a
power for God you would be, if you would only give over your eccen-

tricities and become a Christian . . a chap with your magnetism—in spite of your folly !———"

He impressed on me the fact, that, now I was a senior, more would be expected of me . . that the younger boys would look up to me, as they did to all seniors, and I must be more careful of my deportment before them . . my general conduct. . .

He asked me what I intended making of myself.

"A poet!" I exclaimed.

He spread his hands outward with a gesture of despair.

"Of course, one can write poetry if necessary . . but what career are you choosing?"

"The writing of poetry."

"But, my dear Gregory, one can't make a living by that . . and one must live."

"Why must one live?" I replied fervently, "did Christ ever say 'One must live'?"

"Gregory, you are impossible," laughed Stanton heartily, "but we're all rather fond of you . . and we want you to behave, and try to graduate. Though we can't tell just what you might do in after-life . . whether you'll turn out a credit to the School or not."

"Professor Stanton, I have a favour to ask of you before I go," I asked, standing.

"Yes?" and he raised his eyebrows.

"I want to know if I can have that room alone, over the platform, in Recitation Hall."

"You'll have to ask Professor Dunn about that . . he has charge of room-transfers . . but why can't you room as the other students do? . . I don't know whether it is good for you, to let you live by yourself . . you're already different enough from the other boys . . what you need is more human companionship, Gregory, not less."

"I want to do a lot of writing. I want to be alone to think. I plan to read Westcott and Hort's Greek New Testament all through, again, this winter." . . This was a sop to his religious sentiment. I related how I had first read the New Testament in the Greek, while on a cattle-boat, in the China Seas. . .

"Gregory, you're quite mad . . but you're a smooth one, too!" his eyes gleamed, amused, behind his glasses. . .

"And I want to write a lot of poems drawn from the parables of the New Testament"—though, not till that minute had such an idea entered my head. . .

.   .   .   .

When I was admitted to the study of Professor Dunn and sat down waiting for him among his antique busts and rows of Latin books, I had formulated further plans to procure what I desired. . .

He came in, heavily dignified, like a dark, stocky Roman, grotesque in modern dress, lacking the toga.

I told him of my New Testament idea . . and added to it, as an afterthought, that I also wanted to prosecute a special study of the lyrics of Horace. Though he explained to me that Horace belonged to the college curriculum, his heart expanded. Horace was his favourite poet—which, of course, I knew. . .

I got my room.

I borrowed a wheelbarrow from the barn, and wheeled my trunk down to Recitation Hall, singing.

.   .   .   .

What a hypocrite I had been! But I had obtained what I sought —a room alone. But now I must, in truth, study the Greek Testament and Horace. . .

I figured out that if I enrolled for several extra Bible courses the Faculty would be easier on me with my other studies, and let me cut some of them out entirely.

To make myself even more "solid," I gave out that I had been persuaded to Christianity so strongly, of a sudden, that I contemplated studying for the ministry. I even wrote my grandmother that this was what I intended to do. And her simple, pious letter in return, prayerful with thanks to God for my conversion so signal —in secret cut me to the heart. . .

But it gave me a temporary pleasure, now, to be looked upon as "safe." To be openly welcomed at prayer-meetings . . I acted, how I acted, the ardent convert . . and how frightened I was, at myself, to find that, at times, I believed that I believed! . .

My former back-sliding was forgiven me.

And the passage of Tennyson about "one honest doubt" being more than half the creeds, was quoted in my favour.

.   .   .   .

Field-day! . .

.   .   .   .

I entered for the two-mile, to be run off in the morning . . for the half-mile, the first thing in the afternoon . . the mile, which was to be the last event, excepting the hammer-throw. My class, in a body, had urged me to enter for all the "events" I could . . when the delegation came, I welcomed them, with gratified self-importance, to my solitary room. I invited them in, and they sat about . . on my single chair . . my bed . . the floor. . .

"You see, Gregory, if you win two of these races, we'll get the banner that goes to the class that makes the greatest number of points . . you must do it for us . . we have never yet won the banner, and this is our last chance."

They left, solemnly shaking my hand, as over a matter of vast importance. . .

Hurrying into my track suit, I went out to the Oval. It was three days before the meet.

Dunn was there, with several others, measuring out distances and chalking lanes.

With all the delicate joy of an aesthete I took my slim, spiked running shoes. I patted them with affection as I pushed my feet into them. I removed the corks from the shining spikes. . .

I struck out with long, low-running, greyhound strides . . around and around . . the wind streamed by me. . .

I knew I was being watched admiringly. I could see it out of the tail of my eyes. So I threw forward in a final sprint, that brought me up, my eyes stinging with the salt of sweat, my legs aching . . my chest heaving. . .

"Good boy," complimented Dunn, coming up to me, and patting me on the back . . Gregory, I'm *for* you. I'm so glad you've come out a clean, fine, clear-cut Christian."

.   .   .   .

For the two-mile, the half, and the mile, each—a single athlete was training, his heart set on the record. It seemed impossible that I should win all three races. Yet I did.

I was all nerves and sinews for the two-mile. The night before I had lain awake. I could not sleep so I read a poor translation of the odes of Pindar. But behind the bad verbiage of the translator,

I fed on the shining spirit of the poetry.   With Pindar's music in me, I was ready for the two-mile.

.   .   .   .

Tensely we leaned forward, at the scratch.   I had my plan of campaign evolved.   I would leap to the fore, at the crack of the pistol, set a terrific pace, sprint the first quarter, and then settle into my long, steady stride, and trust to my good lung power .. for I had paid special attention to my lung-development, at "Perfection City."

I felt a melting fire of nervousness running through my body, a weakness.

I bowed my face in my hands and prayed .. both to Christ and to Apollo .. in deadly seriousness .. perhaps all the gods really were. . .

The gun cracked.   Off I leapt, in the lead .. in the first lap the field fell behind.

"Steady, Gregory, steady!" advised Dunn, in a low voice, as I flashed into the second. . .

I thought I had distanced everybody .. but it chilled me to hear the soft swish, swish of another runner .. glancing rapidly behind, I saw a swarthy lad, a fellow with a mop of wiry, black hair, whom we called "The Hick" (for he had never been anywhere but on a farm)—going stride for stride, right in my steps, just avoiding my heels. . .

Run as I might, I couldn't shake him off. . .

Every time I swept by, the crowd would set up a shout .. but now they were encouraging "The hick" more than me.   This made me furious, hurt my egotism.   My lungs were burning with effort .. I threw out into a longer stride.   I glanced back again.   Still the chap was lumbering along .. but easily, so easily .. almost without an effort. . .

"Good God, am I going to be beaten?"   I sensed a terrific sprinting-power in the following, chunky body of my antagonist.

There were only two more laps .. the rest of the field were a lap and a half behind, fighting for third place amongst themselves .. jeered at by the instinctive cruelty of the onlookers. . .

My ears perceived a cessation of the following swish, the tread. Simultaneously I heard a great shout go up.   I dared not look back, however, to see what was happening—I threw myself forward at that shout, fearing the worst, and ran myself blind. . .

.   .   .   .

"Take it easy, you have it!"
"Shut up! he's after the record."

.   .   .   .

The shrill screaming of the girls who had come over, in a white, linen-starched wagon load, from Fairfield, gave me my last spurt. Expecting every moment to hear my antagonist grind past me, on the cinders, I sped up the home-stretch.

The air was swimming in a gold mist. I felt arms under mine, and I was carried off to the senior tent, by my class-mates. . .

Yet I am convinced that I would have been beaten, if my rival had not had the string that held his trunks up, break. He had sunk down on the track, when they had fallen, not to show his nakedness . . and, pulling them up, and holding them, amid great laughter, he had still won second ribbon.

.   .   .   .

I won the second race—the half-mile, without the humour of such a fateful intervention. It was my winning of the first that won me the second. I had just equalled the two-mile record, in the first. . .

I ran that half, blindly, like a mad man. I was drunk with joy over my popularity . . for when I had gone into the big dining room for lunch, all the boys had shouted and cheered and roared, and pounded the dishes with their knives.

.   .   .   .

"Now, Gregory, you've just got to take the mile away from Learoyd . . he's a junior . . you've just *got* to! . . besides, if you don't . . there's Flammer has lost the broad jump . . and we won't win the class banner after all."

Learoyd was a smallish, golden-faced, downy-headed boy . . almost an albino. . . I had seen him run . . he ran low to the ground, in flashes, 'ike some sort of shore-bird.

.   .   .   .

In the class-tent, alone. Dunn had driven my class out, where they had been massaging and kneading my legs . . which trembled and tottered under me, from the excessive use they had already undergone.

I sat down and put my head between my knees, and groaned. Then I straightened out my right leg and rubbed it, because a cramp was knotting it.

"Hello, Gregory!"

The tent-flap opened. The athletic director poked his head in.

"Come on, Gregory, we're waiting for you."

"Wait a minute, Smythe . . I want to pray," I replied simply. Reverently he withdrew . . impressed . . awed. . .

I flung myself on my face.

"Look here, God, I'll really believe in you, if you give me this last race . . it will be a miracle, God, if you do this for me, and I will believe in your Bible, despite my common sense . . despite history . . despite Huxley and Voltaire," then, going as far as I could— "yes, and despite Shelley . . dear God, dear Christ, please do what I have asked."

My hand struck on a bottle of witch hazel as I rose. Impulsively, I drank off half the contents. It sent a warmth through me. I straightened up, invigorated.

"Come on, Gregory . . what's the matter?" it was Dunn, protesting, "we'll have to run off the mile without you, if you don't come."

"I'm ready . . I'm coming."

.   .   .   .

All that I had in my head, when the pistol cracked, was to *run!* . . all I felt about me was only a pair of mad legs.

I licked out, neither seeing nor caring . . almost feeling my way along the rim of the track with my toes, as I ran—as if I had racing eyes in them. There was a continuous roar that rose and fell like the sea. But I neither saw nor heeded. I just ran and ran.

On the home-stretch a fellow came breast to breast with me. It was Learoyd . . running low like a swallow skimming the ground. But it didn't worry me. I was calm, just floating along, it seemed to me.

I saw Dunn throwing his camera into the air, in the forefront of the seething crowd. He was crying for me to come on. The camera fell in a smashed heap, unregarded.

Barely, with my chest flung out, I took the tape . . trailing off . . I ran half a lap more, with my class leaping grotesquely and shout-

ing, streaming across field after me—before I had my senses back
again, and realised that the race was over.

"Did I win? Did I win? Did I win?" I asked again and again.

"Yes, you won!"

"I was being carried about on their shoulders.

"A little more, and we'd have to take you over to the hospital,"
commented Smythe, as he looked at me, while I lay prone on my
back, resting, under shelter of the tent.

"Who—who used up all this witch-hazel?" he asked of the
rubbers. . .

I hid my face in the grass, pretending to groan from the strain
I had just undergone. Instead, I was smothering a laugh at myself . . at the school . . at all things. . .

"God and witch-hazel," I wanted to shout hysterically, "hurrah
for God and witch-hazel."

Then I rose shakily to my feet, and, flinging myself loose from
those who offered to help me, I ran at a good clip, in my sneakers,
dangling my running shoes affectionately—to my solitary room . .
with a bearing that boasted, "why, I could run all those three races
over again, one right after the other, right now . . no, I'm not
tired . . not the least bit tired!"

That night, in the crowded dining hall, the ovation for me was
tremendous.

"I'll smash life just like those races," I boasted, in my heart.

But my triumph and eminence were not to last long.

To be looked up to at Mt. Hebron you had to lead a distasteful,
colourless life of hypocrisy and piety such as I have seldom seen
anywhere before. Under cover of their primitive Christianity I
never found more pettiness. First, you prayed and hymn-sung
yourself into favour, and then indulged in sanctimonious intrigue
to keep yourself where you had arrived.

I could not stand my half self-hypnotised hypocrisy any longer.
A spirit of mischief and horseplay awoke in me. I perpetrated a
hundred misdemeanours, most of them unpunishable elsewhere, but
of serious import in schools and barracks, where discipline is to
be maintained. I stayed out of bounds late at night . . I cut classes
continually. I visited Fairfield . . and a factory town further
south, where I lounged about the streets all day, talking with people.

Professor Stanton, not to my surprise, sent for me again.

Yet I was amazed at what he knew about me, amazed, too, to discover the extent of the school's complicated system of pious espionage that checked up the least move of every student.

Stanton brought out a sheet of paper with dates and facts of my misbehaviour that could not be controverted. . .

"So we will have to ask you to withdraw from the school, unless you right-about-face . . otherwise, we have had enough of you . . in fact, if it had not been for your great promise—your talents!———"

I waved the compliment aside rather wearily.

"I think that if this school has had enough of me, I have had about enough of the school."

I expressed, in plain terms, my opinion of their espionage system.

"Your omnipotent God must be hard put to it when He has to rely on the help of such sneakiness to keep His Book (and I couldn't help laughing at the literary turn I gave to my denunciation) before the public!"

Stanton's eyes flamed behind their glasses.

"Gregory, I shall have to ask you to leave the Hill as soon as you can get your things together," he shouted.

"—which can hardly be soon enough for me," I replied.

"Come, my boy," continued Stanton, as if ashamed at himself for his outburst, and putting his hand on my shoulder, "you're a good sort of boy, after all . . you have so much in you, so much energy and power . . why don't you put it to right uses? . . after your father has made such sacrifices for you, I hate to see you run off to a ravelled edge like this.

"Even yet, if you'll only promise to behave and preserve a proper dignity in the presence of the other students—even yet we would be glad to have you stay and graduate . . and we might be able to procure you a scholarship at Harvard or Princeton or Yale or Brown. Lang says you put yourself into the spirit of Homer like an old Greek, always doing more work than the requirements,—and Dunn says, that you show him things in Vergil that he never saw before."

Moved, I shook my head sadly. I hated myself for liking these people.

"If you mean that I should be like other people . . I just can't . . it's neither pose nor affectation." (He had intimated that some of the professors alleged that as the core of the trouble.) "I guess I don't belong here .. yes, it would be better for me to go away!"

.   .   .   .

That night, unobserved, I stole into the chapel that stood on the crest of the hill, against the infinite stars.

I spent nearly all the night in the chapel, alone. The place was full of things. I felt there all the gods that ever were worshipped .. and all the great spirits of mankind. And I perceived fully how silly, weak, grotesque, and vain I was; and yet, how big and wonderful, it would be to swim counter, as I meant, to the huge, swollen, successful currents of the commercial, bourgeois practicality of present-day America.

.   .   .   .

I pinned up a sign on the bulletin board in the hall, in rhyme, announcing, that, that afternoon, at four o'clock, John Gregory would hold an auction of his books of poetry.

.   .   .   .

My room was crowded with amused students. I mounted the table, like an auctioneer, while they sat on my cot and on the floor, and crowded the door.

At first the boys jeered and pushed. But when I started selling my copy of Byron and telling about his life, they fell into a quiet, and listened. After I had made that talk, they clapped me. Byron went for a dollar, fetching the largest price. I sold my Shelley, my Blake, my Herrick, my Marvell, my Milton .. all. . .

My Keats I could not bring myself to sell. I kept that like a treasure. What I could not sell I gave away.

My entire capital was ten dollars .. one suit of clothes .. a change of underwear .. two shirts. I discarded my trunk and crammed what little I owned into my battered suitcase.

That night, the story of my dismissal from school having travelled about from mouth to mouth, and the tale of my poets' auction —the boys cheered me, as I came into the dining hall—cheered me partly affectionately, partly derisively.

.   .   .   .

In the morning mail I received a letter from the New York *Independent*, a weekly literary magazine. Dr. Ward, the editor, informed me that I possessed genuine poetic promise, and he was taking two of the poems I had recently submitted to him, for publication in his magazine.

. . . .

Like the vagrant I was, I considered myself indefinitely fixed, with that ten dollars. I went to Boston . . hung about the library and the waterfront . . stayed in cheap lodging houses for a few days—and found myself on the tramp again.

. . . .

I freighted it to New York, where I landed, grimy and full of coal-dust. And I sought out my uncle who lived in the Bronx.

I appeared, opportunely, around supper time. I asked him if he was not glad to see me. He grimaced a yes, but wished that I would stop tramping about and fit in, in life, somewhere. . . He observed that my shirt was filthy and that I must take a bath immediately and put on a clean one of his.

In Boston I had ditched everything but the clothes I wore . . and my suit was wrecked with hard usage.

"Get work at anything," advised my Uncle Jim, "and save up till you can rig yourself out new. You'll never accomplish anything looking the way you do. Your editor at the *Independent* will not be impressed and think it romantic, if you go to see him the way you are . . ragged poets are out of date. "

. . . .

At "Perfection City" I had made the acquaintance of a boy, whom, curiously enough, I have left out of that part of the narrative that has to deal with the Nature Colony. He was a millionaire's son: his father, a friend of Barton's, had sent him out to "Perfection City" with a tutor. His name was Milton Saunders. He was a fine, generous lad, but open as the weather to every influence . . especially to any which was not for his good.

One morning I saw him actually remove his own shoes and give them to a passing tramp who needed them worse than he.

"That's nothing, dad's money will be sufficient to buy me a new pair," he explained, going back to his tent, in his bare feet, his socks in his hand—to put on his sneakers while he hastened to the shoe store in Andersonville.

. . . .

Milton had urged me to be sure to come and see him if I chanced to be in New York.

I now called him on the telephone and was cordially invited to visit him, and that, immediately.

The servants eyed me suspiciously and sent me up by the trades-men's elevator. Milton flew into a fury over it. His friend was his friend, no matter how he was dressed—he wanted them to remember that, in the future!

He brought out a bottle of wine, had a fine luncheon set before me. I went for the food, but pushed the wine aside. He drank the bottle himself. I was still, for my part, clinging to shreds of what I had learned at "Perfection City." . .

He rushed me to his tailor. I had told him of my first poems' being accepted.

"Of course, you must be better dressed when you go to see the editor."

The tailor looked me over, in whimsical astonishment. He vowed that he could not have a suit ready for me by ten the next morning, as Milton was ordering.

"Then you have a suit here for me about ready."

"It is ready now."

"Alter it immediately to fit Mr. Gregory . . we're about the same height."

The tailor said *that* could be done.

For the rest of the day Milton and I peregrinated from one saloon back-room to another . . in each of which the boy seemed to be well known. He drank liquor while I imbibed soft drinks . . the result was better for him than for me. I soon had the stomach-ache, while he only seemed a little over-exhilarated.

At his door-step he shoved a ten dollar bill into my hand. I demurred, but accepted it.

"I'd hand you more," he apologised, "but the Old Man never lets me have any more than just so much at a time . . says I waste it anyhow . . but I manage to do a lot of charging," he chuckled.

"Have you a place to stay to-night?"

"Yes . . I have an uncle who lives uptown."

.   .   .   .

When I showed up at my uncle's, that night, I showed him my new rig-out, and explained to him how I came into possession of it. But he did not accept my explanation. Instead, he shook his head in mournful dubiousness . . indicating that he doubted my story, and insinuating that I had not come by my suit honestly; as well as by the new dress suitcase Saunders had presented me with, and the shirts and underclothing.

"God knows where you'll end up, Johnny."

After supper Uncle Jim grew restive again, and he came out frankly with the declaration that he did not want me to stay overnight in the house, but to pack on out to Haberford to my father . . or, since I must stay in town to see my editor (again that faint, dubious smile), I might stay the night at a Mills Hotel . . since my rich friend had given me money, too . . besides my aunt was not so very strong and I put a strain on her.

.   .   .   .

At the Mills Hotel I was perched in a cell-like corner room, high up. The room smelt antiseptic. Nearby, Broadway roared and spread in wavering blazons of theatric gold. I looked down upon it, dreaming of my future fame, my great poetic and literary career . . my plays that would some day be announced down there, in great shining sign-letters.

.   .   .   .

The sound of an employée's beating with a heavy stick, from door to iron door, to wake up all the Mills Hotel patrons, bestirred me at an early hour.

.   .   .   .

I meditated my next move, and now resolved on another try at community life. . . The Eos Artwork Studios, founded in the little New York State town of Eos, by the celebrated eccentric author and lecturer, Roderick Spalton.

I was in such impatience to reach Eos that I did not cross over to Haberford, to drop in on my father. I feared also that my leaving school the second time, "under a cloud," would not win me an enthusiastic welcome from him.

.   .   .   .   .   .

By nightfall I was well on my way to Eos, sitting in an empty box-car. I had with me my new clothes—which I wore—and my suitcase, a foolish way to tramp. But I thought I might as well appear before Roderick Spalton with a little more "presence" than usual. For I intended spending some time in his community.

Characteristically, I had gone to the office of the *Independent*, had not found the editor in, that morning, and had chafed at the

idea of waiting till the afternoon, when I might have had a fruitful
talk with a man who was interested in the one real thing in my
life—my poetry.

.   .   .   .

I reached Rochester safely.   It was on the stretch to Buffalo that
I paid dearly for being well-dressed and carrying a suitcase . . as
I lay asleep on the floor of the box-car I was set upon by three
tramps, who pinioned my arms and legs before I was even fully
awake.   I was forced to strip off my clothes, after wrestling and
fighting as hard as I could.   I floated off into the stars from a blow
on the head. . .

When I came to, I was trembling violently both with cold and
from the nervous shock.   My assailants had made off with my suitcase. . I was in nothing but my B. V. D.'s and shirt.   Even my Keats
had been stolen.   But beside me I found the ragged, cast-off suit
of one of the tramps . . and my razor, which had dropped out of
my coat pocket, while the tramp had changed clothes, and not been
noticed.   Gingerly, I put on the ragged suit. . .

.   .   .   .

I stood in front of the Eos Artwork Studios.

I saw a boy coming down the path from one of the buildings.

"Would you tell me please where I can find the Master?" I asked,
reverently.

The boy gave me a long stare.

"Oh, you mean Mr. Spalton?"

"Yes."

"That's him . . there . . choppin' wood."

There was a young man and an older one, both chopping wood,
in the back of a building, but in fairly open view.

I walked to where they worked with both inward and outward
trepidation, for, to me, Spalton was one of the world's great men.

Just as I reached the spot, the younger of the two threw down
his axe.

"So long, Dad! now I'll go into the shop and tend to those
letters."

I stood in the presence of the great Roderick Spalton himself,
the man who, in his *Brief Visits to the Homes of Famous Folk*, had
written more meatily and wisely than any American author since
Emerson . . the man whose magazine called *The Dawn*, had ren-

dered him an object of almost religious veneration and worship to thousands of Americans whose spirits reached for something more than the mere piling of dollars one on the other. . .

I stood before him, visibly overwhelmed. It was evident that my silent hero-worship was sweet to him. He bespoke me gently and courteously.

"So you want to become an Eoite?"

"Yes," I whispered, bending my gaze humbly before his.

"And what is your name, my dear boy."

"John Gregory, Master!"

"What have you brought with you? where is your baggage?"

"I—I lost my baggage . . all I have with me is a-a r-razor."

He leaned his head back and laughed joyously. His lambent brown eyes glowed with humour. I liked the man.

"Yes, we'll give you a job—Razorre!" he assured me, calling me by the nickname which clung to me during my stay. . .

"Take that axe and show me what you can do."

I caught up the axe and fell to with enthusiasm. The gospel of the dignity and worth of labour that he preached thrilled in me. It was the first time I ever enjoyed working. . .

As we worked the Master talked . . talked with me as if he had known me for years—as if I, too, were Somebody.

There was nothing he did not discuss, in memorable phrase and trenchant, clever epigram. For he saw that I believed in him, worshipped whole-heartedly at his shrine of genius, and he gave me, in return, of his best. For the first time I saw what human language is for. I thought of Goethe at Weimar . . Wilde's clever conversation in London. . .

Never since did I see the real man, Spalton, as I saw him then, the man he might always have been, if he had had an old-world environment, instead of the environment of modern, commercial America—the spirit of which finally claimed him, as he grew more successful. . .

Modern, commercial America—where we proudly make a boast of lack of culture, and where artistic and aesthetic feeling, if freely expressed, makes one's hearers more likely than not, at once uneasy and restive.

    .   .   .   .

That night, at supper, I caught my first glimpse of the Eoites in a body. The contrast between them and my school-folk was agreeably different. I found among them an atmosphere of good-natured greeting and raillery, that sped from table to table. And when Spalton strode in, with his bold, swinging gait (it seemed that he had just returned from a lecture in a distant city early that afternoon), there was cheering and clapping.

Guests and workers joined together in the same dining hall, with no distinctive division. . . I sat next to Spalton's table, and a warm glow of pleasure swept through me when he sent me a pleasant nod.

"Hello, Razorre," he had greeted me; then he had turned to the group at his table and told them about me, I could see by their glances—but in a pleasant way.

．　　　．　　　．　　　．　　　．　　　．　　　．

The next morning I was at work in the bindery, smearing glue on the backs of unbound books. My wage was three dollars a week and "found," as they say in the West. Not much, but what did it matter? There was a fine library of the world's classics, including all the liberal and revolutionary books that I had heard about, but which I could never obtain at the libraries . . and there were, as associates and companions, many people, who, if extremely eccentric, were, nevertheless, alive and alert and interested in all the beautiful things Genius has created in Art and Song. . .

Derelicts, freaks, "nuts" . . with poses that outnumbered the silver eyes in the peacock's tail in multitude . . and yet there was to be found in them a sincerity, a fineness, and a genuine feeling for humanity that "regular" folks never achieve—perhaps because of their very "regularness."

．　　　．　　　．　　　．　　　．　　　．　　　．

Here, at last, I had found another environment where I could "let loose" to the limit . . which I began to do. . .

In the first place, there was the matter of clothes. I believed that men and women should go as nearly naked as possible . . clothing for warmth only . . and, as one grew in strength and health through nude contact with living sun and air and water, the body would gradually attain the power to keep itself warm from the health and strength that was in it.

So, in the middle of severe winter that now had fallen on us, I went about in sandals, without socks. I wore no undershirt, and

no coat . . and went with my shirt open at the neck. I wore
no hat. . .

Spalton himself often went coatless—in warm weather. His main
sartorial eccentricity was the wearing of a broad-brimmed hat.
And whenever he bought a new Stetson, he cut holes in the top and
jumped on it, to make it look more interesting and less shop-new . .
of course everybody in the community wore soft shirts and flowing ties.

We addressed each other by first names and nicknames. Spalton
went under the appellation of "John." One day a wealthy visitor
`ad driven up. Spalton was out chopping wood.

"Come here, John, and hold my horses."

Spalton dropped the axe and obeyed.

Afterward he had been dismissed with a fifty cent tip.

He told the story on himself, and the name "John" stuck.

.   .   .   .

Working in the bindery, I began to find out things about the
community of Eos that were not as ideal as might be . . most of
the illumination of the books was done by girls, even by children
after school hours. The outlines of the letters and objects to be
hand-illumined were printed in with the text, the girls and children
merely coloured them between the lines.

In each department, hidden behind gorgeous, flowing curtains,
were time-clocks, on which employées rang up when they came to
work, and when they left. Also, each worker was supposed to
receive dividends—which dividends consisted in pairs of mittens and
thick woolen socks distributed by the foremen at Christmas time . .
or maybe an extra dollar in pay, that week.

"Two dollars a week less than a fellow would draw at any other
place that ran the same sort of business," grumbled a young book-
binder who was by way of being a poet, "and a pair of woolen mittens or socks, or an extra dollar, once a year, as dividends!"

However, I think that the artworkers had finer lodgings and
board than most workers could have supplied for themselves . .
and the married couples lived in nicer houses . . and they heard the
best music, had the best books to read, lived truly in the presence
of the greatest art and thought of the world . . and heard speak in
the chapel, from time to time, all the distinguished men of the

country . . who came, sooner or later, to visit Spalton and our community. . .

What though the wages were not so big, what though you ráng up the time of arrival at work and the time of departure from it, on hidden time-clocks, what though every piece of statuary, every picture, every stick of furniture, had, on the bottom of it, its price label, or, depending from it, its tag that told the price at which it might be bought! . .

.　　　.　　　.　　　.　　　.　　　.　　　.

Spalton had begun his active career as a business man, had swung out from that, his fertile mind glimpsing what worlds of thought and imagination lay beyond it!

But now Big Business was calling him back again, using him for its purposes.

Oftener and oftener magnificently written articles by him began to appear in his remarkable little magazine, *The Dawn*. And the Ingersoll of Dollar Watch fame crowded out the Ingersoll of brave agnosticism . . and when he wrote now of artists and writers, it was their thrifty habits, their business traits, that he lauded.

"A great man can be practical and businesslike, in fact the greatest of them always are," he defended. "There was Voltaire, the successful watchmaker at Ferney . . and there was Shakespeare, who, after his success in London, returned to Avon and practically bought up the whole town . . he even ran a butcher shop there, you know."

.　　　.　　　.　　　.　　　.　　　.　　　.

"The people expect startling things . . and, as the winds of genius blow where they list—when they refuse to blow in the direction required, divine is the art of buncombe," he jested.

I suppose this applied to his musician-prodigy, a girl of eight, who worked, in the afternoons, in the bindery. And when a visiting party swept through that department, it was part of her job to rise as if under the impulse of inspiration, leave her work, and go to a nearby piano and play . . the implication being that the piano was placed there for the use of the workers when melody surged within them. . .

But she was the only one who played. And she never played except when she was tipped the wink. And it was only one thing— a something of Rubenstein's . . which she had practised and practised and practised to perfection; and *that* rendered, with haughty head, like a little sibyl, she would go back to her work-bench. And if urged to play more, she would answer, lifting her great, velvet eyes in a dreamy gaze, "no, no more to-day. The inspiration has gone." And, awed, the visitors would depart.

.　　　.　　　.　　　.　　　.　　　.　　　.

Back of the bindery stood the blacksmith shop, where MacKittrick, the historian-blacksmith, plied the bellows and smote the anvil.

MacKittrick took a liking to me. For one day we began talking about ancient history, and he perceived that I had a little knowledge of it, and a feeling for the colour and motion of its long-ago life.

"I want you to come and work for me," he urged, "my work is mostly pretty," he apologised, with blacksmith sturdiness, "—not making horseshoes, but cutting out delicate things, ornamental iron work for aesthetic purposes, and all that . . all you'll have to do will be to swing the hammer gently, while I direct the blows and cut out the dainty filigree the "Master" sells to folk, afterward, as art."

"Well, isn't it art?" I asked.

"I suppose it is. But I like the strong work of blacksmithing best. You see, I was born to be a great historian. But destiny has made me a blacksmith," he continued irrelevantly . . "do come out and work for me. I'm hungry for an intelligent helper who can talk history with me while we work."

My transfer was effected. And I was immediately glad of it. "Mac," as we called him, was a fine, solid man . . and he did know history. He knew it as a lover knows his mistress. He was right. He should have been a great historical writer—great historian he *was!*

For two glorious months I was with him. And during those two months, I learned more about the touch and texture of the historic life of man than three times as many years in college could have taught me.

"Mac" talked of Cæsar as if only yesterday he had shaken hands with him in the Forum . . and he was shocked over his murder as if it had happened right after. . .

"Ah, that was a bad day for Rome and the future of the world, when those mad fellows struck him down there like a pig!" he cried.

And Mary, Queen of Scots, was "a sweet, soft body of a white thing that should have been content with being in love, and never tried to rule!" ..

* * * * * * *

"Can you cook?" asked Spalton of me one day, just as Barton had done at "Perfection City."

"No," I replied honestly, thinking back to that experience.

"Fine!" was the unexpected rejoinder, "I'm going to send you out to the camp to cook for my lumber-jacks for a few weeks."

"But I said I couldn't cook."

"You know how to turn an egg in the pan? you know enough not to let ham and bacon burn? .. you know water won't scorch, no matter how long it stands over the fire? ..

"You'll make an excellent cook for lumber-jacks .. so long as it's something to eat that's stuck under their noses, they don't give a damn! .. they're always hungry enough to eat anything .. and can digest anything. ..

"Get ready! I'm sending you out on one of the waggons by noon."

* * * * * * *

Perched on the high seat of the waggon by the side of the driver! The latter was bundled up to the chin .. wore a fur cap that came down over the ears .. was felt-booted against the cold .. wore heavy gloves.

It was so cold that the breath of the horses went straight up into the air like thick, white wool. As we rode by, the passing farmers that were driving into town almost fell off their seats, startled, and staring at me. For there I perched .. coatless and hatless .. sockless feet in sandals .. my shirt flung open, a la Byron, at the neck.

It is true that the mind can do anything. I *thought* myself into being composed and comfortable. I did not mind, truly I did not mind it.

The driver had protested, but only once, laconically:

"Whar's y'r coat an' hat?"

"I never wear any," I explained, beginning a propagandistic harangue on the non-essentiality of clothes. ..

He cut in with the final pronouncement:

"Damn fool, you'll git pneumony."

Then he fell into obdurate, contemptuous silence.

.   .   .   .

The snow was deep about our living shanty and cook-shack in one, but hard-frozen enough to bear a man's weight without snow-shoes. Over the crust had fallen a powdery, white, new snow, about four inches deep.

Every morning, after the "boys" had eaten their breakfast and left for the woods, I went through my exercises, stripped, out in the open .. a half hour of it, finished by a roll in the snow, that set me tingling all over.

One morning I made up my mind to startle the "boys" by running, mother-naked, in a circle, whooping, about them, where they were sawing up fallen trees and felling others.

It was a half mile to where they worked.

For more bizarre effect, I clapped on a straw hat which I found in the rafters—a relic of the preceding summer. . .

.   .   .   .

"Gosh a'mighty, what's this a-comin!" . .

Everybody stopped working. Two neighbour farmers, who had come over for a bit of gossip, stooped, their hands on their knees, bowed with astonishment, as if they had beheld an apparition.

One of the "boys" told me the two held silence for a long time— till I was entirely out of sight again, and after.

Then one exclaimed, "air they any more luny fellers like thet, back at them Artwork shops?"

The incident gave birth to the legend of a crazy man under Spalton's care, whose chief insanity was running naked through snowdrifts.

Spalton had three sons. Roderick was the eldest: named after his father. Level-headed and businesslike, he followed his father's vagaries because he saw the commercial possibilities in them . . though he did so more as a practical man with a sense of humour than as a man who was on the make. Spalton, who knew men thoroughly and quickly appraised their individual natures, had installed Roderick in the managing end of things,—there with the aid of an older head—one Alfoxden, of whom Spalton made too much of a boast, telling everyone he had rescued him from a life of crime; Alfoxden, when younger, forged a check and had served his term for it. Coming out into the world again, no one would trust him because of that one mistake. Spalton, at this juncture, took him in and gave him a new chance—but—as I said unkindly, in my mind, and publicly, he made capital of his generous action.

But Alfoxden was a soul of rare quality. He never seemed to resent "John's" action. He was too much of a gentleman and too grateful for the real help Spalton had extended to him.

Alfoxden was a slight, Mephistophelian man . . with bushy, red eyebrows. And he was totally bald, except for the upper part of his neck, which was fiery with red hair. He had a large knowledge of the Rabelaisan in literature . . had in his possession several rather wild effusions of Mark Twain in the original copy, and a whole MSS. volume of Field's smutty casual verse. . .

.   .   .   .

But I was in the lumber camp, cooking for the "boys." . .

"Hank," Spalton's youngest son (there was a second son, whose name I forget . . lived with his mother, Spalton's divorced wife, in Syracuse, and was the conventional, well-brought-up, correct youth) —Hank worked in the camp, along with the other lumber-jacks.

The boy was barely sixteen, yet he was six feet two in his stocking feet . . huge-shouldered, stupendous-muscled, a vegetarian, his picture had appeared in the magazines as the prodigy who had grown strong on "Best o' Wheat," a prepared breakfast food then popular.

I asked him if the story that he had built his growth and strength on it was a fake.

"Yes. I never ate 'Best o' Wheat' in my life, except ónce or twice," he answered, "I like only natural food . . vegetables . . and lots of milk . . but I draw the line at prepared, pre-digested stuff and baled breakfast foods."

"Then why did you lend them the use of your name?"

"Oh, everybody that has any prominence does that . . for a price . . but I really didn't want to do it. 'John' made me . . or I wouldn't have."

"And now you have your hair cropped close, why is that?"

"I suppose it's all right to wear your hair long . . but, last summer, it got so damned hot with the huge mop I had, that I always had a headache . . so one day I went down town to the barber and slipped into his chair. 'Hello, Hank,' says he, 'what do you want, a shave?' (joking you know—I didn't have but one or two cat-hairs on my face). .

" 'No, Jim, I want a hair-cut.' At first he refused . . said 'The Master' would bite his head off . . but then he did it——

"John wouldn't speak to me that night, at table . . but the other fellows shouted and clapped. . .

"I don't exactly get dad's idea all the time . . he's a mighty clever man, though. . .

"Books? Oh, yes . . the only ones I care about are those on Indians and Indian lore . . I have all the Smithsonian Institution books on the subject . . and I have a wigwam back of the bindery— haven't you noticed it?—where I like to go and sit cross-legged and meditate . . no, I don't want to study regular things. Dad always makes me give in, in fact, whenever I act stubborn, by threatening to send me off to a regular school. . .

"No, I want nothing else but to work with my hands all my life."

. . . .

But, with all his thinking for himself, "Hank" was also childishly vulgar. He gulped loudly as he ate, thinking it an evidence of hearty good-fellowship. And he deliberately broke wind at the table . . then would rap on wood and laugh. . .

I, on my dignity as cook, and because the others, rough as they were, complained to me in private about this behaviour, but did not openly speak against it because "Hank" was their employer's son. I took exception to the good-natured "lummox's" behaviour.

One morning he was the last to climb out from over the bench at the rough, board table. . .

"Hank . . wait. I want to speak to you a minute."

"Yes, Razorre, what is it?" he asked, waiting. . .

"Hank, the boys have delegated me to tell you that you must use better manners than you do, at meals."

"The hell you say! and what are you going to do if I don't?"

"I—why, Hank, I hadn't thought of that . . but, since you bring up the question, I'm going to try to stop you, if you won't stop yourself."

"—think you can? —think you're strong enough?"

"I said 'try'!"

"Listen, Razorre," and he came over to me with lazy, good-natured strength, "I'll pick you up, take you out, and roll you in the snow, if you don't keep still."

"And I'll try my best to give you a good whipping," replied I, setting my teeth hard, and glaring at him.

He started at me, grinning. I put the table between us, and began taking deep breaths to thoroughly oxygenate my blood, so it would help me in my forthcoming grapple with the big, over-grown giant.

He toppled the table over. We were together. I kept on breathing like a hard-working bellows, as I wrestled about with him.

He seized me by the right leg and tried to lift me up, carry me out. I pushed his head back by hooking my fingers under his nose, like a prong.

Then I grabbed him by the seat of the britches and heaved. And they burst clean up the back like a bean pod. . .

Unexpectedly Hank flopped on the bench and began to shout with laughter. . .

My heavy, artificial breathing, like a bellows, for the sake of oxygenating more strength into my muscles, had struck him as being so ludicrous, that he was in high good humour. I joined in the laughter, struck in the same way.

"I surrender, Razorre, and I'll promise to be decent at the table— you skinny, crazy, old poet!"

And he rumbled and thundered again with Brobdingnagian mirth.

.   .   .   .

Back from the lumber camp. Comparatively milder weather, but still the farmers we passed on the road were startled by my summery attire. But by this time the lumber-jacks and I were on terms of proven friendship . . I had told them yarns, and had listened to their yarns, in turn . . the stories of their lives . . and their joys and troubles. . .

I was reported to Spalton as having been a first-rate cook.

I went to work in the bindery again.

.   .   .   .

Every day seemed to bring a new "eccentric" to join our colony. I have hardly begun to enumerate the prime ones, yet. . .

But when I returned to the little settlement a curious man had already established himself . . one who was called by Spalton, in tender ridicule, Gabby Jack . . that was Spalton's nickname for him . . and it stuck, because it was so appropriate. Jack was a pilgrim in search of Utopia. And he was straightway convinced,

wholly and completely, that he had found it in Eos. To him Spalton
was the one and undoubted prophet of God, the high priest of Truth.

Gabby Jack was a "j'iner." From his huge, ornate, gold watch-
chain hung three or four bejewelled insignia of secret societies that
he was a member of. He wore a flowered waistcoat . . an enormous
seal-ring, together with other rings.

He had laid aside a competence, by working his way from jour-
neyman carpenter to an independent builder of frame houses, in
some thriving town in the Middle West . . where, in his fifty-fifth
year, he had received the call to go forth in quest of the Ideal,
the One Truth.

His English was a marvel of ignorant ornateness, like his vest and
his watch-chain and rings. He had, apparently, no family ties.
Spalton became his father, his mother, his brother, his sister, almost
his God. There was nothing the Master said or did that was
not perfect . . he would stand with worship and adoration written
large on his swarthy, great face, listening to Spalton's most trivial
words. . .

Otherwise, he was Gabby Jack . . talking . . talking . . talking . .
with everybody he met . . enquiring . . questioning . . taking notes in
a large, crude, misspelling hand . . trying himself to write. . .

We ran away from him . . Spalton ran away from him . . "this
fellow will be the death of me," he remarked to me, one afternoon,
with a light of pleasure and pride in his eyes, however, at being
so worshipped. "Ah, Razorre, beware of the ignorant disciple!"

There was nothing Jack would not do for Spalton. He sought
out opportunities and occasions for serving him.

And he would guide visitors over the establishment. And, coming
to the office where Spalton usually sat and worked, he was heard
to say once, with a wide-spread, reverential sweep of the hand—
"and this, ladies and gents, is the (his voice dropping to a reverential whisper) 'Sancta Sanctoria.'"

Jack could not see so well with one eye as he could with the
other. A cataract was there which gave that eye the appearance
of a milky-coloured, poached egg. . .

Coming home from Buffalo one evening, he stepped down on the
wrong side of the train, in the dusk. . . perhaps from his eagerness
to sit by his prophet at supper again that night—there being too
long a line leaving at the station, ahead of him.

A freight was drawing out on the track opposite. And Gabby was so huge that he was rolled like a log in a jam, between the two moving trains .. when the freight had passed, he rose and walked. He took a cab to the Artwork Studios.

All in tatters, he hurried to his room and put on another suit. He appeared at supper by the side of the Master. He narrated what had happened, amid laughter and joking. When Spalton wanted to send for his old, frail, white-headed father, the elder Spalton, who was the community doctor, Jack waved the idea aside.

"Oh, no, Master!" (Master he called Spalton, and never the familiar, more democratic John) "Oh, no, I'm all right." ..

The next morning Jack did not show up for breakfast.

At ten o'clock Spalton, solicitous, went up to his room. . .

He shouted for help. He had found his disciple there, huge and dead, like a stranded sea-thing.

·   ·   ·   ·   ·   ·   ·

In Gabby Jack's will .. for they found one, together with a last word and testament for humanity,—it was asked of Spalton that he should conduct the funeral from the Chapel .. and read the funeral oration, written by the deceased himself .. and add, if the Master felt moved, a few words thereto of his own .. if he considered that so mean a disciple deserved it.

·   ·   ·   ·   ·   ·   ·

All work was suspended the day of Jack's funeral.

Spalton eloquently read the curious, crude composition of his disciple .. which had fine flashes, as of lightning in a dark sky, here and there, in it.

Then Spalton began adding words of his own, in praise of the deceased——

"You all know this dear comrade of ours," he began, "this dear friend whose really fine soul, while in the body—went under the appellation of Gabby Jack——"

Here Spalton broke down. He unashamedly dropped into the chair behind the reading-desk and wept aloud. He could say no more. . .

·   ·   ·   ·   ·   ·   ·

In *The Dawn* for the ensuing month he put a wonderful and

beautiful tribute to his disciple . . who had thoroughly loved, and believed in him.

. . . .

On a cold day of blowing snow, "Pete" came tramping in to town . . his high boots laced to the knees, a heavy alpaca coat about him . . he had come all the way from Philadelphia on foot, to add his portrait to our gallery of eccentrics . . but he was not so unusual after all . . there was too much of the hungry hardness of youth in him, the cocksureness of conceit which he considered genius.

Immediately he put Spalton to question . . and everything and everybody to question. . .

He irritated Spalton most by attacking doctors . . (though Spalton himself did so in his magazine) . . Spalton's father was an old family practitioner. . .

But the Master's revenge came.

"Pete" fell sick. Spalton sent for his father to doctor him. And made the old man use a strong horse-medicine on him . . which he himself brought up from the stables. . .

"The boy is such an ass . ." Spalton told me laughingly, "that it's a veterinarian he needs, not a doctor."

. . . .

There was Speedwell, the young naturalist . . a queer, stooping, gentle, shy thing, who talked almost as an idiot would talk till he got on his favourite topic of bird and beast and flower. In personal appearance he was a sort of Emerson gone to weed . . he walked about with a quick, perky, deprecative step. . .

"—queer fish," John remarked of him, "but, Razorre, you ought to come on him in the woods . . there he is a different person . . he sits under a tree till he seems to become part of the vegetation, the landscape . . when I had him out to camp with me last summer he would go off alone and stay away till we thought he had got lost, or had walked into a pond, in his simpleness, and drowned. . .

We followed him, and watched him. . .

There he sat . . in his brown corduroys . . his lock of hair over his eyes . . that simple, sweet, idiotic expression, like sick sunshine, on his mouth. . .

And after a while the birds came down to him . . pecked all around him . . and a squirrel climbed up on his shoulder . . he seemed to have an attraction for the wild things . . it wasn't as if they just accepted him as a part of the surroundings . . the man sat there like a stump till we grew tired watching, and returned to camp. . .

Each day he spent most of the day, immobile, like that. . .

"Say Razorre," the Master continued, after a thoughtful pause, "you know you nuts are teaching me a lot of things. . .

"The trouble with the educated, regular folks is that they lose so much by drawing the line . . often everything that is spontaneous and fine. . . This thing called God, you know, draws the line nowhere. . .

"If 'Crazy' Speedwell fell heir to a large sum of money, his relatives could find a commission of physicians anywhere, who would honestly have him into custody for lunacy . . yet, in some respects, he is the wisest and kindest man I have ever known . . though, in others, he is often such a fool as to try my patience very hard, at times."

   .   .   .   .

Most of us who had arrived at "The Studios" from "foreign" parts, slept in the common dormitory.

We held frequent "roughhouses" there, the younger of us . . to the annoyance of Speedwell. Spalton finally gave him permission to sleep and live, alone, in the shed where the fire-truck and hose was stored. . .

One night, for malicious fun, a beak-nosed young prize-fighter, and several others (including myself) sneaked into his abode while he slept . . thoughtlessly we turned the gas on and tiptoed out again. . .

Not long after he came staggering forth, half-suffocated. . .

Everybody laughed at the tale of this . . at first Spalton himself laughed, our American spirit of rough joking and horse-play gaining the uppermost in him . . but then he recalled to mind the seriousness of our practical joke, and burned with anger at us over what we had done. And he threatened to "fire" on the spot anyone who ever again molested "Crazy" Speedwell. . .

   .   .   .   .

"Old Pfeiler" we called him. . .

Pfeiler had attended one of Spalton's lectures at Chicago.

Afterward, he had come up front and asked the lecturer if he could make a place for him at Eos . . that he was out of a job . .

starving . . a poor German scholar . . formerly, in better days, a man of much wealth and travel. . .

He had spent his last nickel for admission to Spalton's lecture. Spalton brought him back to the Eos Artwork Studios.

There he found that the queer, gentle, old man was as helpless as a child . . all he could be trusted to do was to write addresses on letters . . which he was set at, not too exactingly. . .

I never saw so happy a man as Pfeiler was that winter.

He was a Buddhist, not by pose, but by sincere conviction. He thought, also, that the Koran was a greater book than the Bible . . and more miraculous . . "one man, Mohammed, who left a work of greater beauty than the combined efforts of the several hundred who gave us that hodge-podge, the Bible."

.   .   .   .

Pfeiler had been left a fortune by his father, a wealthy German merchant . . so, like Sir Richard Burton, he had made off to the Near East . . where he had lived among the Turks for ten years . . till, what with his buying rare manuscripts and Oriental and Turkish art, he had suddenly run upon the rocks of bankruptcy . . and had returned from the Levantine a ruined, helpless scholar, who had never been taught to be anything else but a man of culture and leisure. . .

By steerage he made his way to America . . to Chicago . . all his works of art, his priceless manuscripts sold . . the money gone like water through the assiduities of false friends and sycophants. . .

On the bum in Chicago . a hotel clerk, discharged as incompetent—he had forgotten to insist that a man and woman register always as man and wife . . "because it was such hypocrisy" . . finally a dishwasher, who lived in a hall bed-room . . no friends because of his abstractedness, his immersion in oriental scholarship . . his only place of refuge, his dwelling place, when not washing dishes for a mere existence, the Public Library. . .

"Old Pfeiler" drank coffee by the quart, as drunkards drink whiskey. He had a nervous affliction which caused him to shake his head continually, as if in impatience . . or as a dog shakes his head to dislodge something that has crept into his ear. . .

He was as timid as a girl. . .

The common dormitory was no place for him . . I am sorry to confess that, for a while, I helped to make his life miserable for him . . each night the beak-nosed pugilist-lad and I raised a merry roughhouse in the place . . Pfeiler was our chief butt. We put things in his bed . . threw objects about so they would wake him up. One night I found him crying silently . . but somehow not ignobly . . this made me shift about in my actions toward him, and see how miserable my conduct had been. . .

So the next time "Beak-horn," as I called my plug-ugly friend, started to tease the old man, I asked him to stop . . that we had tormented Pfeiler long enough. "Beak-horn" replied with a surprised, savage stare . . and the next moment he was on me, half in jest, half in earnest. I boxed with him as hard and swift as I was able . . but a flock of fists drove in over me . . and I was thrown prone across the form of the old man . . who stuttered with fright and impotent rage, swearing it was all a put-up game between us to torment him further, when I protested that I had not tried to do it.

.   .   .   .

The next morning Spalton sent for me.

"Look here, Razorre, if *you* were not the biggest freak of them all, I could understand," he remarked severely. . .

I tried to explain how sorry I was for the way I had joined in Pfeiler's persecution . . but the master would have none of it . . he told me to look better to my conduct or he would have to expel me from the community. . .

"Gregory," he ended, calling me by my name," somehow I never quite *get you* . . most of the time you are refined and almost over-gentle . . you know and love poetry and art and the worth-while things . . but then there's also the hoodlum in you . . the dirty Hooligan——" his eyes blazed with just rebuke . . I trod out silently, sick of myself, at heart . . as I have often, often been.

.   .   .   .

After that, Pfeiler avoided me. I went up to him in apology. Most contritely I said I was sorry.

"You are a fraud," he cried at me, spluttering, almost gnashing his teeth in fury, "you go around here, pretending you are a poet, and have the soul of a thug, a brute, a coward and bully . . please don't speak to me any more as long as I'm here . . you only pretend interest in spiritual and intellectual things, always for some brutal reason . . even now you are planning something base, some

diabolical betrayal of the Master, perhaps, or of all of us .. I myself
have advised Mr. Spalton, for the good of his community to send you
back to the tramps and jail-birds from whom you come .. you
scum! you filthy pestilence!"

His head was shaking like an oscillating toy .. his eyes were
starting from his head through force of his invective .. he was
jerking about, in his anger, like a dancing mouse. . .

I hurried out of his word-range, overwhelmed with greater shame
than I can ever say.

•   •   •   •   •   •   •

The editor of the *Independent*, Dr. William Hayes Ward, had,
so far, not found room in his magazine for the two poems of mine
he had bought. I was chagrined, and wrote him, rather impetuously,
that, if he didn't care for the poems he might return them. Which
he did, with a rather frigid and offended reply. I was rendered
unhappy by this.

I spoke to Spalton about it.

"Why Razorre, so you *have* come that near to being in print?"
I showed him the poems. "Yes, you have the making of a real poet
in you!"

A day or so after he approached me with— "I'm writing a brief
visit to the home of Thoreau .. how would you like to compose a
poem for me, on him—for the first page of the work?"

"I would like it very much," I said. In a few days I handed him
the poem. A "sonnet," the form of which I myself had invented,
in fifteen lines.

•   •   •   •   •   •   •

For days I lived in an intoxication of anticipation .. just to
have one poem printed, I was certain, would mean my immediate
fame .. so thoroughly did I believe in my genius. I was sure
that instantly all of the publishers in the world would contend with
each other for the privilege of bringing out my books.

Spring had begun to give hints of waking green, when *The Brief
Visit* was issued from the press. I rushed to procure a copy before
it was bound. I was surprised and dumbfounded to find that the
Master had used the poem without my name attached .. just as if
it, with the rest of the book, was from his own pen.

My first impulse was to rush into the dining hall, at breakfast,
waving the sheets, and calling "John" to account for his theft,

before everybody . . then I bethought myself that, perhaps, some mistake had been made . . that the proofreader might have left my name out.

Spalton looked up quickly as I passed by his table. He read in my face that I had already discovered what he had done. He blushed. I nodded him a stiff greeting. I ate in silence—at the furthest table.

In a few minutes he did me an honour he had never shown me before. He came over to where I sat. "Razorre," he invited, "how would you like to take a hike with me into the country, this morning?"

I gave him a swift glance. "I would like it very much."

"Then as soon as you are through, meet me in the library."

I drank a second cup of coffee with studied deliberation—in spite of myself, I was thrilled with the notice that had been shown me before all the others. Already my anger had somewhat lessened.

.   .   .   .

Never had the master been so eloquent, so much his better self, since that first day, at the wood-pile. He strove to throw the magic of his spirit over me with all his power. For hours we walked, the light, pale green of the renewing year about us. But through it all I saw what he was trying to effect . . to impress me so deeply that I would not only forgive him for having stolen my poem, but actually thank him, for having used it—even consider it a mark of honour . . which his eloquence almost persuaded me to do.

Indeed I saw the true greatness in "John" . . but I also saw and resented the petty, cruel pilferer—stealing helpless, unknown, youthful genius for his own—resented it even more because the resources of the man's nature did not require it of him to descend to such pitiful expedients. He was rich enough in himself for his own fame and glory.

And why should he rob a young poet of his first fame, of the exquisite pleasure of seeing his name for the first time in print? . . than which there is no pleasure more exquisite . . not even the first possession of a loved woman! . . . .

We had almost returned to the "Artworks" before I tried to let loose on him . . but even then I could not. Gently I asked him why he had not affixed my name to my poem.

He looked at me with well-simulated amazement.

"Why, Razorre, I never even thought of it . . we are all a part of one community of endeavour here . . and we all give our efforts as a contribution to the Eos Idea . . I have paid you a higher compliment than merely giving you credit . . instead, I have incorporated your verse into the very body of our thought and life."

His effrontery struck me silent. I told him sadly that I must now go away.

"Nonsense," he replied, "this is as good a place in which to develop your poetic genius as any place in the world. I may say, better. Here you will find congenial environment, ready appreciation . . come, let us walk a little further," and we turned aside from the steps of the dining room and struck down the main street of the town.

"I mean bigger things for you, Razorre, than you can guess . . I will make you the Eos Poet—look at Gresham, he is the Eos Artist, and, as such, his fame is continent-wide . . just as yours will become . . and I will bring out a book of your poetry . . and advertise it in *The Dawn*.

His eloquence on art and life, genius and literature, had enthralled and placated me . . his personal wheedling irritated and angered.

"A book of my poems . . without my name on the title page, perhaps," I cried, impassioned, looking him deep in the eyes. He shifted his glance from me——

.   .   .   .

I threw my few belongings together.

Everybody, in saying good-bye, gave me a warm hand-clasp of friendship (excepting Pfeiler), including Spalton, who assured me—

"Razorre, you'll be back again . . despite its faults, they all come back to Eos."

"Yes," I responded, sweeping him off his feet by the unexpectedness of my reply, "yes, in spite of all, Eos is a wonderful place . . it has given me something . . in my heart . . in my soul . . which no other place in the world could have given . . and at the time I needed it most . . a feeling for beauty, a fellowship——"

"Razorre," he cut in, moved, "we all have our faults,—God knows *you* have—mutual forgiveness—" he murmured, pressing my hand warmly again; his great, brown eyes humid with emotion . . whether he was acting, or genuine . . or both . . I could not tell.

I didn't care. I departed with the warmth of his benediction **over** my going.

. . . .

This time I did not freight it. I paid my fare to New York.

. . . . . .

My father . . I must pay him a visit, before lifting my nose in the air like a migrating bird. Where I would go or what I would do that spring and summer, I hadn't the vaguest idea. . .

It seemed but the day before that I had left Haberford. The fat policeman who leaned against the iron railing of the small **park** near the station was there in the same place. The same young rowdies pushed each other about, and spat, and swore, near the undertaker shop and the telegraph office.

But as I walked past the Hartman express office—the private concern which Hartman, the thin, wiry shock-haired Swede, had built up through arduous struggle, beginning with one wagon—

Hartman saw me through the window, and beckoned vigorously for me to step in. . .

"—just got home from another hobo-trip, Johnny?"

"You're almost right, Mr. Hartman."

"A pause. . .

"—been to see your father yet?"

"No, sir, I'm on the way there now . . just arrived this minute, on the train from New York."

"I'm glad I caught sight of you, then, to prepare you." A longer pause . . mysteriously embarrassing, on his part.

"I have something to tell you about him . . —guess you're old enough to stand plain talk . . sit down!"

I took a chair.

"You see, it's this way," and he leaned forward and put his hand on my knee . . "it's women—a woman" . . he paused, I nodded to him to go on, feeling very dramatic and important. . .

"It's Mrs. Jenkins, the widow, that has her hooks in him . . around where he boards . . and, to be frank with you, he's going it so strong with her that he's sick and rundown . . and not so right, at times, *up here!*" and Hartman tapped his forehead with his forefinger significantly. . .

"Now, you're the nearest one to him around here," he went on, "and I'll tell you what we were going to do . . his lodge, of which

I'm a member, was going to give him a trip, to separate him from her, and cure him .. you come back just pat. . .

"Has your daddy any relatives that can afford to entertain him, out in the West, where you came from?"

"Yes, one of my uncles, his brother, is very well off, and would be glad to take him in .. in fact any of the folks back home would," my voice sounded hollow and far off as I answered.

"You're a pretty smart lad .. do you want to go back with him when he goes?"

"No, Mr. Hartman."

"Well, we can tip the porter to take care of him .. but why don't you want to go with him, we will foot your expenses?"

"I have other things to do," I answered vaguely.

He gave a gesture of impatience. . .

．　　　．　　　．　　　．　　　．　　　．　　　．

There was a hush in the house, as I stepped softly up the stairs. The catch of the front door was back. . .

First I went to my room and found all my books intact .. in better condition even, than when I was home with them .. there was not a speck of dust anywhere. Evidently my father was not too sick to keep the place clean .. but then, I meditated he would attend to that, with his last effort.

My books were my parents, my relatives. I had been born of them, not of my own father and mother. My being born in the flesh was a mere accident of nature. My father and mother happened to be the vehicle.

But the place was so quiet it perturbed me.

"Pop!" I called, going toward his bed-room.

The door leading into it slowly opened. The little, dark widow was in there with him.

"Hush! your father is asleep."

A hatred of both him and her shot up quick in my heart. I sensed their abandonment to the sheerly physical, till it took in their whole horizon. It was utterly ignoble. I had a vision of all humanity, living, for the most part, merely for food and sex, letting art and poetry and beauty and adventure pass by, content if they only achieved the bare opportunity of daily wallowing in their mire.

I was bad and mean enough, but the conception of a single poem in my brain, till it found birth on paper, was, I swore, bigger and

finer than all this world-mess at its best. Also there was in me somewhat the thwarted, sinister hatred of the celibate. . .

.　　　.　　　.　　　.　　　.　　　.　　　.

"You mustn't bother your father now," little Mrs. Jenkins interposed, as I started in, "you must let him rest for awhile, and not
wake him."

Through the door, half open, I caught a glimpse of a hollow, wax-
white face . . he looked as if all the blood had been let out of his
body, little by little. The little, pretty, dark woman looked like a
crafty animal . . there was a beady shine of triumph, which she
could not conceal, in her eyes, as she opposed my entering. I smelt
the pungent smell of her physical womanhood. There was a plump-
ness about her body, a ruddiness to her lips, that gave me the
phantasy that, perhaps, the moment before, she had drunk of my
father's blood, and that she was preventing me from going in to
where he lay till a certain tiny, red puncture over his jugular vein
had closed.

"You forget, Mrs. Jenkins, that he is my father."

"You shan't go in . . please, Johnnie . . let him sleep just a
little longer . . as soon as he wakes he asks for another drink!"

"And who put him in this state?" I charged directly, vividly
remembering what Hartman had said. . .

"What, you don't mean to insinuate?"—she gasped.

"I mean nothing, only that I have come home to take care of my
father, till his lodge takes charge of him, and that, for the present,
I want you to please leave me alone with him."

Her small, black pupils dilated angrily. But she did not press
the point of her staying. She had put her hand on my arm cajol-
ingly, but I had shook it off with such evident disgust—founded
partly and secretly on a horror of physical attraction for her—
that drew my morbid, starved nature——

"Very well!" . . but I'll be back this afternoon, early. When
he wakes up and asks for a drink of whiskey . . starts out to get
one . . draw him a glass of water from the faucet, and take your
oath that it's whiskey . . he'll believe you and drink it!"

And she departed, an odor of strong perfume in her wake.

.　　　.　　　.　　　.　　　.　　　.

Had this planet of earth been populated from without? . . there
were evidently two races on it—the race of men—the race of

women—men had voyaged in from some other world in space . .
women had done the like from their world . . to this world, alien
to both of them. And here a monstrous thing had brought them
together like an interlocking fungus—their sex-union . . a function
that monstrously held together two different species of animals
that should not even be on meeting terms.

Thus my morbid fancy ran, as I entered slowly my father's room.

He slept.

On a chair by his bed lay a copy of *Hamlet*, his favourite Shakespearean play. I picked it up, read in it, waiting for him to wake,
while he breathed laboriously.

I became absorbed in the play . . I must write a poem, some time,
called "Hamlet's Last Soliliquy."

.   .   .   .

My father was awake.

I did not know how long he had been so, for his breathing had
not changed and the only difference from his sleeping state was that
his eyes stared, wide and glassy, at the ceiling, as if they compre-
hended nothing.

A feeling of horror crept over my body. This was more than I
had counted on . . my father, helpless on his back and his wits
off gathering wool. . .

"Father!" I put my hand on a talon of his.

He turned his head slightly. Smiled vacuously.

"Father!"

A perturbation clouded his eyes . . that painful struggle toward
comprehension observed in an infant's face.

"Who are you? What do you want?"

"I'm your son—Johnnie! . . and I've come back to take care of
you."

"Johnnie is away . . far off . . on the sea . . in a ship."

And he sighed and turned his face to the wall as if the thought
troubled him, and he wished to dismiss it. Then, in a moment, he
whirled about, changed and furious. He rose to a sitting posture
. . swung his legs out, bringing the bed-clothes a-wry with him. . .

"You are an impostor . . you are not my son . . I tell you again,
he is away . . has been away for years . . as long as I can remember . . perhaps he is dead . . you are an impostor."

He leaped up, full of madness, and seized hold of me.

"Stop, Father, what are you trying to do?"

As I grappled with him, trying to keep him from hurting me—and he was quite strong, for all his emaciation—the horror of my situation made me sick at the stomach, quite sick . . and my mind went ridiculously back to the times when my father and I had eaten oyster-fries together . . "that is the only thing you and this man have in common . . oyster-fries," remarked my mind to me. All the while I was pinning his wrists in my grasp . . re-pinning them as he frantically wrested them loose . . swearing and heaping obscenities on my head . . all the while, I thought of those oyster-fries . . we had saved up a lard-tin full of bacon grease to fry them in . . and fry after fry had been sizzled to a rich, cracker-powdered brown in that grease . . a peculiar smell waxed in the kitchen, however . . which we could never trace to its source . . "a dead rat somewhere, maybe," suggested my father.

When we had used a third of the bacon grease, the dead rat's foot stood up . . out of that can.

We discharged the contents of our stomachs in the sink.

This was the ridiculous incident that possessed my imagination while I struggled with my father.

.   .   .   `   .   .   .

I had my father over on the bed. He fought to a sitting posture again . . got his finger in my eye and made me see a whorl of dancing sparks. With irritation and a curse . . then both laughing hysterically and sobbing . . I bore him back to his pillow. . .

The strength had gone entirely out of him . . now it came into his mind that I was there trying to rob or kill him.

"Spare me, spare me!" he pleaded, "you can have everything in the house . . only don't kill me! My God!"

"Good Christ!" I groaned, as he beat upward, fighting again.

I let him rise, almost palsied with horror.

He perched on the edge of the bed, exhausted,—began groping with one hand, in the air, idly.

"What is it? What do you want?"

"Give me my pants! I don't trust you. I want to go to the corner and get a drink . . give me my pants!"

"Pop, look at me . . stop this nonsense . . you're safe . . I'm your son, Johnnie!"

"That's all very well," he assented with an air of reserved cunning.

"Please believe me," I pleaded.

"All right . . you are my son . . only don't kill me," he responded craftily.

"Father! . . good God!"

He perceived by the emotion of my last exclamation, that at least I was not ill-disposed toward him.

He clutched at the advantage.

"Promise to take care of me till Johnnie comes—he's just around the corner," slyly.

"Pop, what is it you want? What can I do for you?"

"A curious greed flickered in his eyes.

"Get me a drink!"

"All right! I'll get it for you!"

"Let me think! There's none in the house . . none left, Emily said."

"But I brought some with me . . wait a minute." I went into the kitchen, turned on the tap softly, filled a glass half full of water, brought it back to him.

"Here it is."

"I don't like the colour of it."

"Why, it has a nice, rich colour."

"What is it? —Scotch?"

"Yes."

He sipped of it. Made a rueful face. "I don't like the taste of it . . it tastes too much like water," he commented, with a quiet, grave, matter-of-fact grimace that set me laughing, in spite of myself. . .

"Drink it down! I swear it's all right."

He tossed off the water.

"Give me my pants. I want to get out of here."

"Why, wasn't that whiskey that I just gave you?"

"Yes, yes . . but not very good stuff. I know where I can get better."

Humouring him, I helped him into his trousers . . painfully he put on his shirt, neatly tied his tie, while I steadied him. This manual function seemed to better his condition straightway. He startled me by turning to me with a look of amused recognition in his .eyes. He was no longer off his head, just a very sick man.

"Well, Johnnie, so you're back again?"

"Yes, Pop—back again!"

"What are you going to do next?" he queried wearily, seating himself laboriously in an armchair.

"Stay, and take care of you!"

"That will be unnecessary. I have had a rather severe attack of malaria . . that is all . . left me rather weak . . but now I'm getting over it . . had to take a lot of whiskey and quinine, though, to break it up!

"Malaria comes on me, every spring, you know . . harder than usual, this spring, though . . it's made me dotty . . made me say things, at times, I'm afraid!"

We sat silent.

"—need any money?" he was reaching into his pocket.

"No, I don't want a cent!"

"Then take this five dollar bill and go around to the corner saloon and buy me a pint . . what I had is all used up, and the chills are not quite out of me yet."

.   .   .   .

On the way to the saloon I stopped at Hartman's express office . . related the foregoing story. . .

"H'm! yes! . . I see!" . . Hartman braced his thumbs together meditatively, "—from what you say it's pretty serious . . something will have to be done this very day. . .

"Yes, go and get the pint . . let him have a drink of it. And— and keep close to him all the time . . don't," he added significantly, "leave the lady in question in the room alone with him for a single moment."

.   .   .   .

"Have you got the pint, Son?"

"Yes, Father. Here it is . . but just a little!"

"I know what I'm doing!"

He took most of it down at a gulp.

Noticing the anxious look in my eyes.

"Don't worry about me, Johnnie. I can take it or leave it alone . . —always could!"

.   .   .   .

Before Mrs. Jenkins could come back, Hartman anticipated her with a nurse and a doctor. As Mrs. Jenkins came in, chagrin and indignation showed on her face. But she bowed perforce to the situation. She was too wise not to.

"His lodge-brothers are taking care of Mr. Gregory now, Mrs. Jenkins," explained Mr. Hartman suavely, warning her off, at the same time, with a severe, understanding look in his eyes.

She dropped her eyelashes—though with a bit of instinctive coquetry in them—under his straight-thrusting glance.

"Well, I suppose professional care *would* be better than anything I could do for him . . but," sweetly, "I'll drop in from time to time to see if there's any little thing I can do."

.   .   .   .

Deprived of the loving care of Emily Jenkins, though he called for her many times, my father mended his condition rapidly. And, after a long, mysterious conference with Hartman and other members of his fraternal order, he consented to allow himself to be sent West on a visit. But not till they had promised to keep his job as foreman in the Composite Works open for him, till he was well enough to come back.

After I had seen my father off, I stayed in the silent rooms only long enough to pack up my books, which I left in care of Hartman.

I had at last arrived at a definite plan of action.

My grandfather was transacting some sort of business in Washington, as my uncle, Jim, had informed me. There he was living in affluence, married again, in his old age . . just like his former wife.

I had evolved a scheme which seemed to me both clever and feasible, by which to extract from him a few hundred or a thousand dollars with which to prosecute my studies further, and enter, eventually, say, Princeton or Harvard . . perhaps Oxford.

.   .   .   .

I found my grandfather holding forth in a swell suite of offices in the business district of Washington.

Near his great desk, with a little table and typewriter, sat a girl, very pretty—he would see to that! . . evidently his stenographer and private secretary.

As I stood by the railing, she observed me coldly once or twice, looking me over, before she thrust her pencil in her abundant hair and sauntered haughtily over to see what I was after.

Despite the fact that I informed her who I was, with eyes impersonal as the dawn she replied that she would see if Mr. Gregory
could see me . . that at present he was busy with a conference in
the adjoining room.

I sat and waited . . dusty and derelict, in the spick-and-span
office, where hung the old-fashioned steel engravings on the wall,
of Civil War battles, of generals and officers seated about tables
on camp stools,—bushy-bearded and baggy-trousered.

Finally my grandfather Gregory walked briskly forth. He looked
about, first, as if to find me. His eyes, after hovering hawklike,
settled, in a grey, level, impersonal glance, on me.

"Come in here," he bade, not even calling me by name.

I stepped inside, trying hard to be bold. But his precision and
appearance of keen prosperity and sufficiency made me act, in spite
of myself, deprecative. So I sat there by him, in his private room,
keying my voice shrill and voluble and high, as I always do, when
I am not sure of my case. And, worse, he let me do the talking . .
watching me keenly, the while.

I put to him my proposition of having my life insured in his name,
that I might borrow a thousand or so of him, on the policy, to go
to college with . . .

"Ah, if he only lets me have what I ask," I was dreaming, as
I pleaded, "I'll go to England . . to some college with cool, grey
mediaeval buildings . . and there spend a long time in the quiet
study of poetry . . thinking of nothing, caring for nothing else."

"No! how absurd!" he was snapping decisively. I came to from
my vision.

"My dear Johnnie, your proposition is both absurd and——"
as if that were the last enormity—— "very unbusinesslike!"

"But I will then become a great poet! On my word of honour, I
will! and I will be a great honour to the Gregory family!"

He shook his head. He rose, standing erect and slender, like a
small flagpole. As I rose I towered high over the little-bodied,
trim man.

"Come, you haven't eaten yet?"

"No!"

Well, he had a sort of a heart, after all . . some family feeling.

Walking slightly ahead, so as not to seem to be in my company,
old Grandfather Gregory took me to a—lunch counter . . bowing to

numerous friends and acquaintances on the way . . once he stepped aside to a hurried conference, leaving me standing forlorn and solitary, like a scarecrow in a field.

I grew so angry at him I could hardly bridle my anger in.

"—like oyster sandwiches?" he asked.

. . . .

He didn't even wait to let me choose my own food.

"Two oyster sandwiches and—a cup of coffee," he barked.

While I ate he stepped outside and talked with another friend.

. . . .

"Good-bye," he was bidding me, extending a tiny hand, the back of it covered with steel-coloured hairs, "you'd better go back up to Jersey—just heard your daddy is very sick there . . he might need your help."

I thought cautiously. Evidently he knew nothing of my father's having been sent home by his lodge. I affected to be perturbed. . .

"In that case—could you—advance me my fare to Haberford?"

I'd wangle a *few* dollars out of him.

My grandfather's answer was a silent, granite smile.

"—just want to see what you can cajole out of the old man, eh? No, Johnnie—I'll leave you to make your way back in the same way you've made your way to Washington . . from all acounts railroad fare is the least of your troubles."

My whole hatred of him, so carefully concealed while I thought there was some hopes of putting through my educational scheme, now broke out——

"*You*"—I began, cursing. . .

"I knew that's the way you felt all along . . better run along now, or I'll say I don't know you, and have you taken up for soliciting alms."

. . . .

Before nightfall I was well on my way to Philadelphia. For a while I resigned myself to the life of a tramp. I hooked up with another gang of hoboes, in the outskirts of that city, and taught them the plan of the ex-cook that we'd crowned king down in Texas. . .

I kept myself in reading matter by filching the complete works

of Sterne (in one volume) and the poetry of Milton—from an outside stand of a second hand book store. . .

.   .   .   .   .   .

—left that gang, and started forth alone again. I became a walking bum, if a few miles a day constitutes taking that appellation.
I walked ahead a few miles, then sat down and studied my Milton,
or dug deep into *Tristram Shandy*. Hungry, I went up to farm-
house or backdoor of city dwelling, and asked for food. . .

.   .   .   .   .   .

I found myself in the outskirts of Newark again.

I took my Sterne and Milton to Breasted's, hoping to trade them
for other books. I stood before the outside books, on the stand,
hesitating. I was, for the moment, ashamed to show myself to "the
perfesser," because of the raggedness that I had fallen into.

While I was hesitating, a voice at my elbow——

"Any books I can show you?—— any special book you're looking for?"

The voice was the voice of the tradesman, warning off the man
unlikely to buy—but it was the familiar voice of my friend, "the
perfesser," just the same. I turned and smiled into his face, happy
in greeting him, losing the trepidation my rags gave me.

"Why, Johnnie Gregory!" he shook my hand warmly as if I were
a prince. I was enchanted.

"I want to exchange two books if I can—for others!"

"Come right into the back. Breasted, the boss, is out for the
day . . I'm having my lunch sent in, won't you have some with me?"

He acted just as if he hadn't noticed my dilapidation.

I said I'd gladly share his lunch.

He drew my story out of me,—the story of my life, in fact, before
the afternoon wore to dusk.

.   .   .   .   .   .

"Do you think I'm crazy?" I asked him.

"No . . far from it . . " adding gently, with a smile, "sometimes an awful fool, though, Johnnie—if I may say it."

.   .   .   .   .   .

"Won't you stay overnight?"

"No, thanks just the same, 'Perfesser.' "

"I have room enough . . better hang around a few days and look
for a job here."

"It's too near Haberford."

"But I know you'd take a couple of fresh books, if I gave them to you, now wouldn't you?"

My eyes lit up as with hunger.

"This Milton and Sterne are too used-up to be worth a nickel a-piece. Maybe, if I'd keep them, they might be worth something, some day, when you're famous," he joked.

"If you want to give me a couple of books . . how about this Keats and this Ossian? I want the Keats for myself. It will renew my courage. And—the Ossian—will you mail that book on for me, to Eos, to old Pfeiler?"

I had told him, in the course of my talking, about them both.

Pfeiler used often to talk of the greatness of Ossian's poetry . . and how he'd like to possess a volume of it again . . that is, before he grew to hate me.

Maybe if I sent him the book, with a letter, he would think less harshly of me.

. . . .

I tramped through New England. My whole life had settled back into tramping . . only my Keats remained. I read and re-read his poems, not caring to write a line myself.

. . . .

I worked as a dish-washer or pearl-diver for several weeks in Boston, and bought a very cheap second-hand suit.

I shifted my mind like a weather vane and decided against shipping to England, with the forlorn hope of, somehow attending Oxford or Cambridge, and studying English literature there. My old ideal of being a great adventurer and traveller had vanished, and, in its stead, came the desire to live a quiet life, devoted entirely to writing poetry, as the poet Gray lived his.

. . . .

I drifted inland to Concord, a-foot, as a pilgrim to the town where Emerson and Thoreau had lived. I was happy in loitering about the haunts of Thoreau; in sitting, full of thought, by the unhewn granite tombstone of Emerson, near the quiet of his grave.

Toward evening I realised that I had gone without food all day . .

On a hill mounting up toward the West, outside of Concord, I stopped at the house of a market-gardener and asked for something to eat. A tottering old man leaned forward through the half-open door. He asked me in, and set before me a plate of lukewarm beans and a piece of jelly roll. But he delighted the tramp in me by setting before me, also, a cup of excellent, hot, strong coffee.

Afterward when he asked me if I wanted a job, I said yes.

The old man lit my way upstairs to a bed in the attic.

It was hardly dawn when he woke me. . .

A breakfast of soggy pancakes and more beans, which his equally aged wife had prepared. And we were out in the fields, at work. And soon his wife was with us, working, too.

When Sowerby, this market gardener, told me that he was almost ninety I could believe him. He might have added a few more years, with credence.

He went actively about his toil, but yet shaky like a bicycle till it fully starts, when it runs the steadier the more it is speeded. It was work that kept him on his feet, work that sustained life in him. His whole life and pleasure was senseless work.

And yet he was not a bookless man. He possessed many books, mostly the old religious classics. Fox's *Book of Martyrs*, Baxter's *Saint's Rest*, Blair, *On the Grave* . . Jeremy Taylor's *Holy Living* and *Holy Dying*, that gave me a shock almost of painful remembrance—Keats had read the latter when he was dying in Rome . . and there were the New England Divines, the somber Jonathan Edwards whose sermon on the day of doom and the tortures of hell made his auditors faint . . I thought back to the terrifying sermon of the illiterate negro preacher in the Texas jail.

But now old Sowerby read nothing. "I have no time left for a book."

I never met the old man's equal for parsimony. "The last man —the man who worked for me before you came—he was a Pole, who could hardly speak English. He left because he didn't like the food . . yes, that was what he had the impudence to announce . . and you can see that I am not so bad . . don't I give you a slice of jelly roll with your beans, every other night?"

I assented to what the old man said. He had been the milkman to the Emerson and Thoreau families, and, in that capacity, had known both the great men. And I was more eager to hear what he had to say about them, than to draw wages for my work.

But he had little to say about them, except that they were as great fools as the outside world esteemed them great men.

"They talked a lot about work and a man's being independent, earning his living with his own hands, from the soil, but,—did they follow their teachings? . . that's the test. . .

"And I saw them, often, strolling out a-field together, talking and talking a lot of nonsense about philosophy, and going on, regardless, across their neighbours' crops."

And that was the only information I could get of these famous men from their milkman.

. . . .

Sowerby kept pigs under the barn. For economy's sake the cows' dung was shovelled down to them. And over them the outhouse was also built, so that our human efforts might not be wasted. . .

. . . .

One night, despite a hard day's work, I could not sleep. So I went out on the hillside to enjoy the moonlight.

On my way back to the attic I observed a light in the barn. I stopped in to see who was there. It was Sowerby, cleaning out the stable, to the plain disgust of the horses and cows.

I asked him if anything was the matter. I learned that he had risen in the middle of the night and gone to work . . because that was his happiness, his only happiness.

. . . .

Driven by an impulse of distaste for him and his house and market garden, I started to leave in secret. What money was coming to me for my two weeks' work I did not care about—in the face of the curious satisfaction it would give me just to quit, and to have the old man call up to me and find me missing. . .

I heard him pottering back to his bedroom again. . . I waited till he was quiet and back to sleep—then I stole forth in the quiet moonlight near dawn.

It gave me a pleasure to vanish like smoke. I thought of the time when I had that job plowing in Southern California; that time I had driven the horses to the further end of the field, and left them standing there under the shade of a tree and then made off, wishing to shout and sing for the sheer happiness of freedom from responsibility and regular work.

Each time I have made off that way, from a multitude of varying employments, it has not been, surely, to the detriment of my successive employers. I have always decamped with wages still owing me.

. . . .

I swung a scythe for a week for another Yankee farmer, on a marsh where the machine couldn't be driven in—which I was informed was King Phillip's battle ground.

. . . .

I visited the inn where Longfellow was supposed to have gotten his inspiration for *Tales of a Wayside Inn*.

I must see all the literary landmarks, even those where I considered the authors that had caused the places to be celebrated, as dull and third rate. . .

. . . .

With gathering power in me grew my desire to attend college. I would tramp, as I was doing, through the country, and end up at some western university for the fall term.

. . . .

The art workers' community lay in my way at Eos.

I dropped off a freight, one morning, in the Eos yards. . .

The gladdest to see me again was the Buddhist, Pfeiler. He rushed up to me, in the dining hall, that night, and took both my hands in his . . thanking me for my kind thought of him in sending him my Ossian . . avowing that he had made a mistake in his opinion of me and asking my indulgence . . for he was old and a failure . . and I was young and could still look forward to success.

My unexpected dropping-in at Eos created quite a stir.

Spalton welcomed me back, and stood, that evening, before the fire in the sitting room, with his arm about my shoulder . . even as he did so I remembered the picture taken of him and the celebrated poet L'Estrange, together . . their arms about each other's shoulders . . and the current Eos proverb, that Spalton always quarrelled not long after with anyone about whose shoulder he first cast his arm.

. . . .

Already a change was manifest in the little community. Tabled off by themselves sat the workers and the folk of the studios, that night. While the guests who stayed at the inn occupied separate tables.

And there were many secret complaints about a woman they referred to as "Dorothy" . . Dorothy had done this . . Dorothy had done that . . Dorothy would be the ruination of "the shop" . . it would have been better if she had never shown up at the Eos Studios. . .

I asked who was Dorothy. . .

"Don't you know . . we thought you did . . Spalton's new wife . . the one his first wife got a divorce from him for?"

And I heard the story, part of which I knew, but not the final details.

Spalton's first wife had been an easy-going, amiable creature . . fair and pretty in a soft, female way . . a teacher in the local Sunday school . . one who accepted all the conventions as they were . . who could not understand anyone not conforming to them . . life was easier and more comfortable that way. . .

Spalton's originality and genius would in the end have of itself produced a rupture between them . . few women are at home with genius, much as they clasp their hands in ecstasy over it, as viewed on the lecture and concert platform. . .

But the wedge that drove them apart was entered when his first wife, Anne, brought into their married life, Dorothy, a fellow teacher, a visiting friend.

Dorothy was so thin as to be stringy of body. She had a sharp hatchet-face, eyes with the colour of ice in them . . a cold, blue-grey.

She was a woman of culture, yet at the same time she was possessed of a great instinct for organisation and business enterprise— just what was needed for the kind of thing Spalton was trying to inaugurate at Eos. She fell in readily with the Master's schemes . . even with his price-tags on objects of art, his egregious over-valuation of hand illumined books . . which his wife, with old-fashioned honesty, rebuked him for.

An affinity of like-mindedness grew up between Spalton and this intense, homely woman, Dorothy . . whose face, like that of all clever, homely women, grew to a beauty in his eyes, that mere beauty which plastic form can never attain.

There was a local busybody of a minister, and it was he who first intimated to the then Mrs. Spalton that her dear and intimate friend was betraying her. . .

There followed the usual spying and publicity . . Mrs. Spalton won her divorce. . .

.   .   .   .

But this was after several years.   Long before the divorce was granted John and Dorothy were aware of a tangible fruit of their love. . I had often wondered why the Master so ardently, so often, wrote eloquently in defense of the superior qualities of illigitimate children. . .

Dorothy bore their child . . a girl . . and went away to teach in a smart school somewhere in the East, under an assumed name. . .

Now, after many years, Spalton and she married.

.   .   .   .

I saw in the sitting room a wonderful girl.   She had shining, abundant hair, and a face rendered superlatively beautiful by the glowing of vivacity, understanding, feminine vitality behind it and through it, like a lamp held up within.   She was absorbed in the new exhibit of Gresham's that hung on the walls of the guest room . . she wore a short, bouncing, riding skirt, and carried a quirt in her hand.

I walked up to her, fascinated.   Without letting her know who I was I quoted Poe's *To Helen* to her: She stood, smiling sweetly, as if it were the most usual thing in the world, to have a lean, wild-faced stranger address her with a poem.

"That's the way I feel about you!" I ended.

She gave a lovely laugh . . held out both her hands, dropping the quirt on the floor . . took my hands and leaned back gaily, like a child.

"Oh, I know who you are . . you're Razorre . . father wrote me a lot about you . . when I lived East . . you were one of his pet 'nuts'!"

We sat there and conversed a long time.   She talked of Socrates and Plato as if she had broken bread with them . . she discussed science, history, art as if wisdom and understanding were nearer her desire than anything else. . .

She was the child of "John" and Dorothy.

.   .   .   .

Again Spalton asked me to stay, "we need a poet for Eos!"

But I insisted that I must go on and acquire a college educa-tion . . which he maintained would be a hindrance, not a help—

"they will iron you out, and make you a decent member of society—and then, Razorre, God help the poet in you . . poets and artists should never be decent . . only the true son of Ishmael can ever write or paint," he waved.

. . . .

There came to the artworkers one day a young Southern woman, a six months' widow . . she was gentle and lily-coloured and lovely. She had great, swimming, blue eyes, a sensitive red bow of a mouth . . and the lashes of her eyes lay far down on her cheeks. She was the first woman I had met who approximated my poet's ideal of what a woman should be.

I was working for Spalton during my stay, which I meant to make a brief one. I was shovelling coal for him, and firing a furnace.

Wash as I might, I could not remove a faint blackness that clung to the edges of my eyes. This made my eyes glow and seem larger than they were. On such an extraneous and whimsical exterior circumstance hinged the young widow's interest in me.

And I decided that I'd stay a little longer at the Eos Studios . . all winter, if she stayed all winter. And I no longer asked for an easier job. For I wanted my eyes to remain large-seeming, since, half in jest, she admired their present appearance.

She manifested a close and affectionate friendship for me, and all day long all I thought of, as I kept the furnace going, was the evening after dinner, when I could sit close by her reading poetry in a low voice to her.

I leaned over her on every pretext to smell her hair,—her body, through her low-necked dress—to breathe in giddily that delicate fragrance that emanates from the bodies of beautiful women, as perfume from flowers.

Once, in spite of my timidity, I dared place my arm about her shoulders, there in the dark. There was a lecture on over in the "chapel" and mostly everybody had gone to it. Spalton, in passing through where we sat together, asked her if she was coming. "No, she was too tired." She remained sitting by me. Spalton shot me a glance of scarcely concealed resentment and went on. We were left alone.

She began telling me of her deceased husband . . of their devotion to each other . . she applied a dainty thing of lace to her eyes, pausing a moment. . .

"John? may I call you by your name, not by the odious name they have for you here? . ."

She leaned her head against my shoulder.

"Johnnie, you are a fine, sensitive soul, and I know you'll be a great poet some day . . but why don't these people take you more seriously?

"I think it must be your childlikeness . . and your spirit of horse-play, that breaks through at the most inopportune moments, that encourages these fools to treat you with levity." . .

"Dear woman," I began, "dearest woman," and my throat bunched queerly so that I could not speak further.

She stroked my hair. . .

"How old are you?"

"Twenty-three."

"I am just a year younger."

"May I kiss you?" I asked, stumblingly.

"Yes, Johnnie, you may kiss me" . . .

"Why, you dear child, you . . you kiss just like a small boy . ." in a lower voice, "can it be possible that you, with all your tramping, your knowledge of life in books, of people?—"

I bent my head, ashamed, silently acknowledging my inexperience of women.

"No, it's nothing to be ashamed of, dearest boy . . I think you are a fine man—to have gone through what you have—and still——"

Her voice trailed off. She put her arm around my neck, drew me to her, and kissed me!

. . . .

As we sat close together, a brooding silence. Then, with a transition of thought to the practical, she remarked . . .

"I'm angry with these people . . they over-charge for everything."

"Just think of it—I—I feel I may speak of it to you . . we seem to have come so near to each other to-night——"

"They brought my laundry back yesterday, and for one piece of silk lingerie I was charged—guess?"

I couldn't imagine how much.

"Seventy-five cents—think of that!"

. . . .

As the Eoites came tramping back from the lecture, they found us still seated there. At the first footstep we had swiftly moved apart.

I had been half-reclining, my head in her lap, strangely soothed and happy as she ran her fingers through my hair. For a long time neither of us had said a word.

Now I sat apart from her, awkward and wooden.

Spalton did not speak, inclined his head icily, as he strode by.

"He's mad because I didn't come to his talk," she whispered.

"I see my finish," I replied.

. . . .

Now, Spalton was as much in love with Dorothy, his second wife, as I have ever known a man to be in love with a woman. But that could not entirely exclude his jealousy over my sympathetic relation with the "Southern Lady," as the artworkers termed her. And he feared for her on another score. She was, to use a constantly recurring phrase of the Master's, whenever he wished to describe anyone as being wealthy, "lousy with money," and he suspected, not without good cause, that I would warn her against paying exorbitant prices for books and objects of art. . .

. . . .

One night I was the cause of an accident which gave him a handle to seize on.

We were having a musicale. A new musician had come to Eos. The former Eos musician, Von Hammer, the father of the prodigy who played the piano, had quarrelled with the Master and had retired to Buffalo. Where, after a brief struggle as teacher of music, he had turned to playing for the movies. It must have nearly slain the man, for he was a sincere artist, a lover of classical music . . and now compelled to play ragtime and popular melodies for a living.

All that I held of him, despite myself, was an unkind remembrance —his breath had been charnel-foul, and always, when discussing anything, he insisted on taking the lapel of his listener's coat and talking directly into his nose. . .

. . . .

But his successor was playing at an introductory musicale. . .

A tall, alert, dark young man . . Italian-dark . . his eyes shone behind his gold-rimmed glasses, swimming large and distorted under the magnification of the lenses . . his lips were full and red, his moustache of a heavy, bristly black that made them look redder and fuller still, almost negroid.

He played the piano with violent, expert energy . . his favourite work was the "Turkish Patrol," which, Spalton exclaimed, as he applauded vigorously, he would now adopt as the Eos anthem.

The drawing-room was crowded . . a few visiting celebrities . . Eoites, too, but only the quasi-celebrities among them. The mass of the workers was as rigidly excluded now, under the new régime, as ordinary retainers ever are.

I stood by my "Southern Lady." She was in evening dress . . wore a lorgnette . . I trembled as I leaned over her, for I could see the firm, white-orbed upper parts of her breasts . . I was trying to be lightly playful, and was clumsy at it. I took up her lorgnette and toyed with it. I sat on the edge of a table . . and where I sat stood a supposed Greek vase of great antiquity and value.

It is a law that prevails in three-dimensional space that two objects cannot occupy the same place at one time. I dislodged the vase. It came to the floor in a crash . . which stopped the music . . which stopped everything. There fell a dead silence. I looked down at the fragments, hardly knowing what to do. . .

Spalton came over to me . . intensely . . his eyes blazing.

"Razorre, come out into the lobby . . I want to speak to you." I willingly followed him . . he wheeled on me when he had me alone.

"Do you know why we have these paintings of Gresham's hung high up there on the wall?" he asked rhetorically, with an eloquent, upward sweep of his arm, "it's so bums like you . . dirty tramps . . can't wipe their feet on them."

"I am so sorry, so very sorry," I murmured, contrite.

Thinking my contrition meekness, and possibly fear of him, he went to take me by the shoulders. I knocked his hands away promptly and quickly stepped back, on the defensive . . all my reverence for him swallowed up in indignation, rising at last, against his vulgar chiding.

At that moment, my widow, Mrs. Tighe, arrived . . she was weeping. . .

"Don't be hard on the poor boy," she pleaded . . "anyhow, it was all my fault . . and I want to pay you for your vase . . whatever it cost." . .

A momentary flicker of greed lighted the Master's eyes. But he perceived as instantly how unmagnanimous he would appear if he accepted a cash settlement.

"I am not thinking of my financial loss . . beauty cannot be valued that way!" he exclaimed.

"Then you must not blame the boy."

"He is clumsy . . he is a terrible fool . . he is always doing the wrong thing. Oh, my beautiful vase!" and he wrung his hands, lost in the pose. Out he strode through the front door.

.   .   .   .

The musicale had been broken up.

"My poor, dear Johnnie, I am so sorry," murmured the young woman. I was sitting in the large armchair where she had sat the memorable night of the lecture that neither of us attended. She had seated herself on one of the arms.

"You mustn't be despondent!" She was patting my hand.

She mistook my rage at the gratuitous insults Spalton had heaped on me as despondency. She leaned closer against me . . quickly I caught her into my arms, drew her into my lap . . held her little, quiet, amazed face in my hands firmly, as I kissed and kissed her. . . I knew how to kiss now. . .

She rose presently. I stood up and caught her in my arms. Slowly and firmly she disengaged herself . . silently she slid away. She stopped in the shadow a moment before going up the long, winding stairs.

"Good night, my dear poet," she whispered.

She had no sooner disappeared than I started out, my heart beating like a drum to a charge in me. Spalton frequently wrote till late, in his office. I would go over there and, if he was there, call him to account for his insults. There was a light lit within, and I could see him through the window at his desk.

"Come in!" in answer to my knock. "Oh, it's you, Razorre!" and his eyes snapped with fresh resentment. "What do you want? Don't you know that I'm busy on *A Brief Visit?*"

"You know why I'm here!"

"Well?" challengingly.

"I've come for two reasons. I want to apologise to you for breaking that vase . . and I demand an equal apology from you, in turn, for the way you insulted me in Mrs. Tighe's presence."

"You deserved everything I said to you," he replied, rising quietly from his chair.

"I may have deserved it . . but that doesn't alter in the least my intention of smashing your face flat for the way you spoke to me, unless you tell me you're sorry for it."

"My dear Gregory, don't be a fool."

"A fool?" I replied, inflamed further by the appellation applied to quiet me in such a superior tone, "if you'll come on out into the street and away from your own property, I'll show you who's a fool . . you'll find you can't treat me like a dog, and get away with it!"

"Why, Razorre . . my dear, dear boy," calling me by my nickname and taking another tack . . he laid his hand gently on my shoulder and gave me a deep, burning look of compassionate rebuke . . though I saw fear flickering back of it all. . .

"Look here, John," I burst out, never able to hold my wrath long, "I like you . . think you're a great man—but you humiliated me before other people . . and I've come to such a pass in my life that I wouldn't let God Himself get away with a thing like that!"

"Then I apologise . . most humbly!"

"That was all I wanted. Good-night!" But I could not bring myself to leave so abruptly.

"John," I wavered, "you *are* a great man . . a much greater man than you allow yourself to be . . I'm—I'm going away from here forever, this time . . and I—I want you to know how I reverence and love the bigness in you, in spite of our—our differences."

He was pleased.

"And so you're going to college somewhere?"

"Yes."

"Where?"

I had talked much of college being my next aim.

"Either the University of Chicago, or further west."

"I can give you commutation as far as Chicago."

"I cannot accept it."

"You must, Razorre."

.   .   .   .

A week from then I left.

I went up to Mrs. Tighe's room to say good-bye. Awkwardly

and with the bearlike roughness of excessive timidity I put my arms about her, drew her to me tentatively.

"Be careful, poet dear, or you'll hurt me," she warned, giving me a look of fondness. Her left arm was in a sling. She had fallen on the steps a few days before and had broken a small bone in the wrist. "My sweet poet!"

The bandaged arm being in the way, I put my head down in her lap again, as she sat there on the edge of the great, white bed.

She leaned over, turned my face up with her free hand, kissed me full in the mouth. . .

"My sweet poet," she repeated, "good-bye!"

.   .   .   .

While at Mt. Hebron I had chosen German as my modern language. And it was a Professor Langworth's grammar and exercise book that we used as a text-book. Langworth, I learned from the title page, was professor of Germanic languages in Laurel University, at Laurel, Kansas.

And now I bethought me that it would be much better to go to college in Kansas than attend the University at Chicago, where, I felt, education was made an industry, just like pork-packing and the hundred other big concerns in that city. Kansas would encourage individuality more, be less appallingly machine-like.

The great, roaring city bewildered me, and the buildings of the University of Chicago (for I got so far as to ask for the registrar's office) overwhelmed me with their number. And I fled. With the exception of a few days I put in washing dishes in a restaurant there, I stayed no longer, but freighted it southwest to Kansas City . . from whence I rode a freight further to Laurel.

.   .   .   .

In the evening twilight I climbed out of a box car in the railroad yards at Laurel. . .

I enquired my way to the university.

"Up on the hill."

I veered off from the main street of the town . . a length of marching telegraph poles and flat-roofed Western houses. I struck across lots in the cold and dark. I floundered through half-hardened puddles of mud, over vacant lots that afterward seemed to have been conjured up for my impediment by some devil of piquaresque romance. . .

The hill, the very top of it, I had laboriously attained. On all sides the college buildings gloomed in dusky whiteness of architecture.

One of them was lit inside with the mellow glow of electric lights. As I stepped into the vestibule timidly, to enquire my way to Professor Langworth's house (for it was his I decided to seek out first), a group of fragrant, white-clad girls herded together in astonished tittering when they saw me. And I surely looked the tramp, dusty and soiled from my long ride.

I asked them the direction to Langworth's house, but they ignored me, and scattered. Turning in confusion, I ran into a man-student bodily . . excused myself . . the girls, standing further off, tittered again.

"Can you direct me to Professor Gustav Langworth's house?"

The student looked me over curiously. But he was of the right sort.

"Certainly. Come with me. I'm going that way. I'll show you where it is. . ."

.   .   .   .

In silence we descended the hill. . .

"That house, in there a bit, under the trees . . that is where the professor lives."

My knock set a dog barking inside . . the quick, insistent bark of a collie that romped against me, putting up its paws on me when the door was opened by a slim-bodied man of middle height. The man was dressed in a grey suit . . he had a kindly, smooth-shaven face except for a close-cropped pepper-and-salt moustache . . and grey-blue, quizzical, but kindly eyes.

"Here, Laddie, come here!" called the voice of a frail, little woman whose hair was white like wool, and like wool in texture. She sat crumpled up by an open gas fire of imitation logs. She was wry-backed, her right shoulder thrust out into a discernible hunch.

She flung her arm tenderly about the dog, when it came to her. She was, I figured, the professor's mother . . He held a hurried, whispered consultation with her—after I had told him that studying his German book at Mt. Hebron had impelled me to come to Laurel. Which story I could see pleased and flattered him.

I was waiting in the storm porch.

He returned. He thrust his hand into his pocket and fetched forth a two-dollar bill.

"Go downtown to one of the restaurants you will find on the main street. You can get a square meal in one of them for a quarter or, at the most, fifty cents . . a bed for the same price . . climb the hill again in the morning, say about ten o'clock, and ask for me at the German Department . . I am sorry I can't invite you to stay here for the night . . but we have no room . ." and he glanced timidly at the woman whom I had taken to be his mother, but who, I afterward learned, was his wife.

.   .   .   .

I found a restaurant-hotel, as he had directed me, and procured my supper for a quarter . . fried potatoes and a cold slab of steak . . and a big Westerner who wore a sombrero and had a stupid, kindly, boyish face, showed me to a bed . . which also cost but a quarter for the night . . with a scattered ambuscade of bedbugs thrown in for good measure.

In the morning, fried pork chops, pancakes and two cups of coffee—and I set out for the hill.

The place buzzed with activity. The fall term was already in full swing, and students poured in lines up and down both sides of the steep street that led to the college . . girls and boys both, for it was co-educational. They were well dressed and jolly, as they moved in the keen windy sun of autumn.

I was not a part of this. I felt like an outcast, but I bore myself with assumed independence and indifference. I thought everybody was looking at me. Most of them were.

.   .   .   .

Langworth enrolled me as a special student. He himself paid my tuition fee, which was a nominal one. I enrolled in Philosophy, Economics, German, Latin.

My patron, furthermore, slipped a ten-dollar bill into my hand. "For the books you will need."

He directed me to the Y. M. C. A. employment bureau. "They will see that you get work at something, so you can be sure of board and room . . in the early days we did not have things so well arranged. I worked my way through college, too. I nearly perished, my first year. After you settle somewhere, come and see me once in a while and let me hear how you're getting on."

. . . .

My first job was milking a cow and taking care of a horse, for board and room. . . The man for whom I worked was an old, retired farmer.

The disagreeable part of taking care of horses and cows is the smell. My clothes, my room, even the skin of my body, soon reeked with the faint yet penetrating odour of stable and barn.

But I was happy. Many great men had done as I was doing. Always trust me to dramatise every situation!

I arranged my meagre row of text-books on the shelf in my attic. I set Keats apart in a sacred nook by himself.

I sat humming softly to myself, studying my first lessons.

. . . .

"Look," cried a girl, her voice vibrating with the hard sarcasm of youth, "look, there goes Abe Lincoln," to another girl and two boys, who lolled with her on the porch of the house next mine.

I was stabbed with a bitter pang of resentment. For my face was thin and weather-beaten . . my sharp, bent knees never straightened as I walked along, like a man going through snow drifts. Yet I held my head erect, ridiculously erect . . and my chest was enormous through over-development, as my arms and legs were thin.

. . . .

My first few days at Laurel University brought me that beginning of newspaper notoriety that has since followed me everywhere as a shadow goes with a moving object. And then originated the appellation which has since clung to me, that of "The Vagabond Poet."

One morning, when I was hardly awake, there came a knock at my door.

"Just a moment," I called, getting into my shirt and trousers, "who is it?"

"A reporter to interview you."

I opened the door to admit a pale, young chap, who expertly flirted the ashes off a cigarette as he said, leaning his head sidewise, that he represented the Kansas City *Star*. As he spoke his keen grey eyes looked me over impartially, but with intelligent, friendly interest. Though he was dressed in the student's conventional style, even to the curiously nicked and clipped soft hat then predominant, there was still about him an off-handedness, an impudent at-homeness that bespoke a wider knowledge, or assumed knowledge, of the world, than the average student possesses.

The interview appeared the next afternoon.

"VAGABOND POET ARRIVES.

LAUREL ENROLLS BOX-CAR STUDENT."

It made me a nine days' wonder with the students. I caught the men staring at me, the girls shyly observing me, as I strode from class room to class room. . .

But the reek of the stable. It went with me like a ghost everywhere. Maybe it was because I had no change of suits . . I saw that it was noticeable to others, and I sat 'way back, in a seat apart, by myself.

.   .   .   .

Langworth watched my progress narrowly the first few weeks.

One afternoon as I was passing his house he beckoned me in.

"You're making good, and I'm glad of it . . because they're looking on you as my protégé . . holding me responsible for you. Munday, in the Schiller class, tells me you sometimes bring in your daily lesson in *Wilhelm Tell*, translated into blank verse . . and good stuff, too. . . And King says he turns over the most difficult lines in Horace in class for you to translate and construe."

Langworth had only half the truth from King.

Whenever the latter came upon a passage a little off colour, he put me on it, chuckling to himself . . he knew I would go right through with it without hesitation.

.   .   .   .

About this time I received a letter from William Hayes Ward, editor of the New York *Independent*. He informed me that he had taken a poem of mine. And, as indubitable proof, he enclosed a check for five dollars.

Professor Langworth was himself a poet of no mean ability: he was pleased to hear that I had sold a poem to the *Independent*.

.   .   .   .

I was sick of being shunned because I carried stable smells about with me wherever I went.

Also, sanguinely, with the sale of my first poem, I was sure that my literary career had begun, and that from now on I would be enabled to earn my living by my pen, and pay my way as a student, too. So I threw up the job that made me smell so unpleasantly.

．　　　．　　　．　　　．　　　．　　　．　　　．

The city of Laurel had been, in the early days, in the memory of settlers yet living a hale life, a pioneer outpost. Through it flowed a great, muddy river. The flat roofs of its main street still preserved a frontier appearance. It was surrounded by high, wind-swept bluffs.

They still talked of the Quantrell raid and repeated the story of it . . and of how the six men were lynched under the bridge that swung over the dam. . .

At the time of the slavery agitation its citizens had encouraged the negroes to escape, had petted them, idealised them as no human beings of any race should be idealised . . had run schools specially for them where it was considered an honour for the women of the settlers to teach.

Now, the great negro population, at first so encouraged, was crowded into a festering multitude of dilapidated buildings that stood on the flats close by the region where the river coiled through level acres of low-lying country. This place was known as the "Bottoms."

I am trying to give you the flavour of the town.

They had prohibition there, too . . long before it won nation-wide power . . consequently the negroes drove a vast trade in bootlegging . . and a concomitant prostitution of coloured women and girls throve. One or two students on the hill had, to my knowledge, negro mistresses of whom they were fond. . .

The drug stores did a thriving business in the sale of spiritus frumenti—for "snake bite" and "stomach trouble," which seemed to be prevalent and epidemic throughout the community.

．　　　．　　　．　　　．　　　．　　　．　　　．

Saturday was market day for the farmers who lived in the adjoining countryside . . and the livery stables where they put up their horses were also resorts for gambling and the selling of "bootleg" booze. . .

These farmers were a wild lot . . something like European peasants in their smacking of the soil and the country to which they belonged, but with a verve and dash of their own distinctly American.

There were three or four cheap restaurants that catered solely to their trade . . "a square meal for a quarter" . . and a square meal they served . . multitudes of fried stuff . . beefsteak, potatoes, boiled ham, cabbage, heaps of white bread constantly replenished as it was voraciously devoured . . always plenty of hot, steaming coffee. Where these restaurants profited I could never see . . unless by a little bootlegging on the side.

It was to one of them that I repaired when I left my malodorous job. The same one where I had spent my first night in town.

. . . .

Langworth sent for me one day.

"I have heard wild tales about you, Johnnie. I don't usually listen to gossip, but these tales are so recurrent and persistent . . about your going about with the degraded people who live in the Bottoms, that I considered I ought to see you about it."

I confessed that, though I did not drink their bootleg booze, I did have a wide acquaintanceship with the folk of the Bottoms, and that I knew all the rowdies among the farmers . . that I passed a lot of time about the livery stables talking with them. That I often rode out to their farms in the hills and spent Saturdays and Sundays there. I avowed that there people were more interesting to me than the carefully tailored professors and students.

My schoolmates had met me on the streets in company with these wild-looking yokels, sometimes taking them to their waggons when they were too drunk to pilot themselves effectively. And they had applied to me the proverb of "birds of a feather."

. . . .

Before I left, Langworth drew from me the admission that I was away behind in my board bill at the Farmers' Restaurant. My hopes of making immediate money as a writer of poems for the magazines had so far been barren of fruit.

"Sh! sit down a minute and wait." His wife was coming downstairs, querulously, waveringly; her eyes red from weeping.

"Laddie has just died."

"The shepherd dog?" I enquired; for she had spoken as of a human demise.

"Yes, the dog . . but he was human, if anyone was." There was an acidulous resentment in the tone of her answer that indicated that she wanted her husband to send me away.

"She wants you to go," whispered Langworth, humouring his wife like a sick child. He escorted me into the storm porch. "You have no idea," he apologised defensively, "how human a dog can be, or how fond of one you can become. . ."

"What's this?" I asked, taken aback. He had thrust a check into my hand as he shook hands good-bye.

"It's a check I've just endorsed over to you. Royalties on a recent text-book. Please do take it." I had intimated that I would probably be compelled to quit college and go on the tramp again . . confessing frankly, also, that a stationary life got on my nerves at times.

"I want you to keep on, not go back to the tramp life . . we'll make something of you yet," he jested, diffidently, steering me off when he noticed that I was about to heap profuse thanks on him.

"How can I ever thank you———"

"By studying hard and making good. By becoming the great poet I wanted to be."

"But how can I pay this back? It will take a long time———"

"When you arrive at the place where you can afford to pay me back, pass it on to someone else who is struggling as you are now, and as I myself have struggled."

.   .   .   .

Always, always I wrote my poetry and kept studying in my own fashion . . marks of proficiency, attendance at class went by the board. My studying was rather browsing among the multitudes of books in the college library. I passed hours, back in the stacks, forgetting day and night . . recitations . . meals. . .

I was soon in trouble with my professors . . I was always up, and even ahead, with my studies, but I was a disrupting influence for the other students, because of my irregularity.

I discovered wonderful books back there in the "stack" . . the works of Paracelsus, who whispered me that wisdom was to be found more in the vagabond bye-ways of life than in the ordered and regulated highways. That the true knowledge was to be garnered from knocking about with vagrants, gipsies, carriers . . from corners in wayside inns where travellers discoursed. . .

And there was Boehmen, the inspired German shoemaker, who

was visited by an angel, or some sort of divine stranger, and given his first illumination outside his shop . . and later walked a-field and heard what the flowers were saying to each other, seeing through all creation at one glance, crystal-clear.

And there were the unusual poets . . old Matthew Prior, who wrote besides his poems, the Treaty, was it, of Utrecht? . . hobnobbed with the big people of the land . . yet refused all marks of honour . . the best Latinist of the day . . at a time when Latin was the diplomatic language of Europe.

When he wasn't hobnobbing with the aristocracy or writing treaties he was sitting in inns and drinking with teamsters . . had a long love affair with a cobbler's wife, and married the lady after the cobbler died. . .

There was Skelton and his rough-running, irregular rhythmic rather than strictly metrical verses . . mad and ribald . . often tedious . . but with wild flashes of beauty interwoven through his poems . . the poem about his mistress's sparrow . .the elegy on its death . . where he prayed God to give it the little wren of the Virgin Mary, as a wife, in heaven—"to tread, for *solas!*"

And Gay, the author of many delightful fables . . who must wait still longer for his proper niche, because he showed gross levity on the subject of death and life . . he who wrote for his own epitaph:

> "Life is a jest, and all things show it;
>   I thought so once, but now I know it."

For all those who would not keep step, who romped out of the regular procedure and wantoned by the way, picking what flowers they chose, I held feeling and sympathy.

·   ·   ·   ·   ·   ·   ·

The *Annual*, a book published by the seniors each spring, now advertised a prize for the best poem submitted by any student . . a prize of twenty-five dollars. I had no doubt but that the prize was mine already. Not that I had become as yet the poet I desired, but that the average level of human endeavour in any art is so low that I knew my assiduity and application and fair amount of inspiration would win.

I wrote my poem—*A Day in a Japanese Garden,.....*only two lines I remember:

"And black cranes trailed their long legs as they flew
    Down to it, somewhere out of Heaven's blue,"

descriptive of a little lake . . oh, yes, and two more I remember,
descriptive of sunset:

"And Fujiyama's far and sacred top
    Became a jewel shining in the sun."

The poem was an over-laquered, metaphor-cloyed thing . . much
like the bulk of our free verse of to-day . . but it was superior to
all the rest of the contributions.

The prize was declared off. After an evening's serious discussion
the committee decided that, though my effort was far and away
the best, it would not do to let me have the prize, because I was
so wild-appearing . . because I was known as having been a tramp.
And because seniors and students of correct standing at the university had tried. And it would not be good for the school morale to
let me have what I had won.

They compromised by declaring the prize off.

A year after, Professor Black, assistant professor in English
literature, who served on the judging board, told me confidentially
of this . . though he declared that he had fought for me, alleging
how I needed the money, and how I had honestly won the award.

I thought of the couplet of Gay:

"He who would without malice pass his days
    Must live obscure and never merit praise."

.   .   .   .

Outwardly I maintained a bold and courageous rudeness. Inwardly a panic had swept over me . . not the panic of deep solitude
when a man is alone at night in a boundless forest . . I have known
that, too, but it is nothing to that which comes to a man who
knows all society, by its very structure, arrayed against him and
his dreams.

When the ancient Egyptians had finished the building of a
pyramid, they began polishing it at the top, proceeding downward.
And it has been said that on the finished, hard, smooth exterior
even a fly would slip. . .

Huge, granite, towering, the regularised life appeared to me, the life that bulked on all sides . . I saw that it was the object of education, not to liberate the soul and mind and heart, but to reduce everything to dead and commonplace formulae.

On all sides, so to speak, I saw Christ and Socrates and Shelley valeted by society . . dress suits laid out for them . . carefully pressed and creased . . which,—now dead,—it was pretended their spirits took up and wore . . had, in fact, always worn. . .

. . . .

And my mind went back to those happy days at Eos . . happy despite the fly in the ointment. . .

I thought of my Southern widow, Mrs. Tighe.

"Poet," she had once said, "come to my place in the South. I have a bungalow back of my house that you may live in . . write your poems unmolested . . I won't be going there for awhile yet, but I will give you a letter to the caretaker, and you can use the place. And my pantry and ice box will be at your service . . so you'll need do nothing but write."

Now, fed full of rebuffs, I wished I had accepted her offer. And I wrote her, care of the Eos Artworks . . an ingenuous letter, burning with naïve love. . .

She had once told me how she had scandalised the neighbours by painting a little boy, in the nude, in that same bungalow . . the story being carried about by the servants . . and if it had not been for her social prestige!——

I thought there could be nothing pleasanter than living in her place, perhaps becoming her lover. . .

I imagined myself posing, nude, for her canvases. . .

But my brief hope fell to earth. A curt note from a married sister of hers . . who first apologised for having read my letter. . . But Mrs. Tighe was abroad, painting in Spain.

The shock of having someone else, indubitably with a hostile eye, read my letter, in which I had poured forth all my heart, made me almost sick. I was chagrined inexpressibly.

. . . .

The truth was, spring was coming on. Spring affects me as it does migratory fowls. With its first effort of meadow and bough toward renewed flowers and greenness, the instinct for change and adventure stirs anew in me.

The school year was not yet up, but I didn't want to graduate.

.   .   .   .

At that time I had a passion for meeting well-known people.

It was then my only avenue of literary publication, so to speak.
The magazines were steadily returning my deluge of poems— I sent
at least three a week to them .. but to those who had established
themselves I could show my work, and get their advice and notice...

.   .   .   .

Walking along the main street, I ran into Jack Travers, the
young reporter who had dubbed me the "Vagabond Poet," the
"Box-car Bard." ..

"Well, what are you up to now, Gregory?"

"Nothing, only I'm thinking of a trip south to Osageville to
pay a visit to Mackworth, the Kansas novelist."

"That's the stuff .. I need another good story for the *Era*."

"I'm going to make it a sort of pilgrimage a-foot."

"Great! 'Vagabond Poet' Pilgrims to Home of Celebrated Kansan.
It's only ninety miles to Osageville from here .. still rather cold of
nights .. but you'll find plenty of shelter by the way .. start to-day
and I can get the story in in time for this Sunday's *Era*..."

Travers got a camera from a fraternity brother.

"Come on, we'll walk up an alley and I'll snap you just as if you
were on the way..."

"No, I won't do that!"

—"won't do what?"

—"won't fake it .. if you want a picture of me on the way, it will
have to be on the way!"

"Of all the fools! Ain't the alleys muddy enough to be like the
gumbo you'll have to plough through?" he teased. But I wouldn't
allow him to take a fraudulent picture. He had to come with me,
through the mud, grumbling, to the edge of town.

There, on the country road that led in the direction of Osageville,
my feet rooted in gumbo, a sort of thick composite of clay and
mud that clings to the feet in huge lumps, I had my photograph
taken .. actually on the march toward my destination .. no hat
on .. a copy of Keats in my hand.

Travers waved me good-bye. "You'll see the story in the *Era*
Sunday sure," he shouted, in a tone half affection, half irony. I was

nettled at the irony. I wanted it to be looked on as a quest entirely heroic.

.   .   .   .

It began to rain. Far off, like a high, great ship riding on the horizon, rode the hill, with its cluster of university buildings.

My first impulse was to turn back, to quit. That is always my first impulse. The instincts of my bourgeois ancestry against the unusual, the impractical,—the safe-and-sane conservatism of the farmers and clerks and small business men bred in my people for generations! . .

I pushed on through the clinging, maddening gumbo, slithering and sliding. Fortunately, I wore an overcoat, which, after it had reached the saturation point, shed most of the steady, oblique-driving rain that came for miles over the plains in a succession of grey, windy sheets. But my wrists and hands were aching, wet, and my thin, plying legs, to my knees. And the "squash-squish!" of my soaked feet in the mud plodded a steady refrain of misery.

My Keats, at least, was dry. I kept the volume under my belt and against my naked belly.

And I was happy and buoyed up by the thought, which lessened my discomfiture, that Sunday morning thousands of readers in comfortable homes would be reading about me, would gaze upon my photograph.

People looked out of their farmhouse windows at me as if an insane man were stalking by.

It darkened rapidly.

My first night's shelter was in a leaky outhouse. The farmstead to which it belonged had burned down. I might have been taken in at any number of places, but my access of timidity was too great . . it might on the following dawn be followed by as great an effrontery. My year in college had disorganized me, pulled me out of my tramp character. It was no more a usual thing to beg or ask for shelter.

I could not sleep. My muscles were already overstrained from the excessive effort of struggling along in the tenacious mud, like a fly escaping from the edge of spilled molasses.

I had brought a box of small candles for just such an emergency. I lit one after the other, sat on the seat, and read Keats all night

.. in an ecstasy, forgetting my surroundings, my pitiful poverty, my pilgrimage that would seem ridiculous to most.

The rain increased. Outside it drummed and drummed. Inside it dripped and dripped.

And as I sat there, upright, to escape the drip from the leaks, I climbed to a high, crystal-clear state of spirit.

Again I burned through Keats' life as if remembering that it was what I had myself suffered .. as if suddenly I awoke to the realisation that *I* was Keats, re-born in America, a tramp-student in Kansas. . .

And now Severn, my true, faithful friend, was with me .. Severn, who had given up his career as painter to be near me in my last days .. we were on the *Maria Crowther* .. we were still off the coast of England, and I had gone ashore for the last touching of my foot on English soil. . .

There hung the great, translucent star of evening, at that hushed moment of twilight, before any other of the stars had come forth . . .

> "Bright star, would I were steadfast as thou art—
> Not in lone splendour hung aloft the night,
> And watching, with eternal lids apart,
> Like nature's patient, sleepless Eremite,
> The moving waters at their priestlike task
> Of pure ablution round earth's human shores, . ."

The evening star made me dream of immortality and love—my love for Fanny Brawne. . .

Now we, Severn and I, were journeying across the country to Rome .. voyaging, rather, through fields of flowers .. like my procession of Bacchus in *Endymion* .. that was a big poem, after all. . .

Now the fountain played under the window .. where I was to die. . .

"Severn, I feel the daisies growing over me."

"Severn, I—I—Severn .. I am dying .. Severn, lift me up— I——"

"Here lies one whose fame was writ in water." (How they cruelly laughed at that—for a time!)

. . . .

I gave a start, almost a scream of agony . . the candle, somehow, had served me a ghastly trick . . it had cast my shadow backard on the wall, like that shadow cast by the head of the dying poet, as Severn had sketched it . . I ran my hand over my face . . it was hollow and tight-drawn like the face of a consumptive.

The mass of resistance I had to face, for poetry's sake, was too enormous . . my country's motto was not "beauty is truth, truth beauty," but "blessed be that man who can make two hills of corn grow where one bank of violets grew before," . . and my pilgrimage, in that hour of vision, it disgusted me . . for I was making it not to some grand poet like L'Estrange, but to the home of the chief exponent of the "Honest-to-God, No-Nonsense-About-Me Hick School of Literature" . . and associated with him was the syndicate poet, William Struthers, called familiarly Uncle Bill, whose daily jingles run together as prose, were now making him a fortune.

With the coming of dawn the day cleared, the sun glistened on a thousand puddles, making them silver and gold. . .

By walking carefully on the side of the road, I made progress less muddy. I was used to the squashing of the water in my shoes. The weather turned warmer.

.   .   .   .

I found myself on the usual long one-street called Main Street, in the prosperous little city of Osageville. It was Sunday. A corner loiterer directed me to Jarvis Alexander Mackworth's house.

A habitation of sequestered quiet . . as I stood before the door I heard the sunrise song of Rossini's *Wilhelm Tell* . . a Red Seal record . . accompanied by the slow, dreamy following of a piano's tinkle . . like harp sounds or remote, flowing water.

I halted, under a charm. I waited till the melody was at an end before I knocked. A small, pale-faced, pretty little woman answered.

"Does Mr. Jarvis Mackworth live here?"

"Yes. Come in. We have been expecting you. You are the poet, aren't you?"

"Yes, I am the poet."

"You're a good walker . . we didn't expect you before Monday or Tuesday. . . Jarvis, here's the poet-boy from the university."

"My host, unseen within, turned off another Red Seal record he had just started, again to the accompaniment of the piano. . . Kreisler's *Caprice Viennoise.* . .

Jarvis Alexander Mackworth came forth like a leisurely duck, waddling. He was very, very fat. He extended me a plump, white hand . . a slack hand-shake . . but not an unhearty one, rather a grip of easy welcome.

A kind, rubicund, moon-round face, full of large blue eyes smiling a gentle and kindly welcome . . if the face of Shelley's father, plump and methodic-oracular, could have been joined to the wild, shining ecstasy of Shelley's countenance itself—you would have had Mackworth's face before its time. I never beheld such spirituality in a fat man. His stoutness was not unpleasing.

"My boy . . come in . . my God, you're all wet . . you look frail, too." A pity shone in his eyes. "Minnie, call up Ally Merton . . " turning to me, "I have, as you can see, no clothes to fit you . . but Ally might have . . he's about your size, but he carries a trifle more meat on his bones. . .

"Come in and dry yourself before the fire till he gets over."

We sat before the gas-fire of artificial logs.

"Minnie, will you make a cup of tea for this—poor boy," and he lowered his voice at the last two words, realising that I was hearing, too.

"Yes, Jarv!"

.   .   .   .

I sat at the table in the dining room. Jarvis Alexander Mackworth sat on the piano-stool, again playing the piano in rhythm rather than in accompaniment with the records . . it was Caruso now. . .

"A glorious voice, isn't it, young man?" Mackworth asked, as I ate voraciously of the cold roast set before me . . of the delicious white bread and fresh dairy butter, just from the churn of some neighbouring farmer.

"I know nothing much about music," he continued, "—just appreciate it . . —seems to me that's what we need now, more than anything else . . appreciation of the arts . . I like to sit here and pick out the melodies on the piano as the tune runs on. It inspires me. The precious people, the aesthetic upstarts, make fun of Edison and his 'canned music,' as they call it . . but I say Edison is one of the great forces for culture in America to-day. Everybody can't go to New York, London, Paris, Bayreuth . . not to Chicago even . . .

"Beauty must come to Osageville, since Osageville cannot come to Beauty."

I was charmed.

"Mr. Mackworth, you are a great man," I said.

．　　　．　　　．　　　．　　　．　　　．　　　．

A ring at the bell. Ally Merton...

"Ally, this is Mr. John Gregory, poet at large, Villon of American Literature . . let us hope, some day a little more of the Whittier . . Ally——" and the speaker turned to me, "Ally Merton is my right hand man . . my best reporter . . "

He took Merton aside, in private talk . . Ally looked me over with a keen, swift glance that appraised me from head to foot instantly . . sharply but not hostilely . . as one who takes in a situation in a comprehensive instant.

"Yes, Mr. Mackworth, I can do it easily . . if they'll fit him."

There was an impersonality, however, about Merton's cryptic words that annoyed me.

"You are going home with Ally, John," Mackworth said to me, using my familiar name for the first time, "and borrow a suit of his clothes . . and you are coming back with him to dinner . . where you'll meet a very famous person—Miss Clara Martin."

．　　　．　　　．　　　．　　　．　　　．　　　．

Ally's blue serge suit was too short in the legs and arms for me . . otherwise it fitted. His gentleness and unobtrusive quietness entered into me, along with the putting on of his apparel. He led me upstairs in his house.

"Mr. Mackworth has asked me to put you up while you are in town . . because his own house is full at present, otherwise he would accommodate you there . . I guess we can make shift to entertain you properly.

"Here is the bathroom . . if you don't mind my saying it, when you throw the toilet seat up, let the water run from the tap over the wash basin . . my mother and sisters!" he trailed off in inaudible, deprecative urge of the proprieties.

Ally was anything but a small-town product. Suave, socially adroit, an instinctive creature of Good Form. . .

He came into the room he had given me to stay in. I looked like a different man, togged out in his clothes. Ally was surprised that

I could wear his shoes . . he had such small feet . . I informed him proudly that I, too, had small feet. . .

"No, no, that is not the way to tie a tie . . let me show you . . you must make both ends meet exactly . . there, that's it!" and he stepped back, a look of satisfaction on his face . . he handed me a pearl stick pin.

"This is a loan, not a gift," he murmured.

I returned a quick, angry look.

"I don't want your pin."

"No offence meant," he deprecated, "and you must wear it" (for I was putting it aside) "Mr. Mackworth and I both want you to look your best when you meet Miss Martin at dinner to-night" . . I angrily almost decided to take his pin with me when I left, just to fulfill his pre-supposition.

"No, that's not the place to stick it . . let me show you . . not in the body of the tie, but further down," and he deftly placed the pin in the right spot. Then he stepped back like an artist who is proud of having made a good job of bad materials. . .

"You look almost like a gentleman."

I was about to lick into Merton and lend him a sample of a few strong objurgations of road and jail, when I saw myself in the glass. I stood transfixed. He had not meant to be ironic. The transformation was startling. . .

"If you would only keep yourself tidy all the time that way! . . it's easy."

"Not for me . . everything material that I touch seems to fall apart. . . I lose my shirts inexplicably . . my socks . . holes appear overnight in my clothes. Books are the only things I can keep. I am always cluttered up with them."

"Appearances mean everything . . then, if you have the rest, the goods to deliver, there is no place a man might not go nor attain."

I looked the small town reporter over in surprise. I studied him closely for the first time. He belonged to the world, not to Osage-ville . . the world of fashion, of smartness . . a world I despised. My world and his would always be like separate planets. He would consort with people for the mere pleasure of social life with them. The one thing I did not like about him was his small mouth. . but then I did not like my own mouth . . it was large, sensual, loose and cruel.

And his walk .. it was almost dainty mincing. But then my walk was a loose, bent-kneed method of progression...

. . . .

Miss Martin, the celebrated exposer of corrupt millionaires and captains of industry, was dark and tall. She had been good-looking in girlhood. She had fine eyes in a devastated face.

I found myself petted, mothered by her. As soon as she saw me she removed a thread that hung to my coatsleeve.

At supper I was told of a new project. A group of writers, especially of writers who were in revolt against big business and the corruption of the trusts, were about to effect a combination and start what was to be called the *National Magazine;* for it was to be no less than that, a magazine embracing all America, to serve as a re-invigorant and re-corroborant for new national ideals .. really only a tilting against the evils of big combinations, in favour of the earlier and more impossible ideals of small business units—the ideal of a bourgeois commercial honesty and individual effort that could no more be re-established than could the big shoe factory be broken up and returned to the shanty of the village shoe-maker. . . Bryan's dream . . the last effort of the middle classes to escape their surely destined strangulation . . which gave birth to the abortive progressive party.

I was assured by Miss Martin and Mackworth that a poet who could sing American ideals and dreams was needed by them .. Ray Stannard Baker, Peter Finley Dunne, Upton Sinclair, were all to write for them...

I saw clearly that their revolution was a backward-working one. That the country's business could never again be broken up into a multitude of small shops and individual competitors.

Of course, I was at that time a Socialist of the violent, fiery type—with a strong cast toward the anarchism of Emma Goldman.

But it flattered me to be taken, as it were, into the inner councils of such great folk. . .

"Send us some of your poetry, with the right American ring to it, Johnnie," suggested Miss Martin, "and we will make you the poet of the group."

I think that Ally Merton's clothes on me, and his correct tie, made my good impression, as much as my after-talk around the fire-place, where I spun yarns of my strange life and adventures.

.　　　.　　　.　　　.　　　.　　　.　　　.

"You made a hit," commented Ally, as he conducted me back to his house," it's a great opening for you.   Follow it up!"
"I will!"

.　　　.　　　.　　　.　　　.　　　.　　　.

That night I could not sleep.   My blood made a tumult through my body.   Before dawn I had written two poems on national themes; didactic verses, each with a moral of democracy tagged to it, and much about the worth of simplicity in it, and the dignity of honest labour.

Yes, I would be their poet.   And America's poet. . .

And visions of a comfortable, bourgeois success took me . . interminable Chautauquas, with rows of women listening to my inspiring verses . . visits as honoured guest to the homes of great popular leaders like Roosevelt . . dignity and rides in parlour cars, instead of dusty, dirty box cars . . interviews of weight and speeches of consequence . . and the newspapers would drop their undercurrent of levity when I was written about in them, and treat me with consideration.

Finally, I would possess a home like Mackworth's, set back amid shade trees, a house not too large, not too small . . a cook and maid . . a pretty, unobtrusive wife devoted to me. . .

And I would wear white linen collars every day, tie the ends of my tie even . . and each year would see a new book of mine out, published by some bookseller of repute . . and I could afford Red Seal records . . and have my largest room for a library. . .

Middle-class comfort was upon me . . good plumbing . . electric light . . laundry sent out . . no more washing of my one shirt overnight and hanging it up to dry on the back of a chair, while I slept . . and putting it on, next morning, crinkly and still damp.

I was already seduced, if there hadn't been that something in me which I myself could not control!

.　　　.　　　.　　　.　　　.　　　.　　　.

It was when I caught Mackworth on the streets of his town and in his newspaper office that I discovered the man himself.

In our country, especially in the Middle West, everybody watches everybody else for the least lapse in the democratic spirit.

Though he was truly democratic at heart, Mackworth laid it on in theatric outward appearance, in true line with the Kansas tradition of a sockless Jerry Simpson, who went without socks, as the adjective implies, and made Congress on that one platform of his sartorial lack . . of William Roscoe Stubbs, who rode into the office of governor partly on the fact that his daughter could make salt-rising bread . . a form of bread-making cultivated by the hardy pioneers of the state, and now no longer necessary.

Mackworth was "in-legged" . . that is, his legs on the insides rubbed together from the crotch to the knees . . and he wore old patches, hanging there actually in strips . . and, I think, had his trouser-seat patched, too . . and though he could have afforded a car, he drove about, he and his family, in a rickety old two-seated rig, deliberately kept, it seemed, in ill-repair . . and it was such an old ex-plow horse that dragged it about!

His fellow townsmen laughed, but they liked it. "Jarv's all right! No nonsense about Jarv, even ef he is one o' them lit'rary fellers!"

To call everybody by the first name—that was the last word in honest, democratic fellowship.

. . . .

Whether this exterior appearance of Mackworth was sincere or affected in him I never could quite tell. I am almost inclined to believe it was not done for effect,—but out of an Assisian simplicity of heart, as a sign manual of Bourgeois integrity.

If it was an affectation, his personal attitude toward the people with whom he came into contact was not . . in his office everybody loved him, and worked for him with that easy efficiency that comes of good will and respect. . .

Unostentatiously and affectionately he went about helping people.

"We've got a wonderful town here . . very little vice, except that which always will be in every community because it is inherent in human nature . . we have a fine college of our own . . a fine electric plant . . everybody's lawn is well-kept . . nobody in this town need be out of a job . . for miles around us the land is rich in real wealth of waving corn and wheat. . .

Kansas will be the centre, the Athens, of our civilisation, one day. . .

We have a fine Harvey Eating House at our railway station,

managed by a hustler . . you must have Ally take you there for
dinner before you go back to Laurel."

The idealisation of small comfort . . in a case like Mackworth's,
fairly unobjectionable . . but in most cases insufferably stodgy . .
the dry-rot of art, literature, life . . leading to a smug conceit that
in turn ends in that school of "two hills of corn where one cluster
of violets grew before."

No wonder that the *National Magazine*, starting with a splendid
flourish of knight-errantry, degenerated into the mere, "let-well-
enough-alone" thrift-crier it is . . " 'How I Became an Expert Tombstone Salesman' . . 'How I collected Tin Foil After Work-Hours and
Added Three Hundred a Year Extra to My Salary as Stenographer.' . . "

Rather, far rather, the Rockefeller, that shrewd manipulator of
businesses . . with all his parsimony in personal economics . . his
diet of bread and milk . . and his giving away of millions to missions
and scientific institutions. . .

Rather the big Morgan, who knew the old masters as well as he
knew the weaknesses of men . . who hobnobbed, not as a democrat,
but as aristocratic as the best of them, with princes, kings, emperors,
in his grim, forbidding dignity.

This at least presented bigness and romance!

.   .   .   .

"Want to meet Uncle Bill?" and Mackworth led me into a close-
shut room blue-thick with smoke. . .

I coughed and choked. A fire extinguisher should have preceded
our entry.

There sat—the lumbering trot of his typewriter heard long before he assumed visible, hazy outline—William Struthers, known to
the newspaper world as "Old Uncle Bill," the writer of daily prose-
verse squibs on the homely virtues, the exalter of the commonplaces
of life, the deifier of the ordinary.

Uncle Bill's head of strong, black hair stood upright like thick
wire. His thick, stubby fingers trotted like cart horses on and on.
He stopped and drew up a chair for me.

"Of course I ain't calling my stuff poetry," he began deprecat-
ingly, "but I do a lot of good for folks . . folks read my stuff when
they ain't got time to read the real poets."

Instead of flattering him, I gave him, frankly but gently, my opinion of the cornfed school of literature, easing the sting by inferring that he without doubt had bigger things up his sleeve than his so-called prose poems.

What I said struck the right chord.

"Of course a fellow has to make a living first."

(But, in my heart, I thought—it is just as vile for a man to send his wife out as a street-walker, and allege the excuse about having to live, as it is for a poet to prostitute his Muse.)

.   .   .   .

Nevertheless, Mackworth, Uncle Bill and I stood together, in the sunny street outside, posing for the photographer. And I swelled with inordinate pride. Though I knew I was bigger than both of them put together, yet, in the eyes of the world, these men were big men—and having my photograph taken with them was an indication to me, that I was beginning to come into my own.

Perhaps our picture would be reproduced in some Eastern paper or magazine . . perhaps even in the *Bookman*.

.   .   .   .

"Uncle Bill Struthers is an example of what Kansas can do for a man . . " said Mackworth, when we were alone. "Bill, in the old days, was a sort of tramp printer . . clever, but with all his ability in him unexpressed . . he was always down and out . . and drink! It verged on dipsomania. He never held a job long . . though he was a good compositor, he was always on the move from place to place. . .

"Then he came to Kansas where we have prohibition . . and it has panned out in Uncle Bill's case pretty fine.

"He came to work for me . . fell by chance into his prose-poetry vein. It took; was instantly copied in all the newspapers . . of course, I could do it as well, or anyone else with a rhyming turn . . but he was the originator . . and people liked his sturdy common sense, his wholesome optimism.

"Now Bill is happy; his stuff's syndicated—in thousands of households wherever English is spoken his name is a familiar word. He gives whole communities strength to go on with the common duties of life."

"And his drinking?"

"He has conquered that entirely . . once every so often the fit comes over him—the craving for it—then, when Uncle Bill turns up missing, as the Irishman puts it, none of us worries. . .

"We all know he has hitched up his horse and buggy and is off, driving and driving and driving across country, to work the fit out . . no, he never touches anything stronger than tobacco and coffee now. . .

"In a few days he comes back . . no one says a word . . we all know . . and love and respect him. . .

"He's happy now, is Uncle Bill . . married a young wife . . has a home all his own . . money piling up in the bank."

. . . .

Ally Merton smiled quizzically when I spoke of Uncle Bill to him. . .

"Yes, Uncle Bill's a fine, quaint old chap . . whenever he has a tiff with his wife—of course, never anything serious—he locks himself in the kitchen . . closes all the windows . . smokes up terrifically with his corncob . . and plays and plays for hours on end . . his Red Seal records of classical music of which he is so fond.

"This behaviour of his is a well-known joke among us, a joke with his wife, to!" . . the speaker paused, to continue——

"He has a good library and quite a large knowledge of the English poets."

"That makes it all the more terrible," I replied, "for if he wrote his verse-prose out of ignorance, he might be somewhat forgiven . . but he knows better."

. . . .

I gave a lecture on Keats to a woman's club.   They paid me thirty dollars for the lecture. . .

"Well, you surely made a killing . . those old birds will worship you for life," sniggered Ally.

. . . .

Mackworth and I had a farewell talk before I returned to Laurel. We stood again in front of his office, on the sunny street . . he had come out to bid me good-bye.

We talked of the folk poetry of America . . Mackworth recited to me several of the songs and ballads which I have since seen in Lomax's book of Cowboy Songs . . I repeated the tale of how I had collected the jail-songs that I subsequently lost while jumping a freight. . .

"There's lots of poetry in American life . . Stephen Foster Collins scratched the surface of it . . but he was a song writer. . .

"There's poetry on farm, ranch, in small town, big city, all waiting for the transmuting touch of the true singer . . not newspaper rhymes . . neither the stock effusions on Night, Love, Death and Immortality inserted as tail-piece to stories and articles in magazines. . .

"There's the negro mind . . —ought to hear them sing, making up songs as they load and unload boats along the Mississippi . . nobody's ever dug back into the black mind yet—why don't you do these things?". . .

   •   •   •   •   •   •   •

"Good-bye, Mister Mackworth—I've had a fine time!"
"Good-bye, my boy . . be a good boy . . God bless you!"

   •   •   •   •   •   •   •

At the Harvey Eating House the manager brought me out a cardboard box neatly packed, full of all manner of good things to eat. . .

"Good-bye, Ally! thanks for your hospitality, Ally! thank your folks for me again!"

"I will. See you up at Laurel some day soon!"

For Merton was coming to study there, in the fall.

   •   •   •   •   •   •   •

Back in Laurel I resumed my studies again in my intense though haphazard way. Doctors' degrees and graduation certificates did not interest me. I meditated no career in which such credentials would stand me in stead. But the meat and substance of what the world had achieved, written, thought—it was this that I sought to learn and know.

Already the professors were beginning to row about me and report me for cutting recitations. On the score of my scholarship and my knowing my subject they had no complaint. It was that I disrupted their classes and made for lax discipline.

But I seldom cut class deliberately. . . I would find myself lost in a book back in the "stack" as the big room that housed the tiers of books was called. The day would be dusking, the lights of evening glimmering below in town, to my bewildered eyes! The day gone, when I had stepped back among the books at nine o'clock, intending to while away a half hour between classes! (Once it was Sidney's Arcadia that entranced me so).

Or I would set out for class . . hatless . . my hair tousled and long . . in my sandals that were mocked at by my colleagues . . my books under arm . . and fall into a reverie that would fetch me up, two miles or so away, a-stray up a by-road flanked with a farm-house and young cornfields.

Then it would be too late for my schoolday, and I would make a day of it . . would perhaps get acquainted with some farmer and his family, have dinner and supper at his house, and swap yarns with him and the rest of his people.

.   .   .   .

Jack Travers was as proud of my foot-trip to Osageville as if he had accomplished it himself.

"The boys out at the Sig-Kappa house expect three or four kegs of beer in from Kansas City . . come on out and help us to celebrate."

"But I don't drink."

"Go on! you've told me about the time you did what you called 'slopping up' down in Texas!"

"That was only once . . and since then I've become a physical culturist."

"Well, come and join the party anyhow . . it won't hurt you to look on."

My curiosity impelled me to accept the invitation to the "keg party" as such a jamboree was known among the students.

The kegs of beer waited us at the station . . disguised with misleading labels . . "chemicals, handle with care." Tenderly we loaded them on the waggon that had been hired. The driver sat smiling as the solicitious students heaved them up and secured them firmly. . .

We sat dignified and quiet, till the outskirts of the town were reached . . then the whip was brought down and away we whooped, bouncing along the country road. . .

We whipped off down the road into the open country with a roar of singing and shouting. We sat on the kegs to keep them from jumping out, as we urged the driver to ply the whip.

.   .   .   .

There was a corner in a cornfield that bent inward, hidden from the casual passer-by by a grove of Osage orange trees. Here we drew up, jumped out, tenderly conveyed the kegs forth . . the ground we had chosen, in the corner of the field, was too rocky for planting. It was sultry early afternoon, of a late spring day.

The driver was offered a drink.

"Nope," he shook his head, grinning wisely, "I'm a teetotaler."

"Be back for us at dark," we shouted, as he jee-d about, heading toward town again.

"Here's to old Gregory and his first drunk!"

Tin cups had been produced, and the bung of one of the barrels started . . the boys lifted their full, foaming cups in unison.

"Bottoms up!"

I joined in the drinking, despite my previous protestation that I would not. . .

"Where's the old boy that runs this farm?"

"All the family's probably in town, this being Saturday afternoon."

"Let's whoop 'er up, then!"

We sang and shouted at the top of our voices.

The cups had been four times filled.

Though I had poured half of mine on the ground, I already felt dizzy. But also a pleasant tingling, a warmth, was slowly increasing in my nerves and veins and body . . an increased sense of well-being permeated me. I stopped spilling my beer on the ground and drank it eagerly.

Someone proposed races up and down the cornfield. We rolled up our trousers, to make it more hilarious, and ran, smashing through the tender spring growth . . yelling and shouting. . .

Then the game unaccountably shifted into seeing who could pull up the most corn stalks, beginning at an equal marked-off space out in each row and rushing back with torn-up handfuls. . .

The afternoon dropped toward twilight and everybody was as mellow as the departing day—which went down in a riot of gold. . .

A great area of the field looked as if it had fallen in the track of a victorious army, or had been fallen upon by a cloud of locusts.

A chill came in with twilight, and we built a fire, and danced about it.

I danced and danced . . we all danced and howled in Indian disharmony . . wailing . . screeching . . falling . . getting up again . .

when I danced and leaped the world resumed its order . . when I stood still or sat down plump, the trees took up the gyrations where I had left off, and went about in solemn, ringing circles . . green and graceful minuets of nature. . .

"Here's to good old Gregory, drink 'er down, drink 'er down!" I heard the boys, led by Jack Travers, bray discordantly.

"Want 'a hear some songs?" I quavered, interrogating.

"What kind o' songs?" asked a big, hulking boy that we called 'Black Jim,' because of his dark complexion.

"Real songs," I replied, "jail songs, tramp songs, coacaine songs!"

All those Rabelaisan folk-things I had lost while hopping the freight, came surging back, each not in fragments, but entire. Drunk, I did then what my brain since, intoxicated or sober, cannot do . . I rendered them all, one after the other, just as I had copied them down. . .

．　　　．　　　．　　　．　　　．　　　．　　　．

"And more! Gregory, more!" the boys kept shouting.

I sat down and began to cry because I had lost the script. It had all gone out of my head again as quickly as it had come, so that I could not even repeat one they'd asked for.

"Hell, he's got a crying drunk the first thing!"

"Cheer up, old scout . . here's another cupful."

"No . . I don't want any more . . I'm never going to drink again."

And I knocked the cup out of Travers' hand with a violent drunken sweep of negation.

"No use getting huffy about it," someone put in belligerently.

"If anybody wants to fight," it was Black Jim, huge and menacing and morose, advancing. . .

Fight! knives! jails! . .

Ah, yes, I was still in jail . . and Bud and the burly cotton thief were at it. . .

I staggered to my feet.

"Wait a minute, Bud . . I'm coming." I gave a run toward a barrel, sent it a violent kick, a succession of kicks. . .

"Wait a minute! I'm coming!"

"So am I!" grinned Black Jim belligerently, thinking I meant him and advancing slowly and surely.

The barrel burst asunder, the beer sumped and gurgled about my ankles as I stooped and picked up a stave.

"The damn fool's ruined a whole keg."

I was going to lick everybody in the jail, if I must.

"Put that stave down Gregory! put it down, for Christ's sake!"

"Good God! Grab Jim, someone!"

"Don't be a fool .. hold Gregory .. he's got the stave!"

"He'll kill Jim!"

"Or Jim'll kill him!" ..

Then came a shout from nearby.

"I'll heve the law on ye, I will! destroyin' a man's cornfield like a lot o' heathens!"

Yelling and menacing, the farmer and his big, raw-boned son were upon us. They evidently thought that we were all in such a drunken condition that they could kick us about as they choose. They had just driven home from market-day in Laurel.

Everything was mixed up in my head .. but one thing out-stood: I must do my duty by my barrel stave .. as the farmer leaped into the circle he did not notice me staggering on the outskirts. I rushed up and let him have the barrel stave full across the head.

At the same time Black Jim had turned his attention to the rangy boy, felling him at a blow. The boy leaped to his feet and ran away to a safe distance.

"Paw!" he called out, 'I'll run back to th' house an' 'phone th' p'lice."

"Come on, boys, we'd better dig out!"

.   .   .   .

We straggled along in silent, rolling clusters, like bees smoked out, down the road .. we heard the rumble of a waggon .. when we recognised that it was our teetotaler coming back for us. ..

"God, if my old man hears of this I'm done for at Laurel."

"So'm I!"

"If we only lay low and don't go spouting off about it, things will be all O.K."

"We'll send Travers back with a little collection, to fix it up with the farmer, and blarney him out of taking any action."

.   .   .   .

In the morning I had a roaring headache .. as long as I lay quiet there was only the slow, deep regular pulse of pain driving through my head, but when I made an effort to get up, my eyeball throbbed with such torment that they seemed to be starting out of my head. . .

I fell asleep in the broad day again, waking to find Jack Travers standing by my bed, pale and cynical, dusting off the ashes from the end of his eternal cigarette.

"How are you feeling this morning?"

"Rotten," I answered. I sat up and triphammers of pain renewed their pounding inside my racked head.

—"thought you would, so's soon as I got up, I came down to see you."

—"lot of good that'll do."

He whipped a flask out of his hip pocket. "Take a nip of this and it will set you right in a jiffy."

"No, I'll never drink another drop."

"Don't be a fool. Just a swallow and you'll be on your feet again."

I took a big swallow and it braced me up instantly.

"Now, come on with me, Johnnie, I'm taking you in tow for to-day! A fellow who's not used to getting drunk always mopes around after a good time like we had . . I'm seeing you through *the day after* . . you're going to lunch with me at the frat-house and this afternoon there's a sacred concert on in Aeolian Hall that I have two tickets for."

"I'll never drink another drop as long as I live."

"That's what they all say."

.　　　.　　　.　　　.　　　.　　　.　　　.

At the Sig Kappas I met Black Jim, the first one, at the door. He shook hands shyly, laughingly.

"You sure fetched that rube a wallop . . he let one croak out of him and flopped flat . . it would have made a good comic picture."

"Lunch is ready, boys!"

I was made into a sort of hero—"a real, honest-to-God guy."

"You'll have to come to some of our frat jamborees . . Jack'll bring you up."

"We and the Sigma Deltas are Southern fraternities . . we have a hell of a sight more fun than the others . . there's the Sigma Pis—though they have some live birds, they're mostly dead . . and the Phi Nus put on too much side . . the Beta Omicrons are right there with the goods, though."

"I see."

A little freshman made an off-colour remark.

"You'd better go and see Jennie!" advised a genial young senior, who, for all his youth, was entirely bald.

"Jennie, who's Jennie?" I asked, curious.

"Our frat woman!" answered Travers casually.

"Frat woman?" I was groping for further information, puzzled.

"Yes, often a fraternity keeps a woman for the use of its members . . when a kid comes to us so innocent he's annoying, we turn him over to Jennie to be made a man of."

"This innocence-stuff is over-rated. It's better to send a kid to a nice, clean girl that we club in together and keep, and let him learn what life is, once and for all, than to have him going off somewhere and getting something, or, even worse, horning around and jeopardizing decent girls, as he's bound to otherwise."

·　　·　　·　　·　　·　　·　　·

There were signs of failure at the Farmers' Restaurant. The curious farmer-family that ran it were giving it up and moving back into the country again. I was soon to have no place to board, where I could obtain credit.

But it was summer by now, and I didn't care. I meditated working in the wheat harvest.

·　　·　　·　　·　　·　　·　　·

The editors of the *National Magazine* had given a new impulsion to my song—and a damned bad one. Already they had accepted and printed several of my effusions.

I was to sing for them the life of present-day America, the dignity of labour, the worth of the daily, obscure endeavour of the world around me. . .

In other words, instead of flattering one man of influence and power with a dedication, as was done by the poets of the seventeenth and eighteenth centuries, I was to install Demos as my patron, must warp the very tissue of my thought to inform the ordinary man that the very fact that he wore overalls, acquired callouses on his hands, and was ignorant and contemptuous of culture—somehow made him a demigod! I was continually to glorify the stupidity of the people, and always append a moral.

For a time I even succeeded in working myself up into a lathering frenzy of belief in what I was doing.

.   .   .   .   .   -   .

The bedrock of life in the Middle West is the wheat harvest.

There was a man named Carl Bonton who owned a threshing machine. I heard he was in need of hands for the season.

I nailed my few books up in a drygoods box and left them in care of Professor Langworth's housekeeper, the former having gone away to Colorado for the summer. As for clothes, tramp-life had taught me the superfluity of more than a change of shirts and b.v.d.'s.

Bonton looked me over.

"You don't look strong enough . . the work is mighty hard."

"I'm pretty wiry. Try me out, that is all I ask. If I buckle in, I won't mind walking back to town."

Bonton's buckboard carried us the matter of five miles to where his machine, separator and cook-shack stood . . lurking behind a grove of Osage orange trees.

Bonton had brought two other men besides me, as accessories to his gang. We found the gang just tumbling forth from the cook waggon, a small, oblong sort of house on wheels . . a long table in it, with benches . . much like the lunch waggons seen standing about the streets in cities.

"Hello, boys, is it dry enough to begin loadin' yet?"

"Naw; the dew's still as heavy as rain on the bundles."

"We'd best wait a little longer, then."

.   .   .   .

Though it seemed that half the day had wheeled by already, by seven o'clock we rode a-field, and the less experienced of us were hard at it, tossing up bundles to the loaders, who placed them swiftly here and there till the waggons were packed tight and piled high.

I pitched up bundles from below, to an old man of sixty, who wore a fringe of grey beard, like a Mennonite.

"I don't see why Bonton ever hired you," he remarked unsympathetically, peering over the top at me from his high-piled load. Several times I had missed the top and the bundle of wheat had tumbled back to me again. . .

"I can't be reaching out all the time to catch your forkfuls."

"Just give me time till I learn the hang of it."

I was better with the next load. The waggons came and went

one after the other . . there was a light space of rest between
waggons. It was like the rest between the rounds of a prizefight.

From the cloudless sky the sun's heat poured down in floods.
A monotonous locust was chirr-chirr-chirring from a nearby cotton-
wood . . and in the long hedge of Osage oranges moaned wood
doves. . .

By noon I had achieved a mechanical swing that helped relieve
the physical strain, a swinging rhythm of the hips and back muscles
which took the burden off my aching and weaker arms.

That afternoon, late, when the old man drove his waggon up to
me for the hundredth time it seemed, he smiled quizzically.

"Well, here you are still, but you're too skinny to stand it another
day . . better draw your two bucks from the boss and strike out
for Laurel again."

—"that so, Daddy!" and I caught three bundles at once on the
tines of my fork and flung them clear to the top, and over. They
caught the old man in the midriff . . I heard a sliding about and
swearing . . the next moment he was in a heap, on the ground . . on
the other side of the waggon.

"What th' hell did ye do that for?"

I looked innocent. "Do what?"

—"soak me in the guts with three bundles to onct an' knock me
off'n the top of the load?"

"Ever since morning you've been kidding me and telling me I
went too slow for you . . I thought I'd speed up a bit."

After surveying me scornfully for a minute, he mutely reascended
the load, and we finished the job in silence together. . .

We laboured on after sunset till the full moon swung over the
tree-tops.

.   .   .   .

Usually they did not use the cook-shack much . . it was used
while on the road from one wheat farm to another. Usually the
farmers' wives and daughters in the valleys and on the hillsides
vied with each other as to heaping food before the threshers . .
every morning saw mountains of pancakes . . bacon . . eggs . .
ham . . beefsteak . . we laboured like giants, ate like hogs, slept like
senseless stocks.

I climbed to my bed in the haymow that first night. It was
chill enough for the use of my blanket.

I drowsed off, to wake with a jump of all my body from a dream that a giant was pressing down on me, that he had my legs doubled up over me and was breaking them into my breast. . .

The cramps. . .

I stood up and rubbed my legs till the taut tendons softened and stretched . . but when I dared bend them the littlest, the tautening and drawing twisted them again. And so I suffered half the night through, till, in wrathful agony, I stumbled to the watering trough and stood naked-white in the flood of the full moon, rubbing the icy water over my body. . .

The dutiful house dogs . . barking furiously, the two of them rushed at my apparition as I stood up in the trough and splashed. They embayed me as a quarry. I jumped out of the trough and threw stones at them. They backed from my attack and bit at the stones. I stepped back in the water and rubbed myself more. The dogs squatted on their haunches at a safe distance and bayed lugubriously at me and the moon in common.

The rest of the night I lay preternaturally awake, hearing the snoring and murmuring of my fellows in the mow . . hearing the horses as they crunched and whickered . . all the noises of the outside night came in at the open door of the mow. Even the hay began to annoy me as it continually rustled in my ear.

I took my blanket and went to lie on the hard ground, under the water waggon. There I heard the multitudinous insects of the night, and the whippoorwill.

Ordinarily I do not have an appetite for breakfast. That morning I thought I would eat little, but I ended by devouring six eggs, two dozen pancakes, drinking three cups of coffee . . all of which immediately lay like a lump of rock in me. . .

No, I could not keep it up! It was too much of an effort, such frightful labour, for sixteen hours of the day. But I thought of the old man who had jeered at me, and I trudged a-field with the rest, my fork slung over my shoulder . . sore . . I ached in every muscle . . muscles I never knew existed before talked to me with their little voices of complaint.

But after the first load I began to be better. . .

And by noon I was singing and whistling irrepressibly.

"You'll do . . but you'll have to put a hat on or you'll drop with sun-stroke," Bonton remarked.

"I never wear a hat."

"All right. It's your funeral, not mine," and the boss walked away.

.   .   .   .

"Have a nip and fortify yourself against the sun . . that's the way to do," suggested the old driver. He proffered his whiskey flask.

"Nope . . I've plenty of water to drink."

The water boy kept trailing about with his brown jug. I tipped it up to my mouth and drank and drank . . I drank and drank and worked and worked and sweated and sweated . . the top of my head perspired so that it felt cool in the highest welter of heat.

In the hot early afternoon I saw the old man lying under a tree.

"What's the matter?"

—"too hot!"

"Where's your whiskey now?"

—" 'tain't the whiskey. *That* keeps a fellow up . . it's because I'm old, not young, like you," he contested stubbornly.

.   .   .   .

These men that I worked with were unimaginably ignorant. One night we held a heated argument as to whether the stars were other worlds and suns, or merely lights set in the sky to light the world of men by . . which latter, the old man maintained, was the truth, solemnly asserting that the Bible said so, and that all other belief was infidelity and blasphemy. So it was that, each evening, despite the herculean labour of the day, we drew together and debated on every imaginable subject. . .

.   .   .   .

On the third day of my employment by him, Bonton put me at the mouth of the separator, where the canvas ran rapidly in, carrying the bundles down into the maw of the machine. My job was feeding the bundles to it . . up in the air in the back the threshed straw was kicked high, and the chaff whirled in dusty clouds . . from a spout in the side of the separator the threshed grain poured in an unending stream. . .

.   .   .   .

It was difficult to keep the horses from the straw stacks that the daily threshing built up.

Also Bonton speeded so terrifically that much of the grain was shot out into the straw. . .

One night three of the horses made their way to the straw and
ate and gorged . . in the morning one of them was dead and the
other two were foundered. . .

. . . .

The cramps bothered me no more.

The boss came up to me and slapped me on the back.

"—thought you'd sag under," but, putting his hand on my back,
"you've got powerful back muscles, though your arms and legs are
like beanpoles . . a fellow never can tell about a man, till he's
tried out."

. . . .

After nearly a month of the work, Bonton began acting glum
toward me. . .

"Gregory, I'm going to pay you off to-day!"

"—pay me off to-day?"

"Yes."

"What's the matter? ain't I working hard enough?"

"I've no fault to find with your work . . you're a better worker
than most of the men . . in fact they complain that you set too
hard a pace at the separator. . .

"But you argue too much . . keep the men up o' nights debating
about things they never even considered before. And it upsets
them so, what with the arguing and the sleep they lose, that they
ain't up to the notch, next day.

"No, that's the only fault I have to find in you," he continued,
as he counted out sixty dollars into my hand. . . "but," and he
walked with me, disquieted to the road, "but if you'll wait around
till this afternoon, I'll drive you back to town."

"No. It's not over ten miles. I'll walk."

I was glad to be paid off. I was missing my books and my
leisure, longing for the cool alcoves of books in the university
"stack."

"You understand me, I hope . . business is business and work
is work. I've found it doesn't do to argue . . only stirs up trouble. . .

"I hope you don't think all this debating will end after you're
gone? . . Oh, no,—for the next week or so the boys will continue
shooting their mouths off . . the Baptist will fight the Methodist,
and both will join against the Seventh Day Adventist . . and the
one Catholic will be assailed by all hands. . .

"Before you came, no one knew what the other fellow believed, and no one cared .. but now you've started something."

"I'm sorry, Mr. Bonton."

"It can't be helped now .. don't fail to let me know in what magazines your poems on threshing and the harvest will appear."

.   .   .   .

I trudged townward, light-hearted .. a poem began to come to me before I had gone a mile .. at intervals I sat down and wrote a few lines. . .

That fall the *National Magazine* printed *The Threshers* and *The Harvest* and *The Cook-Shack*, three poems, the fruit of that work. All three written on the road as I walked back to town .. and all three didactic and ridiculous in their praise of the worker.

.   .   .   .

Frank Randall, tinsmith and plumber, who ran his shop on the main street, rented me a back room over his store, for two dollars a week. It had been occupied by big Sam, the negro shoemaker, and it was neither in order, nor did it smell very sweet. But I cleaned and aired it, and sprinkled disinfectant about that I had bought at the drug store.

Then I fetched my books down from Langworth's in a wheelbarrow, and I set them up in several neat rows.

I lay back on my cot and looked at them in satisfaction and happiness. I had enough for food and lodging for nearly three months, if I cooked for myself. Two dollars a week for food and two for rent, and I'd do my own washing .. say five a week at the most! that would mean twelve weeks of doing nothing but reading and writing and studying.

The first day of my sojourn over the tinsmith's shop, Sunday, I drew down from the shelf my Heinrich Heine .. in German .. one of the tasks I set myself, during that three months, was the making an intensive study of just how Heine had "swung" the lyric form to such conciseness, such effectiveness of epigrammatic expression.

I opened the *Buch der Lieder* at the poem in his preface—the song of the sphinx in the enchanted wood .. and how it clutched the seeker, the poet, to its monstrous but voluptuous woman's breasts as it ravished his soul with kisses. And the nightingale was singing. . .

"O, shöne Sphinx, O löse mir
Das Rätsel, das wunderbare!
Ich hab' darüber nachgedacht
Schon manche tausand Yahre."

.   .   .   .

Monday morning .. by six or seven o'clock a rustling below, in the shop, by eight, the day's work in full blast .. a terrific pounding and hammering on sheets of tin and pieces of pipe. The uproar threw my mind off my poetry.

I went down to speak with Randall about it. . .

"Frank, I can't stand this, I must leave."

"Nonsense; stay; you'll get used to it."

"No, I must go if the noise keeps up continually like this."

"Well, it won't .. we have a special job to finish .. tin-roofing .. but if you want a place to stay where it is quiet, I have a camp, not far out, on the Ossawatomie, where I go for week-ends. . ."

"Where is it? That would be fine. I'd like to stay there."

"You know where old Farmer Brown lives, by the abandoned church, just outside of Perthville?"

"Yes. That's seven miles out on the Osageville road."

"Take the first turn to the right from his house, going west. It's an unused bye-road and it runs plumb into my cabin. There's a frying pan there .. and some flour .. and bacon .. tell you what .. it's been broken into several times. I'll consider it worth while if you go and live there, and I get no rent from you for it nor the room upstairs .. you'll be alone, God knows—excepting Saturdays and Sundays."

.   .   .   .

I packed my Heine in a bundle .. with my Bible and my Josephus in the Greek, along with Whiston's English version .. and I included a bundle of books on New Testament times that made me groan under their weight. For I planned to begin a four-act play on Judas, and must study for writing that, as well as learn the "how" of the lyric. . .

The stupendousness of the silence of absolute solitude! At first the thoughts run on with a tangle and jangle, a turmoil almost of madness .. then they quiet down into the peace that only a hermitage gives and the objects of life are seen in their true relativity and perspective.

My diet was one of sow-belly, bread, and coffee, and what fish I caught in the sluggish, muddy stream. . .

Saturday, toward sunset, I heard a whooping in the woods. It was Randall coming with a few friends for his week-end, as he had warned. With him, his wild brother, Jack; and Bill, his assistant plumber and man-about-shop.

The drinking had begun before they were in sight of the shack. And it was kept up till late Sunday night . . around a big fire in a cleared space they sang and gambled and drank.

Randall served great hilarity to the party by trying to breed his gelded horse to his mare . . the mare kicked and squealed, indignant at the cheat, looking back, flattening her ears, and showing the vicious whites of her eyes. Several times the infuriated beast's heels whished an inch or so from Randall's head, as he forced the gelding to advance and mount. We rolled on the grass, laughing . . myself included.

Then all stripped to the buff for a swim in the stream . . a treacherous place where the bottom was at times but two or three feet from the surface, and the mud, soft and semi-liquid for five feet more. And there were snags, and broken beer and whiskey bottles all over the bottom where it was decent and gravelly.

Bill, with his solemn dundreary whiskers, leaped high in the air like a frog, kicking his legs and yelling drunkenly as he took off.

"Look out, Bill," I shouted, "it's nothing but mud there!"

But Bill didn't heed me. He hit with a swish and a thud instead of a splash, and didn't come up.

We put out in our rickety boat.

By that luck that favours the drunkard and fool, we laid hold on Bill's feet sticking out, just under the water. We tugged mightily and brought him forth, turned into a black man by the ooze . . otherwise, unharmed.

.   .   .   .

It was not till two hours after midnight that they whisked away townward and left me alone, so that the graciousness of silence could enfold me again. I looked forward to a week's peace, before they descended on the camp again. But I had a premonition that there was to be no peace for me there. For Randall had said to me before he drove away. . .

"You know Pete Willets? Well, he's liable to come here for a

few days, during the week .. a nice quiet fellow though .. won't
disturb you."

The thought of another visitor did disturb me. Though I knew
Pete Willets as a quiet, gentle shoemaker in whom seemed no guile,
I wanted to be alone to think and read and write.

Wednesday noon Pete Willets drove up, accompanied by a grubby
woman whom at first glance I did not relish.

"Hello, Johnnie, Frank said we could use the shack for a day
or two."

"Forever, as far as I'm concerned," I answered, beginning to tie
up my books in a huge bundle as big as a peddler's pack, and as
heavy.

Impatiently tying the horse to a post, they were in the shack
and immediately prone on my bunk.

As I shouldered my load their murmuring voices full of amorous
desire stung me like a gadfly. I hurried off toward Laurel, angry
at life.

     .   .   .   .

I explained to Randall why I had left his camp so soon. He was
gravely concerned.

"I didn't tell Willets he could have my shack to take Gracie there.
This is a bit too thick."

"Who's Gracie?"

"—a bad lot .. a girl that's been on the turf since she was in
knee skirts—as long as I've known her. He loves her. She can
twist him around her little finger. She's going to get him into
something bad some day. He'll do anything she wants. And she's
capable of putting him up to anything."

"Willets is weak, when it comes to women .. don't drink much ..
a hard worker .. everybody likes him. . .

"Did you ever notice his limp .. only slight .. scarcely noticeable,
isn't it? .. he's a corking mechanic as well as shoemaker .. mighty
clever .. now for instance, you wouldn't ever have known, unless
I told you, that his left leg is made of wood?"

"I wouldn't even suspect it."

"—lost his left leg when he was a brakeman .. made that wooden
leg for himself .. it works so smoothly that he's thinking of taking
out a patent on it."

"Why does a woman take to a man with a wooden leg?"

"—makes good money . . and he has a way about him with the girls . . he goes about so quietly. He's so gentle and considerate . . acts, but doesn't say much, you know! that's what they like!

"—damned sorry for his wife and two kids, though; when Willets comes to town again I'm not going to let him have my shack any more . . might be some trouble . . divorce or something."

There was trouble and very shortly. In a month Willets had poisoned his wife . . with rough-on-rats . . and the quiet little shoemaker went to the penitentiary for life . . a life-time of shoe-making.

.   .   .   .

I rented a tent and pitched it on an island in the middle of the Kaw, or Kansas River. There I was alone. I rented a boat to take out my possessions.

I lived naked till I grew brown all over. I studied and read and wrote to my full desire, there in the grateful silence of trees and waters—a solitude broken only by an occasional train streaming its white trail of smoke as it whistled and raced round the curve of shining track toward Laurel.

I read Josephus entirely through, haltingly, line by line, in the Greek. I read all the books the "stack" at the university could afford me on New Testament life and times, in preparation for my play on Judas.

My only companions were a flock of tiny mud-hens with their dainty proud little rooster. I heard them talking in bird-language, saw them paddling with diminutive gravity up and down in the mud, on the island mud-bank just beneath the high place on which my tent was pitched.

When I grew lonesome for company, human company, I swam ashore, my clothes tied on top of my head to keep them dry, and, dressing, walked into Laurel. Where I lounged about for the day on the streets, or in the stores, or in the livery stables . . I knew everybody and everybody knew me, and we had some fine times, talking.

I had access to the local Carnegie Library as well as to the university "stack."

My food did not cost me above a dollar a week. For I went on a whole wheat diet, and threw my frying pan away.

.   .   .   .

I was the tramp, as ever, only I was stationary.

. . . .

The opening days of the fall term came round again. Summer weather, hot and belated, lingered on. I was now more native to the river than to life in a four-walled room and on street pavements.

I debated seriously whether I should return to classes, or just keep on studying as I was, staying in my tent, and taking books out at the two libraries. I knew that they'd allow me to continue drawing out books at the university, even though I attended classes no longer—Professor Langworth would see to that.

Also, most of the professors would whisper "good riddance" to themselves. I camped at their gates too closely with questions. I never accepted anything as granted. The "good sports" among them welcomed this attitude of mine, especially the younger bunch of them—who several times invited me to affairs of theirs, behind closed blinds, where good wine was poured, and we enjoyed fine times together. . .

I was invited on condition that I would not let the student-body know of these *sub rosa fiestas*. Which were dignified and unblameworthy . . only, wine and beer went around till a human mellowness and conversational glow was reached.

. . . .

A trifling incident renewed my resolve to continue as a student regularly enrolled. . .

Though considered a freak and nut, I was generally liked among the students, and liked most of them in turn. . .

They used frequently to say—" 's too bad Johnnie Gregory won't act like the rest of the world, he's such a likeable chap. . ."

As the boys came back to school I went about renewing acquaintances.

The afternoon of the day of the "trifling incident" I was returning from a long visit to Jack Travers and the Sig-Kappas.

It was about ten o'clock when I reached the river-bank opposite my island. There was a brilliant moon up. If daylight could be silver-coloured it was day.

I stood naked on the water's elge, ready to wade out for my swim back to my island. My clothes were trussed securely, for dryness, on my head.

A rustling, a slight clearing of the throat, halted me.

I glanced through a vista of bushes.

There sat a girl in the full moonlight. She had a light easel before her. She was trying to paint, evidently, the effects of the moon on the landscape and the river. Painters have since told me that it is impossible to do that. It is too dark to see the colours. Nevertheless the girl was trying.

I stopped statue-still to find if I had been seen. When assured that I had not, I slowly squatted down, and, naked as I was, crept closer, hiding behind a screen of bushes. And I fastened my eyes on her, and forgot who I was. For the moon made her appear almost as plain as day. And she was very beautiful. And I was caught in a sudden trap of love again.

Here, I held no doubt, was my Ideal. I could not distinguish the colour of her hair. But she was maiden and slenderly wonderful.

I lay flat, hoping that she would not hear my breath as she calmly painted. My heart beat so hard it seemed to shake the ground beneath me.

She, too, was original, what the world would call "eccentric" . . out here, three miles from town, with the hours verging toward midnight . . seated on the river bank, trying to capture the glory of the moon on canvas.

But, unusual as her action was, there was nothing mad about her mode of dressing . . her white middy blouse, edged with blue . . her flowing tie . . her dainty, blue serge skirt and dainty shoes.

I lay there, happy in being near her, the unknown.

After a long time she rose . . gave a sigh . . brushed her hand over her hair.

Fascination held me close as she stooped over . . began leisurely to untie her shoes . . set them, removed, aside, toe to toe and heel to heel, equal, as if for mathematical exactness . . paused a moment . . lifted her skirts, drew off her garters with a circular downward sweep . . drew down her stockings. . .

She sat with her stockings off, stuffed into her shoes,—her skirt up to her hips, gazing meditatively at her naked legs held straight before her.

I was close enough to hear her breathing—or so keen in my aroused senses that I thought I heard it. She wiggled her toes to herself as she meditated.

She paused as if hesitating to go on with her undressing. A twig snapped. She came to her knees and looked about, startled, then subsided again, tranquil and sure of her solitude.

. . . .

She stood in the moonlight, naked. My gaze grew fat with pleasure as it fed on her nakedness. . .

She stepped down to the water's edge, dabbling her outstretched toes in the flow.

Ankle-deep, she stood and stooped. She scooped up water and dashed it over her breasts. She rose erect a moment and gazed idly about.

Then, binding her hair in a careful knot, she went in with a plunge and I saw that she could swim well.

My heart shook and thundered so that its pulse pervaded all my body with its violence. I held in curb a mad, almost irresistible impulse to rush in after her, crying out that I was a poet .. that this was the true romance .. that we must throw aside the conventions .. that no one would ever know.

Then I thought of my skinniness and ugliness in comparison with her slight but perfect beauty. And I knew that it would repel her. And I held still in utter shame, not being good-looking enough to join her in the river.

I lay prone, almost fainting, dizzy, not having the strength to creep away, as I now considered I must do.

I saw her return and watched her as she slowly resumed her clothes, piece by leisurely piece. She folded her camp stool, packed her small easel in a case and started off toward town.

Shouldn't I now intercept her, explain who I was, and offer to escort her along the tracks back to town? For it was surely dangerous for her to come so far into the night, alone. There were tramps .. and the stray criminal negro from the Bottoms .. God knows what else, in her path!

But my timidity let her pass on alone.

I needed the coolness of the water about me, as I swam out to my tent. I forgot my clothes on my head and they soused in the water as I swam. All night I tossed, sleepless. I lay delirious with remembrance of her .. imagined myself with her as I lay there, and whispered terms of love and endearment into the dark.

Who was she? One thing I knew—she must be a student, and an

art student under Professor Grant in the Fine Arts Department.

This was the incident that decided me to enroll again as regular student, and to fold my tent, leave my solitary island, and return to town . . where I sought out Frank Randall, and he again offered me the room I had given up. And he gave me work as his book-keeper, several hours of the day . . which work I undertook to perform in return for my room. In addition he gave me two dollars a week extra.

. . . .

One afternoon soon after my enrollment, I met Ally Merton coming down hill.

"Well, here I am, as I said I'd be," said he.

He was, as usual, dressed to perfection—not a minute ahead of the style, not a minute behind . . gentle-voiced and deferential, learning to be everywhere without being noticed anywhere.

"I see you're still eccentric in dress . . sandals . . shirt open at the neck . . denim too . . cheap brown socks . . corduroys. . ."

"Yes, but look," I jested in reply, "I wear a tie . . and the ends pull exactly even. That's the one thing you taught me about correct dressing that I'll never forget."

"If I could only persuade you, Johnnie, of the importance of little things, of putting one's best foot forward . . of personal appearance . . why create an initial prejudice in the minds of people you meet, that you'll afterward have to waste valuable time in trying to remove?"

"Where are you putting up, Ally?"

"At the Phi Nus" (the bunch that went in the most for style and society) "I'm a Phi Nu, keep in touch with me, Johnnie."

"Keep in touch with me," was Merton's stock phrase. . .

"Mr. Mackworth asked me particularly to look you up, and 'take care of' you . . you made a hit with him . . but he's very much con-cerned about you—thinks you're too wild and erratic."

. . . .

The tinshop was a noisy place, as I have said before. It was as uproarious as a boiler factory. All day long there was hammering, banging, and pounding below . . but I was growing used to it . . as you do to everything which must be.

Keeping Randall's books occupied a couple of hours each morring or afternoon, whenever I chose. All the rest of the day I had free. . .

   .   .   .   .

I had almost come to the conclusion that the girl I had seen in the moonlight had been an apparition conjured up by my own imagination, when I glimpsed her, one afternoon, walking toward Hewitt Hall, where the art classes held session, in the upper rooms. I followed the girl, a long way behind. I saw her go in through the door to a class where already a group of students sat about with easels, painting from a girl-model . . fully clothed . . for painting from the nude was not allowed. They had threshed that proposition out long before, Professor Grant explained to me, once,— and the faculty had decided, in solemn conclave, that the farmers throughout the state were not yet prepared for that step. . .

I sought Grant's friendship. He had studied in the Julian Academy at Paris, in his youth. He invited me to his house for tea, often; where I met many of his students, but never, as I had hoped, the girl of the moonlight. . .

But by careful and guarded inquiry I found out who she was . . a girl from the central portion of the state, named Vanna Andrews.

When Grant asked me to pose for his class, sandals, open shirt, corduroys, and all . . I agreed . . almost too eagerly . . he would pay me twenty-five cents an hour.

My first day Vanna was not there. On the second, she came . . late . . her tiny, white face, crowned with its dark head of hair . . "a star in a jet-black cloud," I phrased, to myself. She sailed straight in like a ship.

When she had settled herself,—beginning to draw, she appraised me coolly, impartially, for a moment . . took my dimensions for her paper, pencil held at arm's length. . .

Slowly, though I fought it back, a red wave of confusion surged over my face and neck. I turned as red as ochre. I grew warm with perspiration of embarrassment. I gazed fixedly out through the window. . .

"You're getting out of position," warned Professor Grant.

Vanna still observed me with steadfast, large, blue eyes. She started her sketch with a few, first, swift lines.

"Excuse me," I rose, "I feel rather ill." I posed, "I've been up all night drinking strong coffee and writing poems," I continued, my voice rising in insincere, noisy falsetto.

"Step down a minute and rest, then, Mr. Gregory," advised Professor Grant, puzzled, a grimace of distaste on his face.

"Isn't he silly," I overheard a girl student whisper to a loud-dressed boy, whose easiness of manner with the female students I hated and envied him for. . .

I resumed my pose. I blushed no more. I endured the cool, level, impersonal glances of the girl I had fallen in love with. . .

"The model 's a little wooden, don't you think, professor?" she observed, to tease me, perhaps. She could not help but sense the cause of my agitation. But then she was used to creating a stir among men. Her beauty perturbed almost the entire male student body.

.   .   .   .

I noticed that her particular chum was a very homely girl. I straightway found charms in this girl that no one had ever found before. And Alice and I became friends. And, while posing, I came before the time, because she, I discovered, was always beforehand, touching up her work.

Alice was a stupid, clumsy girl, but she adored Vanna and liked nothing better than to talk about her chum and room-mate. She took care of Vanna as one would take care of a helpless baby.

"Vanna is a genius, if there ever was one . . she doesn't know her hands from her feet in practical affairs . . but she's wonderful . . all the boys," and Alice sighed with as much envy as her nature would allow—"all the boys are just crazy about her . . but she isn't in love with any of them!"

My heart gave a great bound of hope at these last words.

"Professor Grant's students—about two-thirds of them—have enrolled in his classes, because she's there."

And then I went cold with jealousy and with despair . . one so popular could never *see* me . . if it were only later, when my fame as a poet had come!

.   .   .   .

"Vanna has to be waited on hand and foot. I don't mind though," continued Alice, "I hang up her clothes for her . . make her bed . . sweep and dust our rooms . . it makes me happy to wait on anything so beautiful!" and the face of the homely girl glowed with joy. . .

.   .   .   .

I was poor and miserable. I bent my head forward, forgetful of my determination to walk erect and proud, with a pride I did not possess.

Langworth was coming behind me. He slapped me on the back. I whirled, full of resentment. But changed the look to a smile when I perceived who it was. . .

"Why, Johnnie, what's the matter? you're walking like an old man. Brace up. Is anything wrong?"

"No, I was just thinking."

.   .   .   .

The first cold blasts of winter howled down upōn us. No snow yet, but winds that rushed about the buildings on the hill, full of icy rain, and with a pushing strength like the shoulders of invisible giants out of the fourth dimension . . we men kept on the sidewalks when we could . . but the winds blew the girls off into the half-hardened mud, and, at times, were so violent, that the girls could not extricate themselves, but they stood still, waiting for help, their skirts whirling up into their very faces.

It was what the boys called "a sight for sore eyes."

They stood in droves, in the sheltered entrances of the halls, and occasionally darted out by ones and twos and threes to rescue distressed co-eds.

.   .   .   .

Down in the room over the tin and plumbing shop in which I lived, I found it cold indeed. I could afford no heat . . and, believing in windows open, knew every searching drop in the barometer.

But never in my life was I happier, despite my secretly cherished love for Vanna. For I assured myself in my heart of certain future fame, the fame I had dreamed of since childhood. And I wore every hardship as an adornment, conscious of the greatness of my cause.

Isolation; half-starvation; cold; inadequate clothing;—all counted for the glory of poetry, as martyrs had accepted persecution and suffering for the glory of God.

My two hours of daily work irked me. I wanted the time for my writing and studying . . but I still continued living above the din of the shop that I had grown accustomed to, by this time.

Rarely, when the nights were so subarctic as to be almost unbearable, did I slip down through the skylight and seek out the comparative warmth of the shop . . and there, on the platform where the desk stood so that it could overlook all the store, I wrote and studied.

But Randall said this worried the night watchman too much, my appearing and disappearing, all hours of the night. He didn't relish coming every time to see if the store was being burglarised.

.   .   .   .

The outside world was beginning to notice me. My poems, two of which I had sold to the *Century*, two to *Everybody's*, and a score to the *Independent*, were, as soon as they appeared in those magazines, immediately copied by the Kansas newspapers. And the Kansas City *Star* featured a story of me at Laurel, playing up my freaks and oddities . . but accompanied by a flattering picture that "Con" Cummins, our college photographer, had taken.

Also I was receiving occasional letters from strangers who had read my poems. But they were mostly letters from cranks . . or from girls very, very young and sentimental, or on the verge of old-maidhood, who were casting about for some escape from the narrow daily life that environed them. . .

But one morning a letter came to me so scrawlingly addressed that I marvelled at the ability of the postal authorities in deciphering it. The writer of it hailed me as a poet of great achievement already, but of much greater future promise. . . Mr. Lephil, editor of the *National Magazine*, for whom he was writing a serial, had showed him some of my verse, and he must hasten to encourage me . . I puzzled long over the writer's signature. . . It could not be possible! but it seemed to be inscribed with the name of a novelist famous for his investigations of capitalistic abuses of the people . . the author of the sensational novel, *The Slaughter House*, which was said to out-Zola Zola—Penton Baxter.

I hurried downstairs from my attic, to intercept some friend who would confirm me in my interpretation of the signature.

It was Travers I ran into. I showed the letter to him.

"By Jove! It *is* Baxter!" he cried.

He was as overwhelmed as I had been.

"Say, Johnnie, you must really amount to something, with all these people back East paying such attention to you . . come on into Kuhlman's and have a "coke" with me."

In Kuhlman's, the college foregathering place, the ice cream and refreshment parlour of the town, we joined with Jimmy Thompson, our famous football quarterback. The room was full of students eating ice cream and drinking coco-cola and ice cream sodas.

"Say, let me print this."

"No, but you may put an item in the *Laurelian,* if you want to."

"I must write a story for the *Star* about it."

It would have pleased my vanity to have had Jack put the story in the papers, but I was afraid of offending Baxter . . afterward I learned that it would not have offended him . . he had the vanity of a child, as well as I.

I answered his letter promptly, in terms of what might have seemed, to the outside eye, excessive adulation. But Penton Baxter was to me a great genius . . and nothing I could have written in his praise would have overweighed the debt I owed him for that fine letter of encouragement.

.   .   .   .

So at last I was reaping the fruits of my years of struggle for the poetic ideal—my years of poverty and suffering.

A belated student at college, twenty-five years of age . . a tramp for the sake of my art . . as I sat in my cold room . . propped up by my one overturned chair . . in bed . . betaking myself there to keep from freezing while I wrote and dreamed and read and studied, —I burst out singing some of my own verses, making the tune to the lines as I went along.

"John Gregory, you are a great man, and some day all the world shall know and acknowledge it!" I said over and over again to myself. . .

"And now, Vanna, my love, my darling," I cried aloud, so that if anyone overheard, the auditor would think I was going mad, "now, Vanna, you shall see . . in a year I shall have my first book of poetry out . . and fame and money for royalties will be mine . . then I will dare speak to you boldly of my love for you . . and you will be glad and proud of it . . and be happy to marry me and be my wife!"

.   .   .   .

In the meantime Vanna Andrews was daily seen driving down the streets with Billy Conway, whose father was Governor of a Western State . . as I saw her going by in her fragile beauty, I bowed my head to her, and in return came a slight nod of mere, passing acquaintanceship.

I made friends with Billy, as I had done with Vanna's homely room-mate . . who thought I was becoming interested in her—because I often spoke in Vanna's dispraise, to throw her off the track, and to encourage her to speak at greater length of the woman I loved and worshipped from a-far.

Now I sought through Billy Conway a nearer opportunity for her favour. He approached me one day while we were out on the foot-ball field, practicing formations. I was on the scrub team—whose duty it was to help knock the big team into shape.

"Johnnie, you know Vanna, don't you? . . Vanna Andrews, the art student."

"Slightly," I concealed, thanking God I hadn't blushed straight-way at the mention of her name. . "—met her when I posed for Professor Grant's classes."

"She's a beaut, ain't she?"

"Everybody thinks so."

"Don't you?"

"She'd be perfect, if she weren't so thin," I answered, almost smothering from the thumping of my heart.

"I've often wondered what makes you so cold toward the girls . . when you write poetry . . poets are supposed to be romantic."

"We have a good imagination."

"—wish you'd exercise your imagination a little for me . . I'd pay you for it."

"For what?"

"—writing poems on Vanna, for me."

My heart gave a wild jump of joy at the opportunity.

"I'll think it over. But if I do so, I won't take anything for it."

Billy shook my hand fervently.

"You're all right, Gregory . . it'll help me a lot . . I've got a case on her, I'll admit."

"Come on!" roared Coach Shaughnessy, "get on the job."

He began calling letters and numbers for a play.

And just for a joke, he took "Barrel" Way, the two hundred

pound fullback, aside, and "Rock-crusher" Morton .. he whispered them, I afterward learned, to give me rough stuff, go through me with a bang. . .

"Rock-crusher" took the ball, with "Barrel" for interference .. they came flashing my way.

I was so frenzied with joy over the prospect of getting my poems through to Vanna, even if it was in another man's behalf, that I flung myself forward and brought both stars down with only a yard gained.

Shaughnessy gave a whoop of joyous amazement and the other boys shouted, and kidded "Barrel" and "Rock-crusher," the latter of whom won his nickname from the gentle way he had of hitting his antagonists with his hard knees as he ran into them, and bowling them over .. he was a recruit from the hurdles, who ran "high."

Shaughnessy came over to me.

"Gregory, I want to say right here, I wish you took enough studies, and you could make sub on the big team right off. You're skinny, but you've got the mettle I wish all my boys had."

No sooner was I out of my football clothes than I hurried to Kuhlman's, drank three coco-colas to stimulate me, and went to my room, to write my first poem for Vanna. . .

Nearly every day Billy received a poem from me. Henceforth, when I passed Vanna, I received a gentle, appreciative smile .. but I was too timid even to speak to her .. and too self-conscious of my clothes, which were worn and frayed. . .

· · · · · · ·

There were a few negro students at Laurel. One of them, a girl named Matty Smith, approached me in the library one day, introduced herself as one of the chairmen of the entertainment committee of the First African Methodist Church, and asked me if I would come and give them a talk the following Saturday night. . .

The night came .. I found myself on the platform with the preacher by my side. They had seated me in the chair of honour.

First the congregation prayed and sang .. such singing, so clear and soaring and melodious. It rocked the very church, burst out through the windows in great surges of melody.

I was introduced as their friend, as the coloured man's friend.

I spoke. I read my poems simply and unaffectedly.

Afterward I shook hands all round.

Matty Smith, the negro girl, as black as soot, and thoroughly African, stood by me as introducer. If I had shut my eyes, her manner of speech might not have been told from that of any cultured white woman's. She was as refined and sensitive a human being as I have ever met.

As I walked back to my attic over the plumber shop, it was with head erect and heaving chest. I deemed myself a champion of the negro race. I was almost putting myself alongside of Lincoln and John Brown.

Their reason for inviting me was that I had had a scathing poem printed, in the New York *Independent*, on the lynching of a negro in Lincoln's home State of Illinois.

.   .   .   .

Within two days of my talk at the First Methodist African Church, I met simultaneously in front of the library, two women, each going in opposite directions. . .

"Good afternoon, Mr. Gregory!"

It was Matty Smith. She was hesitating for a cue from me. She wished to stop and thank me again for my speaking.

But from the other side Vanna Andrews was passing.

I ignored Matty with a face like a stone wall.

"Good afternoon!" I bowed to Vanna . . who ignored me . . perhaps not seeing me.

The fearful, hurt look in the negro girl's eyes made me so ashamed of myself that I wanted to run away and hide forever somewhere.

That night I was so covered with shame over what I had done to another human soul, a soul perhaps as proud and fine as any in Laurel, that it was not till dawn that sleep visited me. . .

So I was just as rotten, just as snobbish, just as fearful of the herd, as were these other human beings whom I made fun of as the bourgeoisie.

.   .   .   .

Speaking with Riley, one of the English professors, about the mixture of colours on the hill. . .

"I must confess," he admitted sincerely, "that I feel awkward indeed when a negro student walks by my side . . even for a few steps. . .

Coach Shaughnessy declared himself boldly——

"I'll admit frankly to you, Gregory, but don't, of course, repeat what I say—that I'll never let a nigger play on the football team . . when they sweat they stink too badly . . no, sir, John Brown's State or not, the negro was never meant to mix with the white on terms of equality.

. . . .

It was mainly out of consideration for Langworth, and desire to please him, that I now joined the Unitarian Church, of which all the old settlers of Laurel were members. This included a testy old gentleman named Colonel Saunders, who had been one of John Brown's company, had quarrelled with him,—and who now, every year, maintained, at the annual meeting of old settlers, that Brown had been a rogue and murderer . . a mad man, going about cutting up whole families with corn knives. . .

At this juncture in his speech, which was made undeviatingly every year, a sentimental woman would rise and cry out——

"John Brown, God bless him, whatever you say, Colonel Saunders, his soul still goes marching on——"

"I grant that, madam—that his soul still goes marching on—I *never* contested that—but *where* does it go marching on!"

Then the yearly riot of protests and angry disputation would wake.

And every spring, in anticipation of this mêlée, reporters from the Kansas City papers were sent to cover the story of the proceedings of the Old Settlers' Society.

. . . .

Bob Fitzsimmons stopped off at our town, with his show. Though I couldn't afford to attend the performance, I did race down to the station, go up to him, and ask the privilege of a handshake.

His huge, freckled ham of a hand closed over mine in a friendly manner . . which disappeared up to the wrist. He exchanged a few, simple, shy words with me from a mouth smashed to shapelessness by many blows. He smiled gently, with kind eyes.

I was prouder of this greeting than of all my growing associations with well-known literary figures. And I boasted to the boys of meeting "Bob" . . inventing what I said to "Bob" and what "Bob" said to me, *ad infinitum*.

. . . .

Though the great athlete shared my admiration with the great

writer, yet my staying awake at night writing, my but one meal a
day, usually,—except when I was invited out to a fraternity house
or the house of a professor—and my incessant drinking of coffee
and coco-cola to keep my ideas whipped up—all these things inca-
pacitated me from attaining any high place in athletic endeavour.
I was fair at boxing and could play a good scrub game of football.
But my running, on which I prided myself most—I entered for the
two-mile, one field day, and won only third place. I had gone back
in form since Hebron days.

Dr. Gunning, head of our physical instruction, informed me that,
exercise as I might, I could never hope to be stronger or put on
more weight .. "you had too many hardships and privations in your
growing years .. and you are of too nervous a temperament."

.   .   .   .

But my love for Vanna had regularised me somewhat. I discarded my sandals and bought Oxford ties. And I preserved a
crease in my trousers by laying them, folded carefully, under my
mattress every night. And I took to wearing shirts with white
linen collars. . .

And I kept a picture of the girl I adored, secretly, among my
manuscripts—it was one I had begged of "Con" Cummins, frankly
taking him into my confidence as to my state of heart toward Vanna.
Which confidence "Con" never abused, though it might have afforded
endless fields of fun.

"Con" framed the picture for me.

When alone with it, I often actually knelt to it, as to a holy image.
And I kissed and kissed it, till it was quite faded away.

.   .   .   .

Emma Silverman, the great anarchist leader, came to Laurel,
with her manager, Jack Leitman. I went to the Bellman House,
the town's swellest hotel, to see her. I had never met her but had
long admired her for her activities and bravery.

I found her a thick-built woman, after the gladiatorial fashion .. as she moved she made me think of a battleship going into
action. There was something about her face .. a squareness of
jaw, a belligerency, that reminded me of Roosevelt, whom I had
seen twice .. once, at Mt. Hebron, when he had made a speech from
the chapel platform .. (when I had determined not to join in the
general applause of one whom I considered a mere demagogue—

but, before I knew it, found myself on my feet roaring inarticulately as he strode in) and again, after he had returned from his African expedition, and had come to Laurel to dedicate a fountain set up for the local horses and dogs by the S. P. C. A.

Jack Leitman looked to me like a fat nincompoop. Such a weakling as great women must necessarily, it seems, "fall for." But he was an efficient manager. Possessed of a large voice and an insistent manner, he sold books by the dozen before and after Emma Silverman's lectures. . .

Miss Silverman already knew of me through Summershire, the wealthy socialist editor and owner of *Summershire's Magazine*, and Penton Baxter. It thrilled me when she called me by my first name. . .

Her first lecture was on Sex. The hall was jammed to the doors by a curiosity-moved crowd.

She began by assuming that she was not talking to idiots and cretins, but to men and women of mature minds—so she could speak as she thought in a forthright manner. She inveighed against the double standard. When someone in the auditorium asked what she meant by the single standard she replied, she meant sexual expression and experience for man and woman on an equal footing . . the normal living of life without which no human being could be really decent—and that regardless of marriage and the conventions!

"The situation as it is, is odious . . all men, with but few exceptions, have sexual life before marriage, but they insist that their wives come to them in that state of absurd ignorance of their own bodily functions and consequent lack of exercise of them, which they denominate 'purity.' . .

"I doubt if there is a solitary man in this audience—a married man —who has not had premarital intercourse with women."

All the while I kept my eye on Professor Wilton, who sat near me, in the row ahead . . he was flushing furiously in angry, puritanic dissent . . and I knew him well enough to foresee a forthcoming outburst of protest.

"Yes, I think I can safely say that there is not one married man here who can honestly claim that he came to his wife with that same physical 'purity' which he required of her."

Wilton leaped to his feet in a fury . . the good, simple soul. He

was so indignant that the few white hairs on his head worked up
sizzling with his emotion. . .

"*Here's one!*" he shouted, forgetting in his earnest anger the
assembled audience, most of whom knew him.

There followed such an uproar of merriment as I have never seen
the like before nor since. The students, of course, howled with indescribable joy . . Emma Silverman choked with laughter. Jack
Leitman rolled over the side table on which he had set the books to
sell as the crowd passed out——

After the deafening cries, cat-calls and uproars, Emma grew
serious.

"I don't know who you are," she cried to Professor Wilton, "but
I'll take chances in telling you that you're a liar!"

Again Wilton was on his feet in angry protest.

"Shame on you, woman! have you no shame!" he shouted.

This sally brought the house down utterly. The boys hooted and
cat-called and stamped again. . .

Emma Silverman laughed till the tears streamed down her face. . .

.   .   .   .

During the four days she remained in Laurel her lectures were
crowded.

.   .   .   .

Walking up the hill one day, I overtook Professor Wilton, under
whom I had studied botany, and whom I liked, knowing he was sincere
and had spoken the incredible though absolute truth.

"That woman, that anarchist friend of yours, Gregory, is a
coarse woman!"

I rose to Emma's defence . . but he kept repeating . . "no, no . .
she is nothing but a coarse, depraved woman."

.   .   .   .

At my instigation, the Sig-Kaps gave an afternoon tea for her.
And I was proud to act as her introducer. The boys liked her.
She was like a good gale of wind to the minds and souls of us.

.   .   .   .

I saw Emma and Jack off at the train. I carried two of her
grips for her.

"Take Johnnie with you!" jovially shouted some of the boys—a
motor car full of them—Phi Alphs—as we stepped to the station
platform. . .

She answered them with a jolly laugh, a wave of the hand. . .

"No, I'll leave him here . . you need a few like him with you!"

.   .   .   .

"I have something on my conscience," remarked Miss Silverman to me, "Johnnie, do you really think that old professor was speaking the truth?"

"I'm sure of it, Miss Silverman."

"Why, then, I'm heartily sorry . . and it was rough of me . . and will you tell the professor for me that I sincerely apologise for having hurt his feelings . . tell him I have so many jackasses attending my lectures all over the country, who rise and say foolish and insincere things, just to stand in well with the communities they live in—that sometimes it angers me, their hypocrisy—and then I blaze forth pretty strong and lay them flat!"

.   .   .   .

Professor Wilton was a Phi Alph. From that time he was spoken of as "the only Phi Alph Virgin."

.   .   .   .

The periods when I had rested secure in the knowledge of where my next meal was coming from, had been few. Life had pressed me close to its ragged edge ever since I could remember.

Now I was accorded a temporary relief. Penton Baxter wrote me that he had procured me a patron . . Henry Belton, the millionaire Single-Taxer, had consented to endow me at fifteen dollars a week, for six months. I had informed Baxter, in one of my many letters to him—for we had developed an intimate correspondence— that I had a unique fairy drama in mind, but could not write it because of the harassment of my struggle for bread and life. . . I had laid aside for the present my projected "Judas."

.   .   .   .

Singing all the time, I packed my books in a large box which the corner grocer gave me, and, giving up my noisy room over the tin-shop, I was off to the Y. M. C. A., where I engaged a room, telling the secretary, who knew me well, of my good luck, and enjoining him not to tell anyone else . . which I promptly did myself. . .

I selected one of the best rooms, a corner one, with three windows through which floods of light streamed. It was well-furnished. The bed was the finest I had ever had to sleep in.

Immediately I went to Locker's, the smart students' clothier, and put on a ready-made suit of clothes, of blue serge. And I charged new shirts and little white collars .. and several flowing ties. And a fine, new pair of shoes.

"You sure look nifty," commented Locker, who himself waited on me.

Then I went to a bookstore and plunged recklessly, purchasing Gosse and Garnett's *Illustrated History of English Literature*, in four volumes, an expensive set.

I charged everything on the strength of my endowment, and, of course, in order to gain the credit I sought, I showed Baxter's letter, and pledged each storekeeper not to spread the story. . .

Before nightfall practically the whole student body knew of my good luck. And Jack Travers had found me, lying back, luxuriously clad in my newly acquired, big blue bathrobe, in my morris chair. . .

He looked me over with keen amusement.

Somehow, for several years, my one dream of luxury and affluence had been to own a flowered bathrobe to lounge in, and to wear on the athletic field. I had hitherto had to be content with a shabby overcoat.

On my new sectional bookcase stood a statue of the Flying Mercury, that my eye might continually drink in my ideal of physical perfection. Opposite that, stood my plaster cast of Apollo Belvedere, as indicative of the god of song that reigned over my thoughts and life.

.   .   .   .

"Jack, I want you to come and have supper with me!"

"Johnnie, you are just like a big baby .. all right, I'll dine with you, after I've shot in the story about your endowment to the *Star*."

"Hurry up, then,—it's after five now. I've never had enough money before, to treat you .. it's you that have always treated me."

"Where'll we dine?"

"At the swellest place in town, the Bellman House .. Walsh will charge me." Walsh Summers was the proprietor.

.   .   .   .

Big, fat Walsh welcomed me and Travers.

"No, Johnnie, I won't charge you. Instead, you and Jack are dining as guests of the house."

And he would have it no other way.

.   .   .   .

Ally Merton was right about appearances. To have your shirts laundered regularly makes a man a different being. People that only noticed me before with a sort of surreptitious mockery now began to treat me with surprised respect. Professors invited me even more—the more conservative of them—to dine at their homes.

And it was delightful to have living quarters where there was both hot and cold running water. I took a cold bath, every morning, after my exercise, and a hot bath, every night, before going to bed.

The place was well-heated, too. I no longer had to sit up in bed, the covers drawn to my chin to keep from freezing, while I read, studied, wrote. Nor did I need sit on my hands, in alternation, to keep one warm while I rhymed with the other, during those curious spells of inspiration, those times of ecstasy—occurring mostly in the night—when I would write and write so rapidly that morning would find me often not able to decipher the greater part of what I had written .. five or ten poems in a night .. scrawled madly almost like automatic writing. . .

.   .   .   .

William Jennings Bryan came to talk to us at our school auditorium. His lecture, *The Prince of Peace*, soon degenerated into an old-fashioned attack on science and the evolutionary theory.

The professors sat bored and mute on the platform beside him, while he evacuated the forty-year-old wheeze of "your great-great-great-grandfather might have been a monkey, but, thank God, mine was not!" he won the usual great response of handclapping and laughter with this. . .

And then he held out a glass of water, to prove that miracles might happen, because God, being omnipotent, could, at will, suspend natural laws.

"Look at this glass of water. I hold it out at arm's length, so. If I did not hold it, it would drop to the floor and shatter into pieces. Thus I, by a human act, suspend the law of gravitation .. so God!—" There was huzzaing and applause. Several professors uneasily shifted the crossing of their knees .. one or two stared diplomatically at the ceiling.

I grew angry and sent forth several sharp hisses before I knew what I was doing . . the effect was an electric stillness for the moment. Then a roar of indignant applause drowned my protest. And I stopped and remained quiet, with much craning of necks about me, to look at me.

As the crowd poured out, I ran out into the road, from group to group, and, wherever I found a professor walking along, I vociferated my protest at our allowing such a back-water performance at the State's supposed centre of intelligence.

"But, Gregory, it makes no difference . . the argument is settled, let platform orators like Bryan tilt at windmills all they may."

"The hell it doesn't make a difference! if you professors are worth your salt, you won't let a Chautauqua man get by with such bunco."

. . . .

The writing of my fairy drama progressed amain.

I mailed a copy of it to Penton Baxter, who said that it had genuine merit. Was not great, but showed great promise.

Henry Belton, from London, wrote me that it was beautiful and fine, but too eccentric for production in even the eccentric theatre.

And Belton kept deluging me with Single Tax pamphlets. And I wrote him hot letters in reply, villifying the Single Tax theory and upholding revolutionary Socialism. And he grew angry with me, and informed me that he had meditated keeping me in his patronage longer, but I was so obdurate that he would end my remittance with the six months . . as, in fact, was all that was originally promised me.

I replied that it made no difference . . that I would be always grateful to him. His letters stopped. The money stopped. But I went on living at the Y. M. C. A., charging up rent . . said that I was nearing the end of my rope again, glad because I had shown to myself that I was capable of sustained creative effort.

. . . .

Many well-known men came to Laurel for lectures to the students. Lyman Abbott appeared.

"The ancient bell-wether of the Standard Oil," Travers irreverently dubbed him.

The College Y. M. C. A. accorded him a reception. I was one of those invited to meet him.

After he had delivered a brief talk on God and The Soul, questions were invited—meant only to be politely put, that the speaker might shine. But my question was not put for the sake of social amenity .. though I'll admit, just a little for the sake of showing off.

"Dr. Abbott," I asked, "it is quite possible that there are other worlds in the sky—that, also, the rest of the planets either are or will be, homes for souls, for living beings equal to or higher than our present human grade of development?"

"Yes, yes, that is quite probable."

"Well, then, God, to prove a just God, would have to send his Son to be crucified a million times—once for each world .. for, if He did not, then the souls on these worlds would either be damned without a chance for salvation, or, if God made an exception in their case, that would be an unfair deal—for us to suffer from a fault other worlds are free of."

Dr. Abbott hemmed and hawed.

"It is not yet proven that there are other inhabited worlds. I am only dealing with questions of practical theology," he answered, with some heat and an attempt to be sarcastic.

The members of the Y. M. C. A. were indignant at me for putting a maladroit question.

"It doesn't do to invite Gregory anywhere. You can't tell what stuff he might pull."

"A legitimate question—" egged on Travers at my side, "bump the old boy again, Johnnie."

But I was not given another chance. After a short but painful silence the Secretary rose and put a suave and stereotyped query .. and others filled the breach in rapid succession. And the prestige of the great theologian was salvaged.

Commencement day approached. There came to deliver the address for the day, George Harvey, then editor of *Harper's Weekly*. Travers was assigned to interview Harvey. . .

"The fellow's a pompous big stiff," complained Jack, "the kind that makes a fetish of morning and evening dress .. wears kid gloves .. and a top hat .. he has both valet and secretary with him."

"That's no disgrace. Don't you think, Jack, that we Middle-Westerners only make fun of such people and their habits for the reason that we're either unable to do the same, or do not dare do it because of our jealousy of each other—our so-called hick democratic spirit?"

"There's a lot of truth in that.   But fundamentally I would say
that the newspaper editors who are here this week, holding a conference and tendering Harvey a banquet, *mean* their plainness of
dress and life . . and do not hanker after the clubman's way of life
as Harvey represents it to their eyes . . you just watch for what
Ed. Lowe and Billy Dorgan do to our Eastern chap at the banquet . . they'll kid him till he's sick."

That banquet will live in the memory of Kansas newspapermen.

Harvey, when he entered the hall where the journalists were
already seated, first snapped his top hat sidewise to his attending
valet.   Then he sat down grandly.

Billy Dorgan and Ed. Lowe "rode Harvey around," as Jack
phrased it.   The distinguished editor, with his solemnity, invited
thrusts.   Besides, most of those present were what was denominated
as "progressive" . . Jarvis Alexander Mackworth was there . . and
Alden . . and Tobbs, afterward governor.

.   .   .   .

The next day Travers printed a supposititious interview with Harvey's English valet on how it felt to be a valet of a great man.
Both the valet and Harvey waxed furious, it was said.

.   .   .   .

Arthur Brisbane visited us.   He ran down from Kansas City
over night.   This man was Jack Travers' God . . and we of the Press
or Scoop Club—a student newspaper club of which I had recently
been made a member—also looked up to him as a sort of deity.

Travers informed me reverentially that Brisbane was so busy he
always carried his stenographer with him, even when he rode to the
Hill in an auto . . dictating an editorial as he drove along.

"A great man . . a very great man."

I won merit with Travers by reciting an incident of my factory
life.   Every afternoon the men in my father's department would
bring in Brisbane's latest editorial to me . . and listen to me as I
read it aloud.   To have the common man buy a newspaper for its
editorials—that was a triumph.

And Brisbane's editorials frequently touched on matters that the
mob are supposed not to be interested in . . stories of the lives of
poets, philosophers, statesmen. . .

One of the men who could barely read . . who ran his fingers
along the lines as he read. asked me——

"Who was this guy SO-krats?"

It was an editorial on Socrates and his life and death that brought forth the enquiry .. after I had imparted to him what information I possessed:

"Where can I find more about him, and about that pal of his, Plato?"

. . . .

I was hanging on to my comfortable room at the Y. M. C. A. by bluff. I had not let on to the secretary that my Belton subsidy had stopped. Instead, I affected to be concerned about its delay. But I did this, not to be dishonest, but to gain time .. I was attempting to write tramp stories, after the manner of London, and expected to have one of them accepted soon, though none ever were. . .

Decker, the student-proprietor of the restaurant where I ate every day, was more astute.

"Now look here, Gregory, you just can't run your bill up any higher."

I already owed him fifteen dollars.

I compounded with him by handing him over my *Illustrated History of English Literature*. It was like tearing flesh from my side to part with these volumes.

And now I had no more credit at the Y. M. C. A.

And I went back to Frank Randall, to apply again for my old room over his shop. He was using it now to store old stoves in. But he moved them out.

With a sense of despair, compensated by a feeling of sacrifice for my poetry, I found myself once more back over the tinshop, the hammers sounding and crashing below.

Old Blore, the cancer doctor, lived in a room in the front. All day long he sat drinking rum and sugar .. and shipping out his cancer cure, a white mixture like powdered sugar. Whether it did any good or not, he believed in it himself. . .

I have not written about him before .. there are so many odd characters that I came in contact with that I have not written about .. for this book is about myself. . .

But old Blore .. he came waddling back to me, drunk, as usual, on his rum and sugar.

"Welcome back, Johnnie .. come on, you and Frank, into my room .. we've got to celebrate your return."

Frank and I set down the stove we were moving, dusted our hands off, and followed.

"But I won't drink any of your rum, Ed! It's got too much of a kick."

"—nonsense .. good Jamaica rum never hurt nobody."

We drank several rounds of rum and water, with sugar. And we jocosely joined together in singing the cancer doctor's favourite hymn—"We're drifting down the stream of time, we haven't got long to stay."

Then Frank and Ed. retailed to me the practical jokes they had played on each other since I had been gone from among them .. on big Sam, the chocolate-coloured shoemaker who had his shop next door .. and an obscene one on a half-wit named Elmer, who was one of Frank's helpers .. that, though it was pretty raw, made me choke and gasp with merriment .. and they told me how, one night, they had wired the iron roof in the back, so that about ten cats that were mewling and quarrelling there, received a severe electric shock .. how funny and surprised they'd acted.

.   .   .   .

Most serviceably a check from the *National Magazine* came, for twenty-five dollars .. I had sold them a prophetic poem on airships. The check ameliorated my condition. I saw my way clear to a few weeks more of regular eating.

.   .   .   .

Then, on top of that, one day a telegram came. . .

"Am on my way West. Will stop off visit you at Laurel— Penton."

.   .   .   .

Travers rushed the story to the Kansas City *Star.*

"KANSAS POET HONOURED

AUTHOR OF 'SLAUGHTER HOUSE' TO VISIT HIM"

I waited in a fever of eagerness and impatience for the arrival of this man whom I idealised and looked on as a great man .. the man who had written the *Les Miserables* of the American workingman.

.   .   .   .

Harry Varden, editor of the *Cry for Right*, had been to Laurel a week previously, to address a socialist local, and I had looked him up, at the house of the "comrade" where he was passing the night. The comrade sent me up to Varden's room, where I found the latter just getting out of bed. I shall always think of him in his proletarian grey woollen underdrawers and undershirt. In which he had evidently slept. He had the bed-habits of the masses. And the room was stale with bad air; like the masses, he, too, slept with windows shut.

Varden's monthly magazine *The World to Be*, had occasionally printed a poem of mine . . and I was paid five dollars for each poem.

Varden was a frail, jolly little chap, absolutely fearless and alert and possessed of a keen sense of humour which he could turn, on occasion, even against himself.

I breakfasted with him. He had good table manners, but, from time to time, he forgot himself and smacked his lips keenly. And the egg dripped on his chin as he flashed a humorous incident that had happened to him on one of his lecture trips. . .

After breakfast he and I took a long walk together . . we began speaking of Penton Baxter . . I spoke in high praise of the great novelist . . reverently and with awe.

"Yes, yes," Varden assented, "Penton is all you say, but he has no sense of humour . . and he takes himself and his work as seriously as if the destiny of the human race depended on it . . which is getting in a bad way, for a reformer, you know—gives a chap's enemies and antagonists so many good openings. . .

"When Penton was writing *The Slaughter House* and we were running it serially, his protagonist, Jarl—it seemed he didn't know how to dispose of him . . and the book was running on and on interminably. . . I wired him 'for God's sake kill Jarl.' . .

"Baxter took my telegram much to heart . . was deeply aggrieved I afterward learned . . the dear boy . . he did 'kill Jarl' finally . . and absent-mindedly brought him to life again, later on in his book."

And Harry Varden laughed excitedly like a boy, and he leaned sideways and smote his half-bent, sharp, skinny knee with his left hand. I could perceive that that was a grotesque platform gesture of his, when he drove a comic point home.

·   ·   ·   ·   ·   ·   ·

I was waiting at the station . . where I had shaken hands with Bob Fitzsimmons, and had seen Emma Silverman off. . .

Penton Baxter was due on the eleven o'clock train from Kansas City.

I surely must be on the road to becoming somebody, with all these famous people taking such an interest in me. I remembered Emerson's dictum about waiting in one's own doorway long enough, and all the world would come by.

Was I to be disappointed? It did not seem credible that the great man would make a special stop-off on his way to the coast, just to pay me a visit.

One after another the passengers stepped down and walked and rode away. Then a little, boyish-looking man . . smooth-faced, bright-complexioned, jumped down, wavered toward me, dropping his baggage . . extended his hand . . both hands . . smiling with his eyes, that possessed long lashes like a girl's.

"Are you Johnnie Gregory?"

"Penton Baxter?" I asked reverently. He smiled in response and drew my arm through his.

"This is great, this is certainly great," he remarked, in a high voice, "and I'm more than glad that I stopped off to see you."

He expanded in the sun of my youthful hero-worship.

"Where's the best hotel in town?"

"The Bellman House . . but I've arranged with the Sig-Kappas to put you up."

"Are you a fraternity man?"

"No—a barb."

"I'd rather go to the hotel you named . . but thank the boys for me."

I contended with Penton Baxter for the privilege of carrying his two grips. They were so heavy that they dragged my shoulders down, but, with an effort, I threw my chest out, and walked, straight and proud, beside him.

As we walked he questioned and questioned. He had the history of Laurel University, the story of my life, out of me, almost, by the time we had covered the ten blocks to the hotel.

"Penton Baxter!" I whispered in a low voice to the proprietor,

who, as he stood behind the desk, dipped the pen with a flourish,
and shoved the open register toward his distinguished guest.

.   .   .   .

Travers, of course, was the first to see the great novelist. He
wired an interview to the *Star*, and wrote a story for the Laurel
Globe and the *Laurelian*.

Baxter said he would stay over for two days . . that he didn't
want to do much beside seeing me . . that he would place himself
entirely in my hands. I was beside myself with happy pride.

"This is a glorious country. You must take me for a long walk
this afternoon. I want to tramp away out to that purple bluff
toward the South East."

"We call it Azure Mound."

"Has it any historical interest?"

"—don't know! It might have. Richard Realf, the poet, camped
out about here, on the heights with his men, during the Quantrell
Raid. And there are one or two old settlers in Laurel who were
members of John Brown's company."

Baxter was a good walker. He made me think of Shelley as he
traipsed along, indefatigably talking away, his voice high-pitched
and shrill . . unburdening his mind of all his store of ideas. . .

His head was much too large for his body . . a strong head . .
strong Roman nose . . decisive chin, but with too deep a cleft in it.
His mouth was loose and cruel—like mine. His face was as smooth
as a boy's or woman's . . on each cheek a patch here and there of
hair, like the hair on an old maid's face.

More than a year later his wife confided to me that "Pennie,"
as she dubbed him affectionately, could not grow a beard . . and
she laughed at his solemnly shaving once a week, as a matter of
ritual, anyhow. . .

Each of us went with bent knees as we walked, as if wading against
a rising tide of invisible opposition.

I discoursed of a new religion—a non-ascetic one based on the
individual's spiritual duty to enjoy life—that I meditated inaugurat-
ing as soon as I left college. He advised me to wait till I was
at least Christ's age when he began his public ministry, thirty-
five or six. His face lit with frolic. . .

Then, in rapid transition, he soberly discoursed on the religion he himself had in mind . . instinctively I knew it would not do to make sport of his dreams, as he had of mine.

Harry Varden was right. Where he himself was involved in the slightest, Baxter absolutely had no sense of humour.

Baxter told me of the great men he had met on intimate terms, in the wider world of life and letters I had not yet attained to . . of Roosevelt, who invited him to dinner at the White House . . and of how, at that dinner attended by many prominent men . . by several Senators . . Roosevelt had unlimbered his guns of attack on many men in public office. . . "Senator So-and-so was the biggest crook in American public life. . . Senator Thinggumbob was the most sinister force American politics had ever seen . . belonged to the Steel Trust from his shoes to his hat. . ."

"Suppose, Mr. President," Baxter had put to him, at the same time expressing his amazement at the president's open manner of speech before men he had never even met before . . men perhaps of antagonistic shades of opinion, "suppose I should go out from here and give to the newspapers the things you have just said! How would you protect, defend yourself?"

"Young man, if you did—*as you won't*—" smashed Roosevelt, with his characteristic of clenched right fist brought down in the open palm of the left hand—"if you did—I'd simply brand you as a liar . . and shame you before the world."

"And so it was that Roosevelt expressed himself freely . . and at the same time protected himself."

. . . .

We stood on the top of Azure Mound. Baxter was puffing heavily, for it had been a hard climb.

At our feet extended a panorama of what seemed like a whole State.

The wide-spread fields of wheat, of corn, exalted us.

"God, what a glorious country! . . no wonder Walt loved America . . in spite of the abuses capital has perpetrated in it."

"Walt Mason?" I enquired, mischievously. . .

"No," he responded, seriously, "Walt Whitman."

"But our poet laureate to-day is Walt Mason . . and our State philosopher, the sage of Potato Hill, Ed Howe, is an honest-to-

God stand-patter . . that's Kansas to-day for you, in spite of her
wide, scenic vistas. . .

"Nevertheless," I went on, "Kansas does develop marvellous people . . we have Carrie Nation————"

"And Johnnie Gregory!" put in Baxter.

"I don't want just to belong to Kansas."

It was I who was humourless now, "I'm sick of its corn-fed
bourgeois ideals . . I want to belong to the world—as—you do!"

We trudged back to town.

"What a site for a university! . . the men who put those buildings up there on the Hill must have dreamed greatly . . look at the
sun! . . the buildings are transfigured into a fairy city!"

    .   .   .   .

My office as social manager for Baxter during his stay I conducted badly. I was so excited and flattered by the visit of one
whom I considered one of the first geniuses of the world, that I
hardly knew what I was doing. I listened to all he said as if an
oracle spoke.

I asked him if he would like to meet some of the professors on
the Hill . . I hurriedly gathered together a small group of them
and Baxter gave a talk to them in one of the unoccupied recitation
rooms. Nor did he fail in telling them that in me Kansas had a
great poet in the making . . the professors who were not invited
to my hasty reception considered themselves slighted.

When I saw Baxter off at the station we were calling each other
by our first names.

"Good-bye, Johnnie!"

"Good-bye, Penton!"

"Don't fail to visit me at Warriors' River, this fall, if you can
do so conveniently."

I assured him that I would not fail.

For I had spoken with him of my determination to ship on the
Great Lakes for a few months, to see if I couldn't garner some poetic
material for my poems of modern life that I was writing for the
National Magazine.

"My wife and I will be at Warriors' River till late in the fall.
We're staying at Stephen Barton's Health Home. Barton is a
good friend of mine. . . I am helping him out, since he left New
Jersey, where he was forced, by a series of petty prosecutions, to

give up Perfection City. . . My wife will be glad to see you . . she
knows your poetry already."

.   .   .   .

The weather was warm again. My next to my last college year
was drawing to a close. Not that I was a graduate . . my course
was a special one, and I had not followed even that closely.

"If you'll graduate," Jarvis Alexander Mackworth urged me,
joking in the Kansas fashion, "I will present you with a great
bouquet of beauty roses . . I'd like to see you vindicate Langworth's and my judgment of you. For you have many, many
professors and people on the Hill who don't believe in you, and,
frankly,—say it was a mistake ever to have let you in."

Mackworth was one of the regents of the school.

"In fact, once one of the professors rose, at a meeting, ably
reinforced by several others, to complain that you were actually
crazy, and a detriment to the school."

"And what did you say, Mr. Mackworth, didn't you defend me?"

"Yes, God pity me, I did," he jested. "I remembered how I was
asked to quit here, too. In the days when General Fred Furniss
was also looked on as an unruly, rather undesirable member of the
student body . . we were classmates. . .

"I replied that no doubt you were crazy, you starry young tramp,
you! . . but that I wished some of the professors shared a little
of your virus . . it might make them more alive and interesting."

.   .   .   .

Again I was absolutely starvation-ridden. Several tramp-poems
that I sold to *Everybody's* kept me literally in bread and cheese for
a month. I was still madly in love with Vanna at long distance.

There came an opportunity for me to make a few dollars and to
show off before her, at the same time.

The Copperwell Street Show came to town. They lined the main
street with booths, and outside of town, in a large pasture, circus
tents were pitched, in which the usual one-ringed circus was to be
shown . . and they had six lions in a cage . . advertised as Nubian
lions, the largest and fiercest of their kind . . their trainer never
going in among them except at peril of his life. A gold medal was
offered to anyone who would go in among the lions alone, and make a
speech to the audience from the inside of the cage.

I negotiated with the management, but asked for the medal's

equivalent in money. I was offered twenty-five dollars if I would go in, and repeat my speech, each one of the three nights the show would be held.

I was to go in for the first time that very night . . to clinch my lagging resolution, the story was printed in the local papers. . .

"JOHN GREGORY TIRED OF LIFE

KANSAS POET TO TALK AMONG LIONS,"

Jack Travers was at his facetious best.

Considering myself heroic, and thinking with inner joy how Vanna Andrews would be there, I spent the day in committing to memory the salient points on the nature and habits of lions, from the Encyclopedia Britannica. . .

People looked at me both with amusement and admiring amazement as they saw me about, late that afternoon. . .

"Now tell me the honest truth about the lions," I asked of the trainer.

"They're a pretty bad lot."

"Come on. I've made up my mind to go in, and I'm not afraid."

"—though lions are not as bad as leopards and tigers . . there's no telling when they might jump you . . there's only one chance in a thousand that they will . . but you may bring one up from being a cub . . and, one morning, because of something you can't read in its animal mind—it not liking its breakfast or something—it may jump you, give one crunch, and snuff you out like a candle . . it's that chance that you take that makes it seem brave."

"Thanks, I'll take the chance."

"Are you sure you'll have enough command of yourself to make a speech?"

"—Certain . . I've committed to memory almost all the Encyclopedia Britannica article on lions . . I'm going to give them that. . ."

.   .   .   .

"Gregory! Gregory!" the crowd was calling, half in derisive jocularity, half in uneasy admiration. . .

The trainer shunted me into the cage, after seating his lions in a half-moon on their tubs.

"Quick! Step in! We'll be on the outside ready with hot irons in case anything goes wrong!"

I didn't know whether the trainer was jesting or serious.

"Don't think of them at all. They'll sit still . . you can turn your back to them and face the audience. It will be safe. Only don't make any unexpected, quick motions."

I was in among them. The door clanged behind me.

Nobody jeered now. All was filled with an expectant hush.

Then, as if strange and a-far from myself, I stepped easily into the very centre of the half moon of squatting beasts, and made my speech . . at the end, there was hardly any applause till I was safely out of the cage. . . Then there was a tumult. Shouts, cat-calls, whoops, and a great noise of hearty hand-clapping.

I stood beside the ropes as the people of Laurel surged by, many of them shaking me by the hand . . Vanna came by, with the big football player with her, bulking behind her slight loveliness . . lightly she put a tiny, gloved hand in mine . . a glove neatly mended at the fingers . . congratulating me, half with feeling, half with amusement. . .

"That was reckless and brave, Mr. Gregory."

I was speechless with frightened delight over her words, and the pressure of her hand.

I turned to the trainer before I went to my room over the tin-shop.

"You say the leopards are most dangerous?"

"Yes."

"For twenty-five dollars a night I will go in with them, alone, and run them around with a whip." As I proposed this, in the background of my consciousness was the conviction that by so doing I could win Vanna's love. . .

"No . . the leopards are too uncertain."

.   .   .   .

The papers were full of my deed. And I was not made fun of, but commended. And it was announced (for advertising purposes only, of course) that the management of the show had approached me with an offer to travel as a trainer of wild animals.

The second night I was rather blasé. I shook my finger playfully in the face of one of the seated lions . . to have a sensation of a thousand prickles running sharp through each pore, when the lion responded with an open, crimson-mouthed, yellow-fanged snarl; I smelt the carrion fetor of his breath. I stepped back rather quickly. All the animals grew restless and furtive. Little greenish-amber gleams lit and flickered in their eyes.

I pulled myself together. Deliberately I turned my back on them.

"—So you see plainly, ladies and gentlemen, that a lion is, after all, a much misrepresented, gentle beast."

The trainer was piqued when I walked out, that night.

"I don't want you to tell the people that my lions are harmless and gentle . . if you do that to-morrow night, I'll see to it that you get the medal, and not the money."

The afternoon of the following day, while the girl who trained the leopards was in the cage of the latter, they jumped on her, and tore her back with their claws. Dripping with blood, she whipped them back, inch by inch, into their living-cage, that led by a small door into the big one used for exhibitions. A shiver ran through me at the news of the girl's mishap. I was glad they had not taken me up as regards the leopards. And my being among the lions now also seemed less of a joke. At least, that last night, I felt it not to be, I delivered a constrained discourse and only breathed freely when outside their cage.

.   .   .   .

And in a few weeks my unique and single glory was snatched from me. The show had moved to Salina, and a barber in that town had shaved their keeper in the cage, while the lions sat around.

.   .   .   .

Before leaving for my projected summer as worker on the boats of the Great Lakes, I snatched at a passing adventure: the Kansas City *Post* had me walk from Laurel to Kansas City with the famous walker, Weston.

The man was going across the continent a-foot. When he saw I was sticking the fifty miles or so with him, he became friendly and talked with me of the athletes of former days . . the great runners, walkers, fighters, oarsmen . . and he knew intimately also many well known journalists and literary men of whom he discoursed.

Time and again, like a bicycle pedalled too slow, he stepped awry on so small an obstacle as a cinder, and toppled over on his face like an automaton running down.

"No, no! Don't touch me. I must get up myself . . that's not

in the game . ." his rising was a hard, slow effort . . he regained
his feet with the aid of his metal-tipped cane. . . .

"Keep back! Keep back!" to the people, gangs of curious boys
mostly, who followed close on his heels. And he poked backwards
with the sharp metallic point of the stick. . .

"People follow close on me, stupid, like donkeys. If I didn't
keep that point swinging back, when I slacked my pace or stopped
they would walk right up on me . . ."

.   .   .   .

Dr. Percival Hammond, managing editor of the New York *Independent*, the first magazine to print my poems, came to town . .
to lecture on his favourite topic of international peace.

It occurred to me strongly that I ought to afford him some witness of my gratitude for what his magazine had done for me.

Though broke, I borrowed ten dollars from the owner of a lunch
counter where I ate.

"I want to give a dinner to Dr. Hammond . . his magazine has
helped me as a poet . . it is obvious that I can't give the dinner
at your lunch counter."

Ten dollars was all the lunchcounter man would lend me.

But Walsh Summers of the Bellman House said I could give
a luncheon in honour of Hammond at fifty cents a plate . . he would
allot me two tables . . and a separate room . . and I could invite
nineteen professors . . and he would throw in two extras for Jack
Travers and myself.

I gave the lunch, inviting the professors I liked best.

After dessert and a few speeches I told them how I had borrowed
the money. Hammond privately tried to pay me back out of his
own pocket, but I wouldn't let him.

.   .   .   .

I asked Hammond if he knew Penton Baxter.

"Yes; we printed his first article, you know . . just as we gave
you your start. . .

"Baxter is the most remarkable combination of genius and jackass
I have ever run into. But don't ever tell him that I said that. He has
no sense of humour . . everything is of equal import to him . .
his toothache is as tragic as all the abuses of the capitalist system."

.   .   .   .

On the way to the Great Lakes there are several people I must stop and see, and show myself to.

I stop at Topeka and visit Dad Rother . . a columnist on a newspaper there, of more than local fame . . an obviously honest-to-God bachelor . . he is afflicted with dandruff and his hair is almost gone. He shows me photographs of Mackworth and of Uncle Bill Struthers, each autographed with accompanying homely sentiment.

I catch myself pretending an interest in Rother's column, but really actuated by a desire to plant myself in his mind, and to have a notice in his paper about me . . anything that Dad Rother has in his column is copied in all the Kansas papers.

．　　　．　　　．　　　．　　　．　　　．　　　．

I drop in at a Leavenworth newspaper office, ostensibly to borrow the use of a typewriter.

But the stick or so put in the paper about my passing through Leavenworth pleases me.

General Fred Furniss is stationed at Fort Leavenworth. I must visit him.

．　　　．　　　．　　　．　　　．　　　．　　　．

General Furniss walked in rapidly as if executing a military manœvour, both hands held forth in welcome. He was "Napoleonic" in size, and, also like Napoleon, he carried too much belly in front of him. He wore a closely curling salt-and-pepper beard. . .

He commented on my "military carriage"—asked me if I had ever gone to a military academy. . .

I yielded to an instinct for deprecative horse-play, one of my worst faults, begot of an inferiority-complex.

"No, I've never gone to a military academy, but I've had a hole in the seat of my pants so generally, and I have had to walk erect so much to keep my coat tail well down to hide it, that that is where I acquired my military carriage."

The general's eyes twinkled.

"Take a chair. I have heard of you, Mr. Gregory . . I have watched your work, too. Roosevelt knows about it . . has spoken of it to me . . has remarked: 'there's a young fellow—your poet-chap in Kansas—that will be worth watching . . why is it, Fred, that every man of any talent whatever in Kansas, instantly gets the eye of the nation? . . we're always expecting something big from William Allen White's State'."

.   .   .   .

A week or so of work for a Polish-Catholic farmer . . who locked me out of his house, when he and his family went to mass the one Sunday I was with him. He asked me if I wanted a book to read. As the only book he possessed was Thomas à Kempis' *Imitation of Christ*, I took it, and learned Christian humility, reading it, in the orchard. Surely this farmer was a practical Christian. He believed in his fellow man and at the same time gave him no opportunity to abuse his faith in him. . .

.   .   .   .

It was pleasant, this working for from a few days to a week, then sauntering on . . putting up at cheap little country hotels overnight. I liked it better than tramping. . .

I pitched hay, I loaded lumber, I dug, I planted, I reaped.

.   .   .   .

In lower Minnesota a Swedish emigrant farmer hired me to help him with his hay crop. He and I and his lanky son, Julius . . just coming out of adolescence . . we worked away from sun-up till moon-rise. . .

The first day I congratulated myself for working for that particular farmer. The meat at table was abundant and fresh.

But before my two weeks were up I had grown weary of the diet. They had killed a cow . . and cow-meat was what I found set before me morning, noon, and night,—every day. I complained about it to Julius . . "when we kill a cow ain't we got to eat it?" he replied.

Every afternoon we participated in a pleasant Swedish custom. The two women of the household, the mother and grandmother, with blue cloth rolled about their head for headgear, brought us coffee and cake a-field. . .

"Aeftermittagscaffee," they called it.

It refreshed us; we worked on after that till late supper by lamp, driving back to the house by moonlight.

.   .   .   .

At Duluth I found that a strike prevailed on the Lakes. I was held in doubt whether I ought to sail, for I would have to do so as strike-breaker, which was against my radical code . . but, then, I

had come over-land all the way from Laurel, to voyage the Great
Lakes for the poetry to be found there . . and I must put my
muse above such things as strikes.

I signed on, on a big ore boat, as porter. . .

That means, as third cook; my task the washing and scouring of
greasy pots, pans, and dishes . . and waiting on the firemen and
deckhands at meals.

The *James Eads Howe* took on a cargo of rust-coloured iron ore
at Twin Harbours . . the gigantic machinery grided and crashed
all night, pouring the ore into the hold, to the dazzling flare of
electric lights. . .

Here for the first time I conceived myself to be caught in the
great industrial turmoil. If I were to derive song from this, it
would be song for giants, or rather, for machines that had grown
to gigantic proportions from the insect world . . diminutive men
made parts of their anatomy as they swung levers and operated
cranes. . .

We kicked outward on the long drop down Lake Superior, the
largest of the five Great Lakes. It was like an inland ocean. The
water of it is always so cold that, when a ship is wrecked there,
good swimmers who might otherwise keep up till rescued, often
perish of the cold. . .

Day and night the horizon was smoky-blue with forest fires . . one
afternoon our deck was covered with birds that had flown out over
the water to escape the flames. . .

And once we saw lifted in the sky three steamboats sailing upside
down, a mirage . . and, once, a gleaming city in the clouds, that
hung there spectrally for about five minutes, then imperceptibly
faded out. . .

"That's a reflection of some real city," explained the tall Cana-
dian-Scotch cook . ." once I recognised Quebec hanging in the sky . .
—thought I even saw people walking and traffic moving."

Half-way across to the Soo Canal we ran into my first lake-
storm.

"The sailor on the Great Lakes has a harder time than the ocean
sailor. He can't make his ship run before a storm. He's got to look
out for land on every side."

Right over my bunk where I slept, ceaselessly turned and turned
the propeller shaft. The noise and roar of the engines was ever

in my ears, and the peculiar ocean-like noise of the stokehold . . and the metallic clang of coal as it shot from shovels. . .

The night of the storm the crashing of the water and the whistling impact of wave-weighted winds kept me awake.

I jumped into my clothes and went into the fire-room. Hardly able to keep their feet, the firemen toiled away, scattering shovels-full of coal evenly over the fires, wielding their slice bars . . greeting with oaths and comic curses the awkward coal passer who spilled with his laden wheelbarrow into the slightly lower pit where they stood.

I quit the *James Eads Howe* at Ashtabula, after several round trips in her, the length of the Lakes.

I freighted it to Chicago, where I shipped, again as porter, on a package freighter.

.   .   .   .

The captain of the package freighter *Overland* should have been anything but a captain. He was a tall, flabby, dough-faced man, as timid as a child just out of the nursery.

We had taken on, as one of our firemen, a Canuck, who, from the first, boasted that he was a "bad man". . .

He intimidated the cook right off. He punched in a glass partition to emphasise a filthy remark he had made to the head engineer. He went after me, to bully and domineer me, next.

It looked as if we were in for a hard voyage to the Georgian Bay.

The Canuck, at the very first meal, terrorised the crew that sat down with him. I looked him over carefully, and realised that something must be done.

He flung a filthy and gratuitous expression my way. Silently I stepped back from the mess room, untied my apron, and meant to go in and try to face him down. But at that juncture, my courage failed me, and instead of inviting the rough-neck out on deck, as I had tried to force myself to do, I hurried to the captain's cabin.

The captain said, "Come in!" to my knock. He was sitting, of all things, in dirty pajamas, at a desk . . though it was mid-day . . his flabby, grey-white belly exuded over his tight pajama waist-string . . the jacket of the pajamas hung open, with all but one button off.

I complained to the captain of the bully—repeated how he had

bellowed at me to tell the unmentionable skipper he would receive
his bumps bloody well, too, if the latter did not stick to his own
part of the ship.

I saw fright in the captain's face. . .

"It's up to the chief engineer."

"Either that fellow goes off this ship or I do. You'll have to
hire another third cook."

The boat was sailing in an hour.

I walked back for my few effects. But, on the way back, I took
hold of myself and determined to stick by my guns. I made up
my mind that I would not leave the boat, and that, at the first
hostile move of the bully I would oppose him—besides, what had the
fellow done, so far, besides chucking a bluff?

My opportunity to live up to my resolve came at mess for supper. There was a smoking platter of cabbage set before the boys.

"What the hell! Who wants to eat bloody cabbage."

And snatching up a handful of the dripping, greasy vegetable,
he was about to fling it into the face of one of the men opposite,
when, without giving myself a chance to hesitate, I stepped up
quickly and grabbed the "bad man's" wrist. The cabbage went
high and spattered all over the opposite wall.

The bully glared like an enraged bull at me.

"I'll——"

Quaking in my boots, I made my eyes glare level with his.

"Listen to me, bo," I bluffed, "I ain't much on guff, and I don't
want specially to fight . . but I'm waiter in this mess room and
you don't pull anything like this here, unless you do it over my
dead body."

"That's just what I will do . . I'll—I'll——" and the chap,
pale with what seemed insane rage, started to his feet.

"Ah, sit down!" I commanded, marvelling at my nerve, and pushing him violently by the shoulders back on the bench . . then,
deliberately, I turned my back, and walked away, expecting any
moment to have him on me like a clawing wild cat.

With seeming calm and nonchalance I made the kitchen. With
a semblance of outward serenity I picked up a rag and returned to
wipe off the wall. I was vastly relieved to find that the bluff had
worked.

The Canuck was finishing his meal in silence.

From that moment till the end of the voyage he was as quiet and unobtrusive as anyone could wish him to be. . .

. . . .

I have a curious habit of often waking up in the night from deep slumber, and breaking into laughter over some funny incident or other that has happened to me a long time ago . . I have chuckled over this incident many times . . if that bully only knew how terrorised he really had me ! . .

. . . .

It is impossible to describe the Georgian Bay and the beauty of its thousands of islands . . as we steamed through them in the dawn, they loomed about us through sun-golden violet mists. . . Here as small as the chine of some swimming animal, there large enough for a small forest of trees to grow upon them. . .

. . . .

Another storm . . on Lake Huron . . a fair-sized one.

I was walking along the deck, just after dawn, the waves riding and running and shattering aboard. I carried the dinner bell, was ringing it for breakfast . . when the greatest wave I have ever seen on the Lakes came running, high-crested, toward the boat,—that seemed to know what was happening, for it rose to meet it, like a sentient being. . .

The wave smashed . . hit the galley and washed over the top of it, catching me in a cataract as I hugged close. I was driven hard against the taut cable wire that made our only railing. For a moment I thought the water reaching up from over-side as the vessel lurched would clutch me and suck me down.

A close and breathless call. A rending, splintering sound told me damage had been done. I looked toward the captain's cabin . . and laughed heartily, for all my discomfort and dangerous escape . . for the whole side of the cabin had been stove in,—and, terrified, his eyes sticking out, in his dirty underclothes the captain had been hurtled forth, his face still stupid from sleep though full of fear.

I rushed up to him. His drawers sagged pitiably with wet.

"A close shave, sir!" I remarked.

When I brought him his breakfast he was still trembling.

. . . .

I left the package freighter *Overland*. It was almost time for

the new school year. But Warriors' River lay in my way back to
Laurel, and I determined to stop off and pay a visit to Baxter, at
Barton's Health Home. . .

.   .   .   .

I was disappointed with my summer. In terms of poetic output.
I had written only three or four poems dealing with life on the
Lakes, and these were barely publishable in the *National Magazine*.
I realise now that poetic material is not to be collected as a hunter
goes gunning for game. It cannot be deliberately sought and found.
It must just happen.

Yet all the things that I had seen and been through, I knew,
would live in my mind till they were ready of themselves to get birth
in words. I knew that I had not lost a single dawn nor one night of
ample moon. And there drifted back into my remembrance that night
when the Italian coal-passer had come to my bunk and wakened
me, that I might come forth with him and observe a certain wonderful cloud-effect about the full, just-risen moon, over Huron. . .

I had cursed at him, thought he was trying to make a monkey
of me . . for I had dropped on deck a letter to me from Lephil of
the *National*, and so the crew had learned that I was a poet among
them.

But I was not being spoofed . . actual tears of surprise and
chagrin came into the coal-passer's eyes. Then I had been ashamed
of myself. . .

"Of course I'll go on deck . . mighty fine of you to wake me!"
I slid into my pants and went up the ladder——

To envisage, rapturous, a great, flaming globe of shadowy silver
. . and across it, in a single straight ebony bar, one band of jet-
black cloud . . and the water, from us to the apparition of beauty,
danced, dappled, with an ecstasy of quivering silver. . .

I have met many a man in my wanderings, simple and silent, who
felt beauty like a poet or an artist, without the poet's or artist's
gifts of expression,—with, on the contrary, a queer shame that he
was so moved, a suspicion that, somehow, it was not manly to be
moved by a sunrise or sunset.

.   .   .   .   .

I found Penton Baxter, his wife Hildreth, and their child, **Dan**,
living in two tents, among a grove of trees, near the main building
of the Health Home. These two tents had, of course, board floors,

and there was a woman who kept them in condition . . and there was a rack for towels, and hot water was supplied by pipes from a nearby building. I think the tents were even wired for electric light.

Baxter welcomed me. But I took a room for a week in town, though he urged me to stay with him. But when I had the means I liked better to be independent. I calculated living a week in Warriors' River for ten or twelve dollars. That would leave me thirty dollars over, from what I had earned while working on the *Overland*.

Then, back to the university for my last year of leisurely study and reading, in the face of the desolate poverty that would have defeated many another man, but to which I was used as a customary condition. After that—Paris or London, or both! Kansas was growing too small for me.

.   .   .   .

I have mentioned that Baxter had a head too large for his body. Daniel, his son, slight and frail and barely eight years of age, possessed the same characteristic. . .

I footed it out to Baxter's tents, faithfully as to a shrine, each afternoon. The mornings he and I both occupied in writing. He, on a novel which was the story of the love-life of his wife and himself, and of his literary struggles, called *Love's Forthfaring*; I, on my abortive songs of the Great Lakes that all came forth still-born . . because I was yet under the vicious literary influence of the *National Magazine*, and was writing my verse, trying to be inspired by the concepts of middle-class morality . . or what was even worse, I was attempting to glorify the under-dog; who, if he were the demi-god Socialists portray him, would by no means remain the under-dog.

.   .   .   .

I found Baxter more a-flame than ever for the utter reformation of mankind . . in the way they dressed . . stiff collars hurt the nervous system, pressing as they did, on the spine . . in the books they read . . he wished to start a library that would sell cheaply and bring all the world's great thought and poetry into factory, and every worker's home . . all conventional ideas of marriage and religion must go by the board and freedom in every respect be granted to men and women.

It was good to listen to this sincere, naïve man, still young . .

who would re-make life nearer to the beauty and harmony that Shelley also dreamed for mankind. I lived in a state of perpetual reverence toward Baxter. This man tried to live his ideals, as well as write about them.

In matters of diet I accepted Baxter's theories but, humanly, did not live up to them. He was a vegetarian.

Later I was to learn that he was to himself an experiment station. On his own person he directly and practically tried out each idea . . his wife was also a convertee, slightly reluctant, to his tests . . and his son, perforce. Baxter actually kept a vegetarian dog. "Even carnivorous animals thrive better on a vegetarian diet." But the dog was no corroboration of his theory. It lacked gloss and shine to its coat, and seldom barked.

One afternoon I came upon Dan, Baxter's son, puking in the bushes, not far from the tents.

"What's the matter, Dan," he turned to me, wan, and serious, and with a grown-up look on his face.

"Nothing! Only sometimes the warm milk father has me drink makes me throw up. I'm on a milk diet, you know."

"Does your father know that you can't keep the milk down?"

"Mostly it does stay down . . I guess father's all right," he defended, "maybe the diet will do me good."

"Do you ever get a beefsteak?"

"Father says meat is no good . . maybe he's right about killing animals. He says it wouldn't be half so bad if everyone killed their own meat, instead of making brutes out of men who do the killing for them . . but it is kind of hard on the dog, though," and the little fellow laughed.

.   .   .   .

"I think my boy is going to become an engineer of some sort; he's always playing about with machinery," Penton said to me. . .

"Suppose you let him take a trip with me to town, then? I'm going to look through the Best o' Wheat factory this afternoon, and watch how Best o' Wheat biscuits are made. Perhaps he'd like to see the machinery working!"

"Johnnie, I'll trust him with you, if you'll promise me not to meddle with his diet."

"Of course."

"I don't like people stuffing him full of candy and ice cream. I want to bring him up with a good digestion and sound teeth."

.   .   .   .

Daniel took my hand as we went through the factory from department to department. I enjoyed a paternal pride in the handsome, pale, preternaturally intelligent little fellow.

"Look at the young father!" exclaimed one girl softly to another, with a touch of pathos in her voice, intimating that perhaps I was a widower.

I blushed with pleasure to the tips of my ears, to be thought the father of so prepossessing a child.

It delighted him to look into the huge bake ovens where first the wheat was baked in big brown loaves, before it was broken up into biscuit form. I thought of Hank Spalton and how he was supposed to have grown strong on a diet of Best o' Wheat.

It was customary to serve sight-seers, in a dining room kept for that purpose, with Best o' Wheat and cream, and wheat coffee . . . free. . .

With a little reluctance Dan sat down and ate.

"Hum! that was good; but look here, Buzzer" (that was the nickname he had invented for me) you mustn't tell Mubby."

"Mubby?"

"That's what mother and I call my father."

"Of course I won't tell him . . and now we must go to a restaurant and have something real to eat."

"I can't. I don't dare. But I'll sit and watch you eat."

I ordered a steak, and persuaded Dan, finally, to have one too.

"If it's not good for people to eat, why does it taste so good?" mooted Dan meditatively. . .

"Now I'll be in for it," he added, as we walked out of the door and started back to the Health Home.

"But your father need never know."

"At first I thought it might be all right to fool him just this once. But I mustn't. I've promised him I'd never lie to him about what I ate, and I must keep my word . . he'll whip me, perhaps."

"Does he whip you much?"

"Not very much . . only when I need it . . and then when I cry, he stops—so it is never very hard!"

I laughed at the boy's frank philosophy. . .

"But daddy's so funny . . not at all like other daddies," wistfully.

.   .   .   .

I did not grow friendly enough with Mrs. Baxter even to call her by her first name of Hildreth . . during that brief visit. . .

Hildreth Baxter was always moving about leisurely, gracefully, like some strange, pretty animal. Not shy, just indifferent, as if processes of thought were going on inside of her that made an inner world that sufficed, to the exclusion of all exterior happenings.

She had a beautiful small head with heavy dark hair; large, brown, thoughtful eyes . . a face so strong as to be handsome rather than beautiful. She walked about in bloomers, languidly conscious that her legs were graceful and lovely. . .

To her I was, at that time, merely one of her husband's visiting friends. . .

.   .   .   .

After little Daniel had manfully squared himself with his conscience, Penton did not whip him. He came to me.

"I did not punish my boy: because it was you, Johnnie, that tempted him," and he flushed angrily. "I'm sure you didn't consider what you were doing. If I thought you did it out of deliberation, I would never speak to you again . . you must learn not to tamper with the ideals of others, Johnnie."

I apologised. I spoke of my reverence and regard for him and his greatness. I asked him to forgive me, which he did. And, as I pronounced him to be as great at Shelley, the Rousseau of America —his naïve, youthful face wreathed with smiles and peace fell between us again.

.   .   .   .

"I am thinking of going to live at Eden, the Single Tax Colony not far from Philadelphia . . I want you to come there and visit us in the spring. In the meantime don't let them make you bourgeois in Kansas . . don't let them smash you into the academic mould."

"They haven't so far, have they?"

"But what in the world are you going back to Kansas for?"

"Because I have them trained there to accept me. I can do

pretty much as I choose at the university. But mainly I want to write my four-act play in earnest—my New Testament drama, *Judas*. And I know of no better place to go to."

"Good-bye, and don't fail to pay me a visit in the spring."

"I will . . for a few weeks . . on my way to Paris."

"Paris? How are you going to get there?"

"I'll take a few cars of cattle east to New York from the Kansas City stock yards . . and I'll work my way across on a cattle boat."

"Good-bye! I wish I had your initiative!"

"Good-bye! Mrs. Baxter . . glad to have met you!"

"Good-bye, Mr. Gregory," and she dropped my hand quickly and turned on her heel, walking away with easy grace. I admired the back of her legs as she disappeared into her tent.

"Good-bye, Dan!"

"Good-bye, Buzzer!"

"Daniel," called Mrs. Baxter from the interior of her tent, "you mustn't call Mr. Gregory that!"

.   .   .   .

At Laurel again, I found it still a month before fall session. All summer I had lacked my nude sunbaths to which I had become accustomed. So again I sought my island.

.   .   .   .

I rented my room over the tinshop again, and was soon in the thick of the fall term. By this time I had my contemporaries on the hill very much puzzled.

Henry Belton, the Single Tax millionaire, had come to Kansas City. He was so diminutive as to be doll-like. He had to stand on a box to be seen, when he spoke from the floor, at the banquet tendered him . . and I had gone in to Kansas City as his guest, and had been seated on his right hand—I, in my painfully shabby clothes.

The professors and students could not see why I made such a stir with prominent people, how I held their friendship despite my eccentricities and deep poverty.

.   .   .   .

"I can't help you any more," observed Belton to me, as we sat in the lobby of the Coates House where he was putting up.

"Who the hell's asking you to help me?" I replied. "I came down from Laurel with no ulterior motive; I came just to pay you a

visit, and to thank you personally for giving me six months of freedom from economic worry while I wrote my fairy drama . . anyhow,
please remember that it wasn't me you helped, but Poetry!"

"It's too bad you can't be a Single Taxer," he sighed. "I like
you, Gregory, and I'd put you on my pension list if you'd only
shift some of your fanaticism for poetry to the Single Tax cause."

Since then I have been frankly sorry that I did not play the
hypocrite to Belton, in order to be put on a pension for several
years. I might have achieved great verse during the leisure so
afforded for calm, creative work.

·　　　·　　　·　　　·　　　·　　　·　　　·

I started a poetry club on the Hill . . I determined that it should
be anarchistic in principle . . we should have no officials . . no dues
. . not even a secretary to read dull minutes of previous meetings . .
we should take turns presiding as chairman. And the membership
was to be divided equally with girls.

·　　　·　　　·　　　·　　　·　　　·　　　·

But the school year had begun unhappily for me. I did not find
Vanna there. I went to visit her homely roommate.

"Vanna has gone off to Arkansas . . she is teaching school down
there for the winter."

"Thank God she's not married somebody!" I cried, forgetting,
and giving myself away. Then Vanna Andrews' roommate saw
at last that it was not she I was interested in. She gave way
to invective.

"You! a worthless tramp like you! A crazy fool! . . to dare
even hope that Vanna Andrews would ever love *you!*" In a torrent
of tears she asked me never to speak to her again.

I was sorry I had not procured Vanna's address before I had
betrayed myself. But, anyhow, I wrote her a long letter and
sent it in care of the university registrar.

Flamboyantly I confessed my love . . rehearsed the story of my
worship of her from afar. . .

For a month, every day, I sent her a bulky envelope full of
mad verse and declarations of undying love. As the letters were
not being returned, she must be receiving them.

One morning, with trembling hands and a pounding heart that
nearly bore me down, it acted so like a battering ram on the

inside, I drew a delicately scented envelope from my mailbox . . addressed in a dainty hand.

I kissed the letter again and again before I tore it open . . it was well that I did it then. I would not have kissed it afterward.

It was filled with stinging rebuke for my presumption . . if I had a shred of the gentleman in me I would cease troubling her . . I had caused her exceeding annoyance by my deluge and torrent of absurd letters . . she did not care for me . . she thought my poetry was bad . . and why had I behaved so brutally toward her former roommate? . .

I saw that the homely girl had not been remiss in writing to Vanna about me. . .

My reply was a very poetic letter.

"I will trouble you no more," I ended; "but do not destroy my letters and poems, for, long after your wonderful beauty has become a mere handful of oblivious dust blowing about the stones of the world, you will be famous because a great poet loved you . . a poet whom you unwisely and ignorantly scorned."

   .   .   .   .

Dr. Van Maarden, the Dutch psychiatrist and playwright, author of *De Kleine Man*, was to come to Laurel to deliver his celebrated lectures on "The Socialisation of Humanity." . .

Professor Dineen, a flabby, feminine little fellow, one of our professors of philosophy, and hated by the dean of his department because he was a real philosopher, despite his physical ludicrousness,—and had published a book which the critics were hailing as a real contribution to the world of thought——

Dineen had engineered the bringing of the semi-radical Van Maarden to Laurel. . .

"For such men are needed here . . to rouse us out of the petty, dogmatic ways of our crude pioneers. . ."

"Van Maarden is a remarkable man," continued Dineen; "he writes plays, poems, books of economic philosophy, novels . . recently he tried to start a co-operative colony for Dutch farmers in South Carolina, but it went on the rocks . . and now Van Maarden, for all his genius, is practically stranded here in America.

"It is, or ought to be, one of the duties of an educational centre like Laurel, to aid such men . . men who travel about, disseminating ideas, carrying the torch of inspiration . . like Giordano Bruno, in former days."

Van Maarden came . . a little, dapper, black-bearded man . . but a very boy in his enthusiasm. He advanced many doctrines at variance with even the political radicalism of Kansas.

But whether it was his winning way or his foreign reputation, he was accepted gravely, and ideas won consideration, enunciated by him, that would have been looked on as mad, coming from me. . .

Again the faculty were nonplussed . . puzzled. . .

Dineen, Van Maarden and I were together much. And the latter found more delight in the time when he could discuss freely and unacademically with me than when he was invited to formal teas and dinners by the weightier members of the faculty and community.

It was psychic research that we particularly discussed. Van Maarden was the greatest scholar in the Mystic, the Occult, the Spiritualistic that I have ever met. He claimed to be able to go out of the body at will and see what any friend was up to at any time, in any out-of-the-way place in the world. . .

When I jested that such a faculty might sometimes prove embarrassing to his friends, he laughed and slapped me on the back.

   .   .   .   .

Dineen was a queer little chap. He roomed de luxe at the Bellman House.

One night, during a cyclone that swept the town and the adjacent country, a fragment of roof was lifted off the hostelry in which he dwelt. The women-servants and waitresses were thrown into a panic. One, who collapsed on a lounge in the upstairs hall, swore that Dineen had felt of her leg as she lay there. A scandal was started. I know that Dineen, in his European fashion, was free with his hands, when he meant no harm. He had merely laid his hand on the girl's leg, in friendly fashion, and asked if she was hurt.

But the nasty Puritan mind of the community went to work, and the story was hawked about that Professor Dineen, taking advantage of the cyclone, had tried to "feel the girl up."

This, and the fact that he had been a friend of mine (after my forthcoming scandal it counted strongly against him) later effected in his being requested to resign from the faculty.

But the real cause of the brilliant, strange man's persecution

was the jealousy of the dean of the philosophical department of
the former's real ability.

.   .   .   .

"We must do more for this man than we have . . he is a genius
. . he has not enough money to return to Europe on. . .

"He has written a curious, mad play called *Iistral* . . one
dealing with psychic phenomena, which we ought to put on. . .

"That way we'll net him three or four hundred dollars."

It was Dineen who spoke.

We chanced to be walking up the Hill together.

.   .   .   .

The school cheer-leader was tall and statuesque, and his voice
was deep and resonant . . but, though pleased with his stature and
his vocal qualifications, Van Maarden decided on me to play the lead
in his abnormal play . . I did not possess as fine a voice, but I knew
the mystics almost as well as he did . . I believed in spiritism, and
would be accordantly sympathetic with the author's ideas. . .

.   .   .   .

The rehearsal of the play progressed. Van Maarden, receiving
from Dineen's own personal bank-account a substantial advance
on the expected receipts from the two performances, returned East,
and sailed away for Holland.

But an intimate friend of Penton Baxter's, before he left, he
related to me many fine things about the latter, and spoke in special
admiration of his wife, Hildreth.

.   .   .   .

I rehearsed and rehearsed.

I fought and fought with the directress, a teacher of elocution,
who tried to make me mouth my words in the old style.

She swore that she would get rid of me as Iistral (pronounced
Eestral), if it were not for the fact that it would seriously
embarrass her to try others for the part, the time of production
being so near.

Dineen upbraided me for being insubordinate. . .

I asked Dineen please to believe in me, and watch results.

My idea of acting was to go into the part, be burned alive by
it . . to recite my lines naturally.

I was proud of myself. I was to act as lead in a play by a
world-celebrated author, in its premier American production.

The story of it was that of a young poet-student, Iistral . .
eccentric . . a sensitive . . who had, while tutoring the children of a
count, fallen in love with the countess, his wife . . on the discovery
of the liaison, she had committed suicide in a lake on their private
grounds. . .

The play opened up with the young student, Iistral, come back
home, after the wife's death. . .

The tragedy had affected him strangely.

He wore a Hindoo robe, let his beard grow like a Yogi . . was
irritated with the unimaginative, self-seeking smugness of the
grown-ups.

He found in Lisel, a little niece of his, the wise, innocent, illumi-
nated imagination of childhood.   And he associated with her,
teaching her the mystic meanings of flowers in the garden.

But he lived for one thing only—the coming of the voice of
Egeria, as he called the spirit of the dead countess. . .

Her voice came to him continually . . preluded by strains of
music . . he lived from day to day with her lovely speech, a
clairaudient.

As long as nothing material was involved, he was regarded as
merely a gentle eccentric . . by his relatives and the bourgeoisie. . .

But as soon as word came that he had inherited a fortune through
the death of a rich uncle in America—the attitude of the people
around him changed.   His relatives began intriguing to have him
declared insane.

But the village burgomaster, ordinarily decent, saw through their
artifices. . .

Goaded and goaded, finally Iistral assailed his pestering relatives
with a shovel with which he was working among the gentle flowers
in the garden . . at his customary task of tending them with Lisel . . .

And now the burgomaster, bribed, had reason to adjudge him
insane.

And Iistral was dragged off, wailing, to the asylum.

.   .   .   .

With my clothes in literal rags I went through the rehearsals,
attended classes, kept up my athletics. . .

Often I woke up in the night, crying out, with tears rolling
down my cheeks, the lines of unhappy Iistral . . the spirit-woman
Egeria grew real as flesh and blood to me. . .

"Egeria! Egeria!——"

I woke, time and again, and heard my own voice, like the voice of another, calling her name in the dark.

.   .   .   .

"You mustn't take the play so desperately .. remember it's just a play .. you rehearse as if the whole thing were a part of your life."

"Some of the boys," I replied, "some of the football boys lost ten or twelve pounds in our Thanksgiving game at Kansas City last fall .. why do you rebuke me for taking art and beauty as seriously as athletes take a football match?"

.   .   .   .

Two days before the play, as I was walking by the Bellman House, I saw Jarvis Alexander Mackworth standing there, come up from Osageville for a regents' conference. . .

"Hello!" the dear, good man called, "you heavenly bum! You starry young tramp!"

His eyes were twinkling in appreciative merriment over his quaint phraseology.

"What are you doing in Laurel, Mr. Mackworth?"

I noticed that he did not wear his many-patched trousers, but was well dressed. . .

—"attending a regents' meeting, young man,—where I suppose I'll have to stand up in your defence again. . .

"It's a good thing you don't run after the women, Gregory, or your case would be entirely lost."

(Yet Mackworth didn't know of the dirty trick that had been played on me:

One of the boys from the school, running wild down in Kansas City, had, with a curious sense of humour, given my name as his .. to the "girls" in various houses of prostitution. . .

And "do you know Johnnie Gregory?" and "when is Johnnie Gregory coming to see us again?" other students were asked who frequented the "houses.")

"And what are you up to now?" asked Mackworth.

—"acting .. in Van Maarden's *Iistral* .. leading rôle!"

"You look skinnier than ever!"

"I am taking the part seriously, and it's bringing me down. I like to do real things when I get a chance, Mr. Mackworth .. and

I am going to make the two performances of *Iistral* memorable ones."

"You need a new suit of clothes very badly."

"I know I do. But I have no money, and no credit."

"We'll see about that, my young Villon."

Mackworth took me to one side and thrust a fifty-dollar bill into my hand.

I hurried down to Locker, the clothier. . .

In a very little while I was again walking by the Bellman House, completely togged out in new apparel from head to heel.

Mackworth was still standing there, and he laughed with astonishment at the lightning-quick change in my appearance. . .

"You're a card, Gregory!"

He afterward repeated the story with gusto. . .

.   .   .   .

The day before the night of our first performance at the Bowersby Opera House, Jack Travers, always turning up, came to me with a smile of faint sarcasm on his face——

"How's the great actor, eh?"

"Don't be an ass, Jack!"

"I've got a good proposition to make for advertising the show —and there'll be a lot of fun in it, too. . .

"Suppose we kidnap you, take you out somewhere in the country —then, after a day or so—find you bound, in a farm house. . .

"Of course it would compel them to put off the performances for a few days . . but look at the excitement; and the stories in the papers! . . afterwards you could go on tour through all the principal cities of Kansas."

The idea fascinated me, in spite of myself. . .

"But how about Dineen? He'd go nearly crazy!"

"There's where a lot of the fun would come in. And to see the way Gertie Black, the elocution teacher, would carry on! . ."

But after a long pause of temptation I shook my head in negation of the suggestion. . .

It *would* be a lark, but I had pledged Dineen that I would give him no more trouble with my vagaries. . .

And, besides, I didn't trust Jack Travers—once they had me in their power, he and his kidnappers might hide me away for several weeks . . to "bust up" the play entirely; would, I wisely reflected, be, to Travers, even a greater joke than merely to delay its production.

And I wanted this time to show my enemies that I could be depended on in affairs of moment. . .

. . . .

We had to have recourse to Kansas City for our costumes. And we were more fortunate in them than the cast of *She Stoops to Conquer* had been the year before . .

Costumes had then been rented for them which left the children mysteriously itching, driven to the inexplicable necessity of scratching in embarrassing localities. . .

The poor girls especially were terror-stricken . . and many of the boys were too innocent to conjecture what was the matter . . at first they thought that the rented costumes had imparted some obscure skin disease to the entire company . . and word was conveyed to the costuming firm that they were to be sued. . .

But when it was discovered that an indecent sort of vermin was the cause, the case was dropped. . .

Suit could not be conducted on such grounds. . .

But the joke was passed around and caused considerable merriment among the wise ones.

. . . .

The only thing I allowed the elocution teacher and directress to do was to put on my make-up for me . . including the sticking to my face of a close Van Dyke beard. . .

I refused to avail myself of her instruction for acting, as I perceived that was all bosh. . .

. . . .

The curtain went up, I sitting there, the orchestra softly breathing Massenet's *Elegy*—meant to be the music sent from the spirit world, the melody that I, Iistral, heard, whenever my dead mistress was present. . .

The orchestra finished the melody. It stopped and left the house in expectancy.

A mistake had been made on the entrance-cue of little Lisel, my child-nephew.

There I sat, in my strange robe, like a bath-robe, with stars cast over it, waiting.

I knew something had gone wrong.

Several girls (of course everyone in the audience knew me) began to titter at my strange appearance, in my apotheosised bathrobe, in my close Van Dyke beard. . .

I knew inwardly that in a moment all the house would be laughing . . at first out of sheer nervousness over the delay in the progress of the play—then from genuine amusement. . .

I threw my will, my entire spirit, against the incoming tide of ridicule which would wreck the play even with the rising of the curtain.

I pictured to myself the beautiful woman who had drowned herself; I burned with her unhappiness . . I felt her hovering near me . . I thought of the lovely passion we had known together . . I *was* Iistral.

I was not on a stage, but in a room, holding actual and rapt communion with my spirit-bride, Egeria! . .

"Egeria! Egeria!" I sobbed . . and tears streamed down my face.

I was miserable, without her, in the flesh . . though she was there, beside me, in soul!

.   .   .   .

I was aware of the audience again. I was proud and strong in my confidence now. The tittering had stopped. The house was filling with awe. I was pushing something back, back, back—over the footlights. I did not stop pushing till it had reached the topmost galleries. . .

I *had* them. . .

The applause after the first act was wonderful.

"Great! You're great . . you've vindicated my belief in you entirely!" Dineen was shouting, as he clapped me on the back, beside himself.

"Oh, I knew I'd do it! . . I want a drink!"

"Here's some grape juice!" Gertie Black held out a glass to me. . .

"No, I won't drink that stuff," I replied, with all the petulance and ill-humour traditionally allowed a star.

A Sig-Kapp, whom I had got into the play as a supe, slipped me a drink of real booze. . .

.   .   .   .

I had to run to the toilet three times before the second act, I was so nervous and excited.

"For God's sake, keep it up!" urged Dineen.

"For Christ's sake, let me alone, all of you,—I know what I'm doing," this, as the elocution teacher tried to press home some advice. . .

.   .   .   .

During the second act I was as electric as during the first, but now I allowed myself to see over the foot-lights and recognise people I knew. I even overheard one girl say to another, "why, Johnnie Gregory is handsome in that Van Dyke!"

"Yes, he has a fine profile . . he looks quite distinguished."

.   .   .   .

Before the curtain for the third act, Jack Travers worked his way back through the props to my dressing room. . .

"Sh! I've brought a nip of something real for you, Johnnie!"

"Bill already has given me some. It's enough! I don't want any more!—wait till the last act, and then I'll take it!

"I don't want it *now! Do you hear!*" I almost screamed, as he mischievously insisted.

The bell rang for the third curtain. . .

The news had come for Iistral that his rich uncle in America had died and left him a fortune . . now his family would try and have him adjudged insane, in order to lay hands on the wealth for their own uses. . .

That third act went off well. . .

"But you skipped a few lines in that act, Mr. Gregory," warned the directress, concerned.

"Oh, let me alone, will you!" I returned, enjoying the petulance of stardom to the full. . .

"Remember the fight-scene at the finish," she persisted," just *pretend* to strike with the shovel . . you might hurt someone!" anxiously.

"I am going to act the thing realistically, not as a matter of stage-craft."

She tiptoed away. And I had the satisfaction of hearing her instruct the boys who acted as guards, and who were to seize on me— in my moment of physical exasperation——

"Grab him before the cue, just a trifle before it! I think Mr. Gregory is going to forget himself!"

.   .   .   .

I swung the shovel high in the air, making at all my relatives, crying out terms of reproach . . sobbing. . .

In the audience, everybody sat still with wonder.

The actors scattered from my brandished shovel, just as they would have done in real life . . the directress had schooled them to crowd about me so as to mask the action.

But the action needed no masking. It was real.

The two guards were on me,—boys who, in everyday life, were big football men on the freshman team. . .

I fought them, frenzied, back and forth over the stage, smashing down the pasteboard hedge, falling . . getting up again. . .

But, though the scenery went down, the audience did not laugh, but sat spellbound.

I was finally dragged away . . on the way to the asylum, half my costume torn from my body . . and I kept crying aloud . . for mercy . . for deliverance . . after the curtain had long gone down. . .

"Big Bill" Heizer gave me a thump in the ribs.

"For God's sake, Mr. Gregory" (he had called me "Johnnie" always, before) "it's only play-acting . . it's not real . . quit it . . it gets me."

.   .   .   .

The audience went wild with applause. I had won Laurel's complete approbation—for the day, as I had won Mt. Hebron's, that fall Field Day, long before!

.   .   .   .

Travers had slipped me just one shot of whiskey before the last act went on. He had tried to persuade me to drink more. He was in my dressing room. . .

.   .   .   .

I could hardly stand, from the weakness of excitement and exertion.

After the play was over———

"*Now* you can give me the rest of the bottle."

"We'll drink it together . . to your success, Gregory!"

"Yes—you devil!" I replied, fond of him, "you'd have had me reeling drunk, that last act, if I had listened to you."

And I gave him an affectionate clout in the ribs.

.   .   .   .

Again the professors were urging me to become more "regular" and pointing out the great career that awaited me—if I only would work.

There was some subsequent talk of sending the play to Osageville, Topeka, Kansas City. . .

But the faculty opposed it . . it would not be proper to send girls and boys out together, travelling about like a regular theatrical company.

. . . .

As it had been said that I was going to take up the career of animal trainer,—after my going into the cage with the lions—so it was now pronounced, and reported in the papers—Travers saw to that—that I meditated a career as a professional actor. . .

. . . .

Gleeful, and vastly relieved, Professor Dineen slipped me twenty-five dollars out of his own pocket.

Several fraternities showed indications of "rushing" me, after my star performance . . but my associations with the odd characters about town and the wild, ignorant farmers of the lower type that drove in each Saturday from the adjacent country, made them, at first, hesitate . . then utterly drop the idea. . .

. . . .

Broke, I now wrote a long letter to Jarvis Alexander Mackworth.

I boldly complained of my poverty, inasmuch as it deterred me from my work.

"I have now proven my case," I wrote him,—"my poems have appeared in the *Century*, in *Everybody's*, in *Munsey's*. . .

"I have acted, as well, as a professional in a first-rate play, by a great European dramatist . . giving Kansas the distinction of being the first to produce *Iistral* on the American stage. . .

"*Now* I want to finish my four-act play on Judas. To do so I must have enough to eat and a place to sleep, without being made to worry about it, for a year. . .

"Can't you help me to a millionaire?"

Mackworth answered me generously, affectionately.

In two weeks he had procured my millionaire . . Derek, of Chicago, the bathtub magnate . . how much could I get on with?

I wrote that I could do with seven dollars a week. . .

Mackworth replied not to be a fool—that Derek was willing to make it fifteen, for a year's duration. . .

I replied that I could only take enough to fill my simplest wants. . .

Derek jocosely added fifty cents to the sum I asked—"for postage stamps"— . . for one year, week in, week out, without a letter from me except those indicating changes of address, without sending me a word of advice, criticism, or condemnation, no matter what I got into . . Derek sent me that weekly stipend of seven dollars and fifty cents! . . .

    .   .   .   .   .

I settled down to consecutive literary work.

Lyrics I could write under any condition. They came to me so deeply from the subconscious that at times they almost seemed like spirit-control, which, at times, I am sure they had been, till I set the force of my will against them. For I was resolved that what *I* wrote should be an emanation from my own personality, not from dead and gone poets who used me for a medium.

But when it came to long and consecutive effort, the continual petty worry of actual penury sapped my mind so that I lacked the power of application. . .

With Derek's remittances this obstacle was removed. . .

I had soon completed the first act of my apostolic play. . .

And then I plunged into a scrape, together with my fellow members of the press or "Scoop Club," as it was more popularly known, which halted my work mid-way. . .

    .   .   .   .   .   .

Our common adventure derived its inception from a casual remark of Jack Travers', at one of our meetings. . .

Ever since Arthur Brisbane had come to Laurel, Jack had been on his toes. . .

"Brisbane brought me a breath of what it must mean to be a big newspaper man in the world outside," said Travers, as he stretched and yawned, "why don't we," he continued, "*start* something to show 'em we're alive, and not dead like so many of the intellects on the Hill!"

"—s all right to talk about starting something . . that's easy to do. The hell of it is, to stop it, after you've got it started," philosophised "The Colonel" . . .

"Just what is it that you propose starting?" asked practical, pop-eyed Tom Jenkins.

"Oh, anything that will cause excitement!" waved Travers, serenely.

"If you boys really want some excitement . . and want to do some service for the community at the same time,—I've got a scheme to suggest . . something I've been thinking over for a long time," suggested Jerome Miller, president of the club. . .

"Tell us what it is, Jerome!"

"The Bottoms . . you know how rotten it is down there . . nigger whorehouses . . every other house a bootlegger's joint . . blind pigs . . blind tigers, for the students. . .

"We might show up the whole affair. . .

"—how the city administration thrives on the violation of the law from that quarter . . how the present administration depends on crime and the whiskey elements to keep it in power by their vote. . .

"*That* would be starting something!"

"I should say it would!" shouted Jack Travers, ablaze with enthusiasm.

"Then we might extend operations," continued the masterful, incisive Jerome, "and show up how all the drug stores are selling whiskey by the gallon, for 'medicinal' purposes, abusing the privilege of the law."

"But how is all this to be done?"

"Through the *Laurelian?*"

"No . . I have a better plan that that . . we might be able to persuade 'Senator' Blair and old Sickert, joint editors of the *Laurel Globe*, to let the Scoop Club run their paper for a day—just as a college stunt!"

"They'd never stand for it!" I averred, innocently.

"Of course they wouldn't—if we let them in on what we were up to!—for they are staunch supporters of the present administration —but they won't smell a rat till the edition is off the press . . and then it will be too late to stop it!"

"In other words," laughed Travers, blowing a cloud of cigarette smoke from his nose, "they'll think they're turning over their paper, *The Globe*, to a bunch of boys to have some harmless fun . . a few sophomoric jokes on the professors, and so forth. . .

"And they'll wake up, to find we've slipped a real man-size sheet over on them, for the first time in local history!"

"It'll raise hell 's all I've got to say!" sagely commented the prematurely bald "Colonel," his eyes glinting merrily.

"It'll be lots of fun," remarked Travers, characteristically, "and I'm for it, lock, stock, and barrel."

"That's not the reason I'm for it; I'm for it for two reasons," reinforced Jerome Miller magisterially, "first, because it will put the Scoop Club on the map as something more than a mere college boys' organisation; secondly, because it will lead to civic betterment, if only temporary—a shaking up where this old burg needs a shaking up . . right at the court house and in the police station. . .

"But, make no mistake about it,—it's going to kick up a big dust!

"Also, remember, no one is going to stand by us . . even the Civic Betterment League, headed by Professor Langworth—your friend, Johnnie—will be angry with us—say our methods are too sensational.

"And the university authorities will say we shouldn't have done it because it will give the school a black eye . . it will be Ibsen's *Enemy of Society* all over again! . . ."

Immediately some of our more conservative members set themselves against the "clean up" . . but Jack Travers and I delivered eloquent, rousing speeches. And the decision was more for full steam ahead.

.   .   .   .

"Senator" Blair was easily deluded, and persuaded to turn his paper over to us, for one day.

Our strong-featured, energetic president, Jerome Miller, together with the suave, plausible Travers, went to see him, deputation-wise, where he sat, in the Laurel *Globe's* editorial office,—white and unhealthy-looking, a great, fat slug of a man, with the slug's nature, which battens on the corruption of earth.

He liked the idea of the publicity his paper would get through the stunt of the "boys." He did not guess the kind of publicity he would really come into.

During the three weeks that we had before we were to bring out the paper we grew quite proficient in the tawdry life lived in the "Bottoms."

We found out that most of the ramshackle "nigger" dives were owned by a former judge . . from which he derived exorbitant rents.

We located all the places where booze was sold, and ascertained exactly how much whiskey was disposed of in the town's drug stores for "snake bite" and "stomach trouble." We discovered many interesting things—that, for instance, "Old Aunt Jennie," who would allow her patrons any vice, but demurred when they took the name of "De Lawd" in vain—"Old Aunt Jennie" ran a "house" where the wilder and more debauched among the students came (in justice to Laurel University, let me add, very few) girls and boys together,— and stayed for the night—when they were supposed to be on trips to Kansas City. . .

Travers and "The Colonel" and I were half-lit for two weeks. . .

That was the only way to collect the evidence.

I drank but sparingly, as I loafed about the joints and "houses."

Jerome Miller did not drink at all . . and was the spirit and soul of our activities.

.   .   .   .

"Senator" Blair came out with a humorous editorial the night before we were to take the day's charge of his paper.

He headed his editorial "A Youthful Interim . . Youth Must Be Served!"

He was laying down his pen, he wrote, for a week-end holiday . . he had dug a can of bait and would go fishing, turning all the care and trouble of a newspaper over to youth and eagerness . . would forgot all his troubles for a few days. . .

The editorial made us roar with laughter . . Blair didn't know the trouble that was preparing for him.

.   .   .   .

I wrote a poem for the Scoop Club Edition of the Laurel *Globe*. . .

> "The Bottoms now I sing, where whiskey flows
>   And two-cent makes life coleur de rose,
>   Where negro shanties line the sordid way
>   And rounders wake by night who sleep by day—"

.   .   .   .

By noon of the day, hints of what was coming were riding the winds of general report. . .

Carefully we read the proofs.

At last there it was—all the data, statistics, and details of the town's debauchery and corruption . . damning, in cold type, the administration, and the aquiescent powers in the university.

We ourselves had not as yet begun to perceive what it would lead to—a state-wide scandal that would echo in the Chicago, San Francisco and New York newspapers, and result in severe criticism of the university faculty for remaining blind to such a condition of affairs . . and how there would be interrogations in the Kansas Legislature and a complete shake-up of the political power in Laurel.

. . . .

News of the forthcoming exposé spread mysteriously in "The Bottoms" before the paper was off the press. To avoid the coming storm, already negro malefactors and white, were "streaming" as Travers phrased it, "in dark clouds" out of town, for brief sojourns, beyond reach of the compelling subpoena, in Kansas City, Missouri.

By five o'clock the edition, an extra large one, had been almost exhausted, and people were lining up at the newspaper office, paying five cents a copy. . .

"Senator" Blair rushed back, having heard of what he called our "treachery" and abuse of his confidence, over telephone. . .

He looked sick and worried, as if he had run in all the way from the little lake, five miles from town, where he had gone for his week-end of idyllic, peaceful fishing. . .

"You've ruined me, you boys have!" he almost sobbed, collapsing fatly in his chair, then he flamed, "by God, I'll have you each investigated personally and clapped in jail," . . which threat, however, he did not even try to carry through. . .

Instead, his paper, and the other two town papers, tried to turn off the affair as a mere college joke, played on a whole community. . .

But we had expected just such action—rather the executive genius of Jerome had expected it—for which reason we had confronted the readers of the *Globe* with damning facts and statistics, carefully gathered, which presented an insurmountable barrier to evasion.

And as we also had expected, the Civic Betterment League was also dead against us. . .

"Why," cried Langworth to me, "why didn't you bring all the evidence to us, and let *us* proceed calmly and soberly with the case?"

"Professor Langworth, you are a friend of mine, and a very good

one—but you know very well that the conditions exposed you people
knew of all along . . and for years you have dallied along without
acting on it."

"We were biding the proper time!"

"The reason you never started something was your fear of in-
volving the university in the publicity that was sure to follow! . . "

Langworth was a good man, but he knew I had him. He hemmed
and hawed, then covered his retreat in half-hearted anger at me. . .

"You know well enough, Johnnie Gregory, that all you boys did
it for was to 'pull a stunt'—indulge in a little youthful horse-
play."

"Granted—but we have effected results!"

.   .   .   .

"What results? merely a lot of trouble for everybody!"

"The Civic Betterment League now has a chance afforded it to
make good . . we've provided you with the indisputable data, the
evidence . . it's up to you, now, to go ahead."

"So God help me, Johnnie, sometimes you make me wish I had
never sponsored you here."

.   .   .   .   .   .

The editor of the *Globe* made a right-about-face-repudiating us.

Jack Travers, in the style of his beloved Brisbane, put an editorial in the school paper, the *Laurelian,* addressed to Blair, beginning, "Get back into the collar of your masters, you contemptible
cur."

.   .   .   .

The usual thing took place. Most of the worst criminals were
mysteriously given ample time to make their get-away . . probably
aided in it. The humorous side of the resulting investigation and
trials of various minor malefactors were played up almost exclusively.

Little by little the town dropped back to its outward observance
of not seeing in its civic life what it did not care to see, and which
no one could radically remedy till human nature is itself different.

.   .   .   .   .   .

The school year was drawing to a close, my last year at Laurel.

Professor Black, of the English department, had assured me that,
if I would tone down a bit, I could easily win a scholarship in his
department, and, later, an assistant professorship.

But I preferred my rambling, haphazard course of life, which was less comfortable, but better for the freedom of mind and spirit that poets must preserve. . .

　　　·　　　　·　　　　·　　　　·　　　　·　　　　·　　　　·

Dr. Hammond, when I had given him that luncheon on the borrowed money, had taken me aside and informed me that one of the professors—an influential man on the Hill (beyond that, he refused to identify him further) had advised him, Hammond, not to accept the luncheon in his honour. . .

"We don't approve generally of Gregory, on the Hill, you know. . . "

And Hammond had, he told me, replied——

"I'm sorry, but Mr. Gregory is my friend, and Dr. Ward, our literary editor, looks on him as a distinguished contributor to the *Independent*, and a young writer of great and growing promise" . . so the luncheon was given . . I wonder if the protesting professor was one of those invited, and if so, if he attended? . .

I saw clearly that I could never fit into the formal, academic life of the college—where professors were ashamed to be seen carrying packages and bags home from the stores, but must have them delivered . . for fear of losing their social status!

　　　·　　　　·　　　　·　　　　·　　　　·　　　　·　　　　·

There was a park on the outskirts of town where I loved to lōaf, when the weather was sunny,—a place where the blue jays fought with the squirrels and the leaves flickered in the sun . . sometimes I lay on the grass, reading . . sometimes I lounged on a bench . . I read my Greek and Latin poets there . . and my English and German poets . . and, when hungry, I sauntered home to my bread and cheese, or, now that I was in receipt of Derek's weekly stipend, to a frugal meal at some lunch counter. I dearly liked rib-ends of beef. . .

One day, when I was in my park, lying on my belly, reading Josephus, I was aware of the deputy sheriff, Small, whom I knew, standing over me. . .

"Oh, it's *you*, Gregory!"

"Yes, what's the matter, Deputy Small? what do you want?"

"People who drove in from the country complained about your lying here."

"Complained about my lying here? what the hell! . . look'e here,

Jim Small, there's no ordinance to prevent me from lying on the grass."

"Well, Johnnie, you either got to git up and sit, proper, on a bench, or I'll have to pull you in, much as I dislike to do it."

"Jim, you just 'pull' ahead, if you think you're lucky . . it'll be a fine thing for me . . I'll sue the city for false arrest."

Deputy Small was puzzled. He pushed his hat back and scratched his head. . .

"Jim, who put you up to this?"

"The people what saw you lying here, as they drove in, stopped off at the office of the *Globe* . . it was 'Senator' Blair telephoned the courthouse——"

"Blair, eh? . . trying to get even for what we boys did with his dirty paper . . he knows I like to lie out here and read my books of poetry!"

I was thoroughly aroused. I jumped to my feet.

"Jim, do me a favour, and arrest me . . and I'll sue you, the city of Laurel, and 'Senator' Blair . . all three of you!"

"—guess I won't do it . . but *do* sit on the bench . . I ask it as a personal favour, Johnnie."

"As a personal favour, Jim, till you are out of sight. Then I'll go back to the grass."

That night Blair, cocksure, had the story of my arrest in the paper. But, as it happened, he was too previous. . .

Jerome Miller and Jack Travers joined me in going to the office of the *Globe*, the next morning. . .

After we had finished telling him what we thought of him, the "Senator" begged my pardon profusely, and the next day a retraction was printed. . .

.   .   .   .

And now school was over at Laurel.

And I determined to bum my way to New York, and, from there, ship on a cattleboat to Europe. Where I would finish writing my play, *Judas*.

Farewell to Laurel!——

I went up to the athletic field and ran my last two miles on its track, at top speed, as good-bye to its cinders forever!

I walked, with a guilty feeling of too much sentimentality, back into the "stack" at the university library. I took down book after book of the great English poets, and pressed my cheek to them in long farewell .. first glancing cautiously around, to be sure that no one was near to observe my actions. . .

I did not say good-bye to Langworth or my other professor friends, as they had already left for their summer vacations.

· · · · · · ·

I sat in Joe Deacon's room, talking, that last night of my sojourn in Laurel. . .

"Good old Joe" we called him, because he was possessed of all the old-fashioned virtues, and unassumingly lived up to them. He was a fellow member of the Scoop Club, an associate teacher in the School of Journalism, and taught during the summer session. . .

Long, long Joe and I talked .. of everything young idealists discuss or dream of. We ended with a discussion of the sex question. I reiterated what he already had heard me say, that I had had so far no sex experience. He confessed that he, also, had had none .. maintained that a decent man should wait, if he expected a woman to come pure to him. . .

I spoke ardently in favour of free love.

He assented that, theoretically, it was the thing .. but there were a multitude of practical difficulties that made for favour of the convention of marriage. . .

"No, if a convention is wrong, it is the duty of everyone who knows the right in his heart, to help smash that convention. . . "

"You just wait," I boasted imaginatively, "and I'll show you!" "Maybe, Joe," I concluded, for I knew what I said would tease him, "maybe, when I reach the East, I shall break loose." Then I added —and to this day I cannot imagine what put it into my head to say it—what fantastic curl of thought, unless perhaps a premonition of what was soon to come to pass——

"Penton Baxter has invited me to pay him a visit at Eden, a Single Tax Colony just outside of Philadelphia, before I go on to Europe via cattleboat .. maybe I'll take him up, go down there, and run away with his wife .. she's a mighty pretty woman, Joe!"

Joe was scandalised at my remark—the effect I had wished for.

· · · · · · ·

But after the uproar broke, Joe stoutly maintained that our

elopement had all been a frame-up, alleging his conversation with me as proof .. as who would have not?

. . . .

Reduced again to my barest equipment, and having left as my forwarding address the office of the *National Magazine*, in New York, I hopped a freight shortly after dawn. It was a fast, through freight. Because of lack of practice I boarded it clumsily, and almost went to my death under its grinding, roaring wheels, there in the Laurel freight-yards. I sat, trembling with the shock to my nerves, on the bumpers.

I hopped off at Argentine, just outside of Kansas City.

I found a camp of tramps and joined with them. We drank coffee together. . .

But, somehow, the scales had fallen from my eyes. My old idealisation of the life of the tramp, somehow or other, was entirely gone—an idealisation that had, anyhow, been mainly literary, induced by the writings of Jack London, Josiah Flynt and Maxim Gorky.

Now, as I listened to their filthy talk .. their continual " 'Jesus-Christ'-ing" over everything they said, I grew sick of them. I got up and walked away stiffly—never again to be a tramp.

The reporter of the *Star*, who covered the stockyards, took me to a little sturdy cattle merchant, who agreed to ship me to New York, in care of five carloads of calves .. for a fee of ten dollars. I persuaded him that I would mail him that ten on arrival at my point of destination .. I have never done so .. when I had it, I needed it more for myself .. and, anyhow, I earned that ten.

. . . .

My duties with the calves were not many .. merely to walk along the sides of the five cars in my keeping, and see that the calves kept on their legs and did not sprawl over each other .. sometimes one of them would get crushed against the side of the car, and his leg would protrude through the slats. And I would push his leg back, to keep it from being broken .. I made my rounds every time the freight came to a halt.

There were other cars, filled with steers, sheep, and pigs.

Each kind of animal behaved according to its nature, during the trip. The steers soon accepted their cramped, moving life rather stolidly. The calves acted as if dumbfounded, in stupefied, wide-

eyed innocence .. the sheep huddled as sheep dō .. but the big fat
porkers were the most intelligent .. like intelligent cowards that
fully know their fate, they piled in heaping, screaming, frenzied
masses .. in scrambling heaps in the centre of their cars .. suffocating, stinking, struggling closer and closer together and leaving
great, bare areas unoccupied on either end. . .

"A pig has no sense in a car .. or anywhere."

"Seems to me they have .. they act as if they know what they're
in for, at the other end of the line."

"By golly, that's true! I never thought of it that way before!"
So conversed the head brakeman and I.

My calves soon grew to know me. They bleated, in a friendly manner, as I walked by, overseeing them, when the freight stopped.

.   .   .   .

We had bumped along as far as Buffalo. There the stock were
driven down an incline into yards fenced in with white-washed
boards, for their second rest, required by law,—before launching on
the last leg of their journey down the middle of New York State,
and along the Hudson .. consigned to Stern and Company of New
York. . .

Some of them were to be butchered there and afford apartment-
dwellers lamb stew, tenderloins, and pork chops .. others to be driven
aboard cattleboats, for Europe. . .

.   .   .   .

At Buffalo I was ripe for a change. Also I wished to pick up
threads of former experiences and acquaintanceships .. to have a
good gossip about the Eos Art Community .. I called up Laston
Meunier who had been at Eos and whom I had first met there .. who
loved bohemian ways, and welcomed wandering artistic and literary
folk at his home in Buffalo.

"Where are you now?" Laston asked, over the phone.

"I'm calling you from the stockyards," and I told him what I
was doing. . .

"Come on up to my house, and forget your five carloads of
calves .. they can weather through the last jump, to New York,
alone .. what does it matter? .. they're going to be butchered in a
few days."

Looking about this way and that, to make sure I was unseen, I took my grip in my hand, hopped aboard a street car outside the stockyards, and abandoned my calves to their destiny.

Meunier welcomed me. He invited me to stay at his house for several weeks. His pretty, young wife, smiling whimsically, showed me to a room she had already set in dainty order for me.

.   .   .   .

Meunier had gone to his office. . .

Nichi Swartzman, the tall Japanese genius, showed up, and Bella Meunier, Nichi, and I ate breakfast together.

Swartzman was, and is, a magnificent talker . . a torch of inspiration burned brightly in his brain, with continual conversational fire.

But he must have his drink. Several of them. Which Laston's wife poured for him abundantly.

After breakfast I sprawled on the floor . . I always sprawl on floors instead of sitting in chairs. . .

Swartzman and Bella Meunier and I talked and talked and talked . . of Poe . . of Baudelaire, of Balzac. . .

Then Nichi launched forth on a long disquisition on Japanese and Chinese art, and Mrs. Meunier and I gladly remained silent during the whole morning, enchanted by the vistas of beauty which Swartzman's words opened for us.

"Why," I thought, "must such a man lack audiences? If civilisation were in its right mind, he would hold a chair in some great university, and lecture daily to hundreds . . this man is *alive*. His fire wakes kindred fire . . why must we leave the business of teaching to the corpse-minded, the dead-hearted? like so many of our professors and teachers!"

I found out afterward that Nichi Swartzman was utterly irresponsible as he was brilliant.

.   .   .   .

Laston Meunier dug up poor old Fritz Von Hammer, the former Eos pianist—whose breath was still as fetid as ever . . who still insisted on seizing you by the coat lapel and talking right into your nose—dug him up from the moving picture house, where he played.

Von Hammer wept over the piano, as he found himself free again to play as he wished. . .

The party was in my honour. There were present about a dozen guests, picked from Buffalo's bohemia. They sat about on the floor on cushions.

Swartzman recited Poe's Black Cat, with gestures and facial con-
tortions that were terrifying. His huge, yellow, angular Japanese
face grimacing near the ceiling .. he was six foot six, if anything. . .

His recitation was done so well that, when he had finished, we sat,
for a moment, in frightened silence, like children. Then we stormed
him with applause.

"Now play the Danse Macabre," cried Nichi, to Von Hammer. . .

"I can't do it without a violin accompaniment."

"Try it for me . . and I shall dance the Dance of Death for
you."

Von Hammer said he would do his best . . after much persuasion
and a few more drinks. . .

And Nichi Swartzman danced. . .

We saw, though we did not know it, the origin of modern futurist
dancing there. Nichi danced with his street clothes on . . wearing
his hat, in ghoulish rakishness, tipped down over his eyes . . inter-
wreathing his cane with his long, skeletal, twisting legs and arms . .
his eyes gleaming cat-like through merest slits. . .

At three o'clock in the morning we were all drunk. Before we
parted we joined in singing shakily but enthusiastically *Down in
Bohemia Land.*

●   ●   ●   ●   ●   ●   ●

Meunier, fulfilling his promise to me, paid my fare to New York.
I soon walked into the office of the *National Magazine.*

Clara Martin was there, and Allsworth Lephil, the managing
editor, and his assistant Galusha Siddon.

As I sat in the office, they gave me a sort of impromptu reception.

Ray Sanford strolled in, as fresh-complexioned as an Englishman.
He was, they said, preparing a series of articles on the negro problem. And I met a little, bustling, sharp-eyed man, with much of the
feminine about him,—his face lifted as if on an intuitive intellectual
scent. . . Carruthers Heflin . . he wore a close-cropped salt-and-
pepper beard, like a stage-doctor. He was busy with a series of
articles to be entitled, *Babylons of To-day* . . exposing the corruption of our modern American cities.

I spoke to them of my projected trip to Europe.

"I think you're foolish to run off to Europe just at this time in
your life. Now is the time you should establish yourself here. Be-

sides, Jarvis Mackworth has written us that you're writing a book while Derek, the Chicago millionaire, stakes you."

"Yes, that's true. But couldn't I write it in Europe as well as here?"

"You'd find too many distractions."

"Where would you go first?" asked Clara Martin.

"Paris!"

"That would be absolutely fatal for a young man of your disposition. You need to sit quiet and write for a few years .. you've been over the map too much already."

"Baxter has just been in here .. he's writing us a sensational novel exposing society. He spoke to me about you," Lephil remarked,—"said he wished we'd put a tag on you and ship you down to his Eden colony."

There was a pause. Miss Martin thoughtfully tapped her forehead with a pencil.

"I don't think it would be good for Johnnie to go down to Eden and put up with Penton," she interjected, "they're too much alike."

"Ally Merton is in New York," Galusha Siddon informed me. He's working on the *Express*. He wants you to run down and see him."

.   .   .   .

Merton had come to New York the year before, to work on the *Express*. Mackworth had gotten him the job. Ally was as meticulously dressed as ever. His eyes swept me from head to foot, with an instinctive glance of appraisal, as he shook hands.

"Come on up on the roof. The paper wants a photo of you .. to go with a story I'm writing about you."

.   .   .   .   .   .

I rather resented all my friends' way of talking to me, as if I were a child to be discussed, ordered about, and disposed of. But I humoured them by playing up to their patronising spirit .. even playing horse with them continually on the sly, and having lots of fun that they didn't suspect.

.   .   .   .   .   .

The next morning I was in the office of the *Independent*, visiting with the literary editor, good old Dr. William Hayes Ward. He was a man of eighty years .. a scholar in English and the Greek and Latin classics. ..

Once, when on a vacation he had written me that, as pastime, he had read the whole of the *Iliad* and *Odyssey* over again. In the Greek, of course.

His abused eyes floated uneasily behind a double pair of lenses . . a dissenting minister . . of the old school . . he seemed to me far more youthful, more invigorating, than any of my other more youthful friends in the literary and magazine world.

We talked and talked of poetry. He brought down a huge treatise on English versification, translated from some German scholar's life-research—to prove a point . . he discussed what Sidney Lanier—whom he had known—might have done with metrics, had he only lived longer. . .

And "no . . no . . take my advice," he said, "don't go down to Eden." There was something so vaguely deprecatory in his voice that it brought from me the question—"why not? isn't Penton Baxter all right?"

"Oh, yes," in the same deprecatory tone,—"he's all right enough, alone—but, together, you'd be like two balloons without ballast. He might get you, or you might get him, into some sort of mess."

"Why Dr. Ward, what do you mean?"

"Penton is always protesting about something or other,—always starting fantastic schemes. . he's just finished with his Parnassus Palace experiment, which brought him a lot of newspaper notoriety . . which is to me distasteful, extremely distasteful . . yet Baxter," he added hastily, "is a real force . . he can think of more original projects in a given space of time than anyone else I know."

"I look on him as a great and wonderful man!"

"Mark my word, Mr. Gregory, you'll find yourself in some sort of mix-up if you go down to Eden to live with him. You're both too mad and inflammable to be in the same neighbourhood."

Using all his powers of persuasion, Dr. William Hayes Ward tried to explain to me how I owed it both to Mr. Derek and Mr. Mackworth to finish my play.

"Have you no place else to go to, beside Eden?"

"I could run out to Perfection City—and camp out there."

"Now that's a good idea . . why not try that?"

.   .   .   .

"Johnnie. had your lunch yet?" it was Dr. Percival Hammond,

the managing editor, who was asking, leaning out from his cubby-hole where he sat before his desk.

"No, sir!"

"Come and share mine!"

I said good-bye to Dr. Ward and walked down the corridor to where Hammond sat. He looked more the fashionable club man than ever, though he did have a slight sprinkling of dandruff on his coat collar. I was quick to notice this, as I had been quick to notice Miss Martin's few, close-scizzored hairs on her fine, thinking face.

Lunch!

But I was not to be-taken out to a meal in a restaurant, as anyone might expect, but Hammond sat me down on a chair by his side, and he handed me a glass of buttermilk and a few compressed oatmeal cakes.

.   .   .   .

I had stayed over night at the Phi-Mu House, at Columbia, with Ally. I had stayed up nearly all night, rather, arguing, in behalf of extreme socialism, with the boys .. till people, hearing our voices through the open windows, had actually gathered in the street without.

"You're utterly mad, but we like you!" said one of the boys.

In the morning, before I clutched my suitcase in my hand and started for Perfection City, Ally showed me something that had come in the morning mail, which startled me. It was a clipping from the Laurel *Globe* — a vilely slanderous article, headed, "Good Riddance." ..

And first it lied that I had run away from my "confederates" of the Scoop Club, leaving them to bear the onus of the investigation of the town's morals .. which was, of course, not true .. I had made a special point of going to the sheriff and asking him if I would be needed. If so, I would defer my trip East. And he had replied that it would be all right for me to go. . .

But the second count—the personal part of the story, was more atrocious .. it intimated that I had, during my sojourn at Laurel, been an undesirable that would have made Villon pale with envy .. an habitué of the Bottoms .. that I had been sleeping with negro women and rolling about with their men, drunk.

I was so furious at this that I dropped my suitcase, clenched my hands, and swore that I was straightway going to freight it back and knock all his teeth down "Senator's" Blair's throat . . the dirty sycophant! The lousy bootlicker! the nasty, putty-bodied slug!

.   .   .   .   .   .

Once more Baxter wrote me, urging me to come to Eden. He told me his wife would welcome me . . and jested clumsily that his secretary would be just the girl to marry me and take care of me. . .

Jested? I did not know the man yet . . he meant it.

.   .   .   .   .   .

Though I was possessed of a curious premonitory warning that I must not accept his invitation and was, besides, settled in a hut by the lake shore, yet I was tempted to go to Eden. . .

For one thing, Perfection City was no longer the place of ideals it had been . . it was now a locality where the poorer bourgeoisie sent their wives and children, for an inexpensive summer outing. . .

Wavering this way and that, I sent a telegram which clinched the matter.

"Will leave for Eden to-morrow morning. John Gregory."

.   .   .   .   .   .

Not far from the little suburban station to which I had changed, lay the Single Tax Colony of Eden. When I dropped off the train and found no one to greet me, I was slightly piqued. Of a labourer in a nearby field I inquired the way to Eden. He straightened his back, paused in his work.

He gave me the direction— "and there by the roadside you'll find a sort of wooden archway with a sign over it . . you step in and follow the path, and that will take you right into the centre of the community. But what do want to go to Eden for? they're all a bunch of nuts there!"

"Maybe I might be a nut, too!"

The old man laughed.

"Well, good-bye and good luck, sonny."

Soon I reached the gateway, trailing my heavy suitcase . . heavy mostly with manuscripts. . .

A woodland path led me into what seemed, and was, a veritable forest; boughs interlaced above, with glimpses of blue sky between. In interspaces of trees wild flowers grew. Luxuriant summer was abroad.

I stepped out of the forest straightway into the community. It was in a beautiful open space like a natural meadow.

There stood the houses of the colonists—Single Taxers, Anar-chists, Socialists, Communists,—folk of every shade of radical opinion .. who here strove to escape the galling mockeries of civilisa-tion and win back again to pastoral simplicity.

It was a community such as William Morris or some Guild Social-ist of a medieval turn of mind might have conceived. It was the Dream of John Ball visualised.

> "When Adam dolve and Eve span
> Who was then the gentleman?"

Toy houses picturesquely set under trees that fringed the Com-mon .. houses with different, quaint colours .. the "green" in the centre carefully cropped as if nibbled by sheep .. well-kept paths of parti-coloured stone, as if each pebble had been placed there by hand. . .

Everything here was born obviously of the Arts and Crafts move-ment, a movement which seeks to teach that each shall make and build for himself .. if clumsily, yet uniquely .. the product to be something at least individual and warm from the maker's personality.

I thought of Jusserand's *English Wayfaring Life in the Middle Ages*. If the Canterbury Pilgrims, led by jolly Harry Bailey, their host, had burst out from the woods, on horseback, singing and jesting, I should not have considered their appearance an anachronism. . .

A tousle-headed girl-child in rompers which she was too big for, pointed me Baxter's house, the largest in the community.

There seemed to be no one home when I dropped my suitcase on the front porch. . .

I knocked vigorously. No one came. I waited a long while.

"A hell of a way to welcome me!" I meditated, my egotism hurt. Again I knocked.

"Come in! do come in!" a gentle voice bade—it was Mrs. Baxter's.

I pushed the door open and stepped in. I set down my heavy suitcase with a thump, on the bare, hardwood floor of the large room in which I found myself—a room sparsely furnished, its walls lined with books. It had one large window, under and along which was built in, a long, wide shelf made into a sort of divan, promiscuous with cushions.

Propped up with a disordered heap of these cushions sat Mrs. Hildreth Baxter, in blouse and bloomers; she was reading.

"Why, Johnnie Gregory!" she cried, swinging her graceful, slim legs down, and rising, coming toward me, extending her hand in greeting. . .

"Why, Johnnie Gregory—YOU here!"

"Yes, didn't you!——"

"I *knew* I was right . . Penton maintained it was to-morrow you were due—Darrie sided with him—Darrie is a friend of mine who is visiting us, from Virginia—but Ruth, Mubby's secretary," she finished, relapsing into her intimate petting name for her husband, (Mubby is short for "My hubby")— "Ruth sided with me, though we had quite an argument about it."

"And you and Ruth were right!"

"Yes, I was right," she assented, leaving "Ruth" out, with naïve egoism.

"Sit down in the morris chair . . you look dusty and heated . . I'll entertain you . . I'm all alone . . Penton is dictating an article to Ruth. Darrie's washing her hair. I'm the only member of the Leisure Class. I'm lazing here, reading Gorky's latest novel."

What an engaging, pretty, naïve, little woman this was! I commented inwardly. A sweet aroma of feminine health breathed from her body, bosom, hair—a tumbly black mass—as perfume breathes from a wild flower.

Strangely enough, I felt calm and happy in her presence; at home, as I had never been with any woman or girl before.

Up to this moment, when alone with a woman, timidity had touched me to ice, while inwardly I had trembled with suppressed passion and fright.

Set in the midst of a group of women, I shone. As at the university, when I used to visit whole sorority chapters at once, and, with from five to ten girls seated about me in the parlour, talk brilliantly and easily and poetically with all of them. Left alone with any *one*, my mouth dried like sand, my tongue clove to my palate, I shook all over as with a palsy.

With Hildreth Baxter I was straightway, marvellously, at my ease. We talked of Keats—she seemed to know all of his verse by heart. . .

Shelley—she quoted his less-known fragments. . .

"O World! O Life! O Time!—"

"O world! O life! O time!
   On whose last steps I climb,
      Trembling at that where I had stood before;
   When will return the glory of your prime?
      No more—Oh, never more!

"Out of the day and night
   A joy has taken flight;
      Fresh spring, and summer, and the winter hoar,
   Move my faint heart with grief, but with delight
      No more—Oh, never more!"

"Surely that does not express your feelings—and you still a young and beautiful woman?"

"No, but I am profoundly moved by the sad beauty of it; and by the fact that perhaps Poe got his refrain of 'nevermore' for his *Raven* as a reminiscence from it."

She laughed engagingly with feminine inconsequence and stooped down to recover a slight, silver bracelet that had slipped off over one of her small hands. I caught a brief glimpse of the white division of her breasts as she stooped over. The vision stabbed my heart with keen enjoyment that pained. . .

Already we were caught up in a current of mysterious fellow-feeling that was soon to bear us onward to the full ocean of frank love and passion. Though at this time neither she nor I perceived it.

.   .   .   .

Penton came in . . the little, handsome, red-faced man, with his Napoleonic head too large for his small, stocky body . . his large, luminous eyes like those of the Italian fisher boy in the painting . . his mouth a little too large . . his chin a trifle too heavy-jowled. His hands were feminine . . but his feet were encased in heavy shoes that made them seem the feet of a six-foot day labourer. . .

Ruth, his secretary, coming close behind him,—was tall, not ungraceful in an easy, almost mannish way . . slab-figured . . built more like a boy than a young woman dangerously near the old maid. She too wore bloomers. Her face was tanned. It was too broad and placid for either prettiness or beauty, but a mischievous tilt to the nōse and large calm hazel eyes kept her this side of mere plainness. . .

Penton glanced from me to his wife, from his wife to me, in one look of instinctive inquiry, before he addressed me. . .

"Well, Johnnie, here you are . . East at last . . and about to become a real literary man."

"He's been here a full hour . . we didn't want to interrupt you—" his wife explained.

"Your work is too important for the world"—I began sincerely and reverently.

Baxter beamed. His being expanded under my worship.

He caught both my hands, friendlily, in his.

"Welcome to Eden," then, introducing, "this is my secretary, Miss Ruth Hazlitt; she's been quite keen to meet you . . we've talked of you a lot . . she knows your poetry and thinks you're a genius, and will some day be recognised as a great poet."

Ruth Hazlitt nodded, shy, took my hand in introduction.

"Darrie, oh, Dar-*rie!*" called Baxter . . "a Southern society girl, but a mighty good radical already," he explained to me, *sotto voce,* as we heard sounds of her approach.

Mary Darfield Malcolm came in, in a flimsy dressing gown of yellow, with blue ribbons in it, her hair wet and still done up in a towel. Superbly she trusted to her big eyes of limpid brown, and to the marble-like pallour of her complexion, the twin laughing dimples in her cheeks . . she added her welcome to the others . . easily, with a Southern way of speech that caught each recalcitrant word by the tail and caressed its back as it came out. . .

  . . . .

That afternoon, at Baxter's suggestion, he and I launched forth on a walk together. . .

"There is some beautiful country for walking about here."

  . . . .

"Darrie, will you and Ruth have the veal steak cooked by six o'clock?"

I noticed that he did not include his wife. Also, I looked at him in amazement . . a look the significance of which he instantly caught. . . Steak? Meat?

"I've done a lot of experimenting in dietetics," he explained, "and I have finally been brought to face the fact, after years of vegetarianism, that there's nothing like a good steak for a brain-worker. It's easily digested and affords ready nourishment . . vegetables, yes . . but it takes up so much vital energy to digest them . . the meat-eating races are the dominant races of the world . . but," he flashed quickly, "I always try to be logical and consistent. If I eat meat, I must be willing to kill the animal I eat. I must not stand off in dainty horror over the butcher's trade, while I live by it."

"Surely you don't mean that you do your own butchering?"

"No . . not that . . but I've proven to myself that I can kill . . we had a dog, a mongrel, that attached itself to us . . tore up everything in my study . . tore the sheets and pillow slips on the beds . . I took it out into the woods," he ended gravely, "and killed . . shot it . . of course I had to summon up all my resolution . . but I did it."

While admitting the almost childlike exactness of my friend's logic, I could not help smiling to myself at his grotesque sincerity. . .

We walked far . . through green fields . . over flashing brooks . . through lovely woodland vistas . . we paused on the top of a hill, with vistas all about us . . just as we had done on Azure Mound in Kansas. . .

"I asked you to take this walk with me in order to tell you something. . . Johnnie, you're my friend, and that is why I don't want you to stay at my house with us. I want you to put up at the Community Inn, at my expense . . eat your meals with us, of course."

I was surprised. He did not want me in the house *because I was his friend!* . . in silence I waited his further explanation. . .

"Yes," he continued, "I want to spare you trouble . . Hildreth and I, you see," he proceeded with painful frankness, "are quite near the breaking point . . I don't think we'll be together very many months longer . . and . . and . . I don't want you to become involved . . for I'm simply desperate."

"But, Penton, how could I become involved?"

"Johnnie, you don't know women, or you wouldn't ask . . especially women of my wife's type . . hysterical, parasitic, passionate, desperate. . . I tell you what, you stay at the inn!"

A pause;—I was startled by what he said next:

"Besides, it's time you had a mate, a real mate . . and I," he proceeded with incredible gravity, "I have been urging Ruth, my secretary, to take you .. you and she would be quite happy together .. she can support herself, for instance .. that would place no economic burden on you."

"Really, Penton!" I demurred.

I was learning how utterly bookish, how sheerly a literary man Penton Baxter was .. and how absurd, at the same time. How life never drew near him, how he ever saw it through the film of his latest theory, and tried to order his own, as well as everybody else's life, to jibe with it. . .

.   .   .   .

"Penton, it is a matter of indifference to me where I put up. It was you who invited me to come to Eden .. but I won't mind staying at Community Inn, as I can only be with you for a couple of weeks, anyhow .. I'm due to take a cattleboat for Paris, for Europe, as soon as I have *Judas* finished."

.   .   .   .

Supper .. veal steaks served on a plain board table outside the big house, under a tree. We waited on ourselves. We discussed Strindberg, his novels and plays .. his curious researches in science .. Nietzsche. . .

Afterward, having eaten off wooden plates, we flung the plates in the fireplace, burning them .. Ruth washed the knives, forks, spoons. . .

"It's such a saving of effort to use wooden plates and paper napkins .. so much less mere household drudgery .. so much more time for living saved."

I had taken my suitcase and was about to repair to the much-discussed inn. But Penton asked me to wait, while he had a conference with the three women of the household.

Soon he came out, smiling placidly and blandly.

"Johnnie, I'm sorry about this afternoon .. I've been rather hasty, rather inhospitable .. you are not to go to the inn, but stay with us. The girls have persuaded me .. the tent, down beside the little house, is yours all summer, if you like."

.   .   .   .

I found the tent in a clump of trees .. it had a hard board floor, a wash-stand, table, chair, and cot.

Along with the rest of the household, I retired early .. but not to sleep.

I lit my big kerosene lamp and sat propped up with the pillows, reading, till late, the poetry of Norah May French, the beautiful, red-headed girl who had, like myself, also lived in Eos, where Roderick Spalton's Artworks were. . .

She had been, Penton informed me, when he handed me her book, one of the famous Bohemians of the San Francisco and Carmel art and literary crowd. . .

After a brief career of adventurous poverty, she had committed suicide over a love affair.

Her poetry was full of beauty and spontaneity . . a grey mist dancing full of rainbows, like those you see at the foot of Niagara. . .

I must have read myself to sleep, for the lamp was still lit when I woke up early with the dawn . . it was the singing of the birds that woke me on my second day at Eden. . .

Working on farms, in factories, on ships at sea, being up at all hours to catch freights out of town had instilled in me the habit of early rising; I would have risen at dawn anyhow without the birds to wake me.

Turning over for my pencil, which I ever keep, together with a writing pad, at my bedside, to catch the fleeting poetic inspiration, I indited a sonnet to Baxter (all copies of which I have unfortunately lost or I would give it here) in which I sang his praises as a great man of the same rank as Rousseau and Shelley.

In spite of the fact that I was fully aware of all his absurdities and peccadilloes, the true greatness of the man remained, and still remains, undimmed in my mind.

. . . .

High day. I walked along the path, past the little house where Baxter sequestered himself when he wished to be alone to think or write; it was close to my tent, around a corner of trees. I tiptoed religiously by it, went on up to the big house where the three women slept, as if drawn to their abode by a sort of heliotropism.

The whole house stood in quiet, the embodiment of slumber.

. . . .

A lank, flat-chested woman came up the path from the opposite direction . . dressed drab in one long, undistinguished gown like a Hicksite or Quaker, without the hood . . her head was bare . . her fine, brown hair plaited flat.

"Good morning!"

"Good morning," she replied, a query in her voice.

"I am John Gregory, the poet," I explained; "I arrived yesterday on a visit to the Baxters."

She said she had heard of me . . she opened the door and went into the house. I followed.

She was the wife of Anarchist Jones, of whom I had already heard the household speak—as a difficult, recalcitrant member of the colony.

The Joneses were very poor. They had two children and lived in a mere shack on the outskirts of the community. Jones was a shoemaker. His wife came twice a week to clean up and set things to rights in the Baxter menage—his two houses. I took care of the tent myself, while I was there. . .

By this time Darrie, Ruth, and Mrs. Baxter were up. I sat in the library, in the morris chair, deeply immersed in the life of Nietzsche, by his sister. Nevertheless I was not so preoccupied as not to catch fugitive glimpses of kimonos disappearing around door-corners . . women at their mysterious morning ritual of preparing themselves against the day.

Comfortable of mind, at ease in heart and body, I sat there, dangling one leg over the arm of the chair. I was much at home in the midst of this easy, disjointed family group.

.   .   .   .   .   .

We were, the four of us—Darrie, Hildreth, Ruth, and I—seated together at our outdoor table, scooping out soft-boiled eggs.

Hildreth Baxter had boiled my two eggs medium for me . . to the humorous, affected consternation of Darrie and Ruth, which they, of course, deliberately made visible to me, with the implication—

"You'd best look out, when Penton's lazy little wife waits on you . . she is the one who generally demands to be waited on, and if——"

.   .   .   .   .   .

And now, for the moment, all of us were combined against the master of the house . . furtively and jocularly combined, like naughty children. . .

Hildreth smuggled forth her coffee percolator, which she kept hidden from her husband's search . . and we soon, by the aid of an alcohol stove, had a cup of fragrant coffee a-piece . . which Darrie made. . .

"Penton swears coffee is worse than whiskey, the rankest of poisons. We have to hide the percolator from him."

"He lies a-bed late, when he wakes. He lies there thinking out what he will later on dictate to Ruth . . we can finish before——"

But just then Penton himself came hurrying up the path from the little cottage.

When he saw what we were doing he gave us such a look of solemn disgust that we nearly smothered with laughter, which we tried to suppress.

"When you take that percolator off the table——" he stood aloof, "I'll sit down with you."

Then we laughed outright, not in disrespect of him, but as children laugh at a humorous incident at school.

"Oh, yes, it might seem funny . . so does a drunken man who gives up his reason to a drug seem funny . . but it's no more a joke than that . . coffee is a vile poison . . I have a sense of humour," he continued, turning to me, "just as keen as the next one . . but I know, by scientific research, just how much damage that stuff does."

.   .   .   .

I read my sonnet to Penton, in a grave, respectful voice.

Peace was patched. We then sat together, under the chequered shade of the big tree which towered over our table . . Baxter waxed as eloquent as an angel . . the wonderful, absurd, little man.

Daniel came romping out for breakfast.

.   .   .   .

Penton reached for the morning's mail. He climbed into the hammock and read, with all the joy of a boy, the huge bunch of press clippings about himself, his activities, his work . . a daily procedure of his, I was to learn. He chuckled, joked, was immensely pleased . . handed me various items to read, or read choice bits aloud to all of us.

After all, though I pretended to criticise, to myself . . yet, in my heart, I liked his frank rejoicing in his fame, his notoriety, and only envied him his ability to do so.

.   .   .   .

I returned to my tent to work, as I had planned to do each morning, on my play *Judas*. The dialogue would not come to me . . **I** laid it aside and instead was inspired to set down instantly the blank verse proem to the play :——

"A noise of archery and wielded swords
All night rang through his dreams.　When risen morn
Let down her rosy feet on Galilee
Blue-vistaed, on the house-top Judas woke:
Desire of battle brooded in his breast
Although the day was hung with sapphire peace,
And to his inner eye battalions bright
Of seraphim, fledged with celestial mail,
Came marching up the wide-flung ways of dawn
To usher in the triumph-day of Christ. . .
But sun on sun departed, moon on moon,
And still the Master lingered by the way,
Iscariot deemed, dusked in mortality
And darkened in the God by flesh of man.
For Judas a material kingdom saw
And not a realm of immaterial gold,
A city of renewed Jerusalem
And not that New Jerusalem, diamond-paved
With love and sapphire-walled with brotherhood,
Which He, the Master, wrestled to make plain
With thews of parable and simile——
So ' 'tis the flesh that clogs him,' Judas thought
(A simple, earnest man, he loved him well
And slew him with great friendship in the end);
'Yea, if he chose to say the word of power,
The seraphim and cherubim, invoked,
Would wheel in dazzling squadrons down the sky
And for the hosts of Israel move in war
As in those holy battles waged of yore' . . .

　　　·　　　·　　　·　　　·　　　·　　　·　　　·

"Ah, all the world now knows Gethsemane,
But few the love of that betraying kiss!"

　　　·　　　·　　　·　　　·　　　·　　　·　　　·

I did not have to be very long at Eden to learn that the community was divided into two parties: the more conservative, rooted element whom success was making more and more conservative,—and the genuinely radical crowd. The anarchist, Jones, led the latter group, a very small one.

As far as I could see, this anarchist-shoemaker held the right. On my third day in Eden my interest in the community life about me led me to inquire my way to the place where Jones lived .. a shack built practically in its entirety of old dry goods boxes .. a two-room affair with a sort of enlarged dog-kennel adjunct that stood out nearer the road—Jones's workshop.

The man looked like the philosopher he was—the anarchist-philosopher, as the newspapers were to dub him .. as he sat there before his last, hammering away at the shoe he was heeling, not stopping the motions of his hands, while he put that pair aside, to sew at another pair, while he discoursed at large with me over men and affairs.

"What is all this trouble I'm hearing about?" I asked him.

"Trouble?—same old thing: Alfred Grahame, when he founded, started, this colony, was a true idealist. But success has turned his head, worsened him, since,—as it has done with many a good man before. Now he goes about the country lecturing, on Shakespeare, God, the Devil, or anything else that he knows nothing about. . .

"But it isn't that that I object to .. it is that he's allowing the original object of this colony, and of the Single Tax Idea, to become gradually perverted here. We're becoming nothing but a summer resort for the aesthetic quasi-respectables .. these folk are squeezing us poor, honest radicals out, by making the leases prohibitive in price and condition."

He stopped speaking, while he picked up another pair of shoes, examined them, chose one, and began sewing a patch on it. . .

He rose, with his leathern apron on, and saw me out. . .

"—glad you came to see old Jones .. you'll see and hear a lot more of me, the next week or so!" and he smiled genially, prophetically.

He looked like Socrates as he stood there .. jovially homely, round-faced .. head as bald as ivory .. red, bushy eyebrows that were so heavy he shrugged them. . .

"I'm just beginning the fight (would you actually believe it) for free speech here . . it takes a radical community, you know, to teach the conservatives how to suppress freedom. . .

"You must come around to the big barn Friday night, after the circus."

"—the circus?"

"Oh, we have a circus of our own every summer about this time . . we represent the animals ourselves . . some of us don't need to make up much, neither, if we only knew it," he roared.

"After the imitation circus, the real circus will begin. I have compelled the announcement of a general meeting to discuss my grievances, and that of others, who are not game enough to speak for themselves."

.   .   .   .

I found nobody but Hildreth—Mrs. Baxter—at home, when I returned. She was lying back in the hammock where Penton lounged to read his news clippings . . near the outdoor table . . dressed easily in her bloomers and white middy blouse with the blue bow tie . . her great, brown eyes, with big jet lashes, drooping languourously over her healthy, rounded cheeks . . her head of rich, dark hair touseled attractively. She was reading a book. I caught the white gleam of one of her pretty legs where the elastic on one side of her bloomers had slipped up.

Alone with her, a touch of my old almost paralytic shyness returned . . but the pathway to my tent lay so near her hammock I would almost brush against its side in passing. . .

She looked up. She gazed at me indefinitely, as if coming back from a far dream to reality.

"Oh, Johnnie Gregory! You?" fingering her hair with flexible fingers like a violinist trying his instrument.

"Yes!" I stopped abruptly and flushed.

"Did Jones like you?"

"I think he did."

"Jones is an eccentric . . but nine-tenths of the time he is right in his contentions . . his moral indignations . . it is his spirit of no compromise that defeats him."

With that she reached out one hand to me, with that pretty droop of the left corner of her mouth, that already had begun to fascinate me. . .

"Help me up . . a hammock's a nice place to be in, but an awkward thing to get out of."

I took her hand and helped her rise to a sitting posture.

"Ruth's in the little house typing . . Penton and Darrie are a-field taking a walk."

I paused where I was. Mrs. Baxter stood directly in the pathway that led to my tent. And the second act of *Judas* had begun to burn in my brain, during my vigorous walk back from Jones's shack. . .

.   .   .   .

"In the yard of an inn at Capernaum. On the left stands the entrance to the inn. In the extreme background lies the beach, and, beyond, the Sea of Galilee. A fisherboat is seen, drawn up on shore. Three fishermen discovered mending nets, at rise of curtain."

The stage was set for the second act. I must get the play finished in the rough. I owed this much to Mr. Derek, who was faithfully backing me—if not to my own career . . and already I had succeeded in interesting Mitchell Kennerley, the new young publisher, in my effort. After the book was disposed of . . then Europe . . then London . . then Paris, and all the large life of the brilliant world of intellect and literature that awaited me.

But, at the present, one small, dainty, dark woman unconsciously stood in my pathway. I looked into Hildreth Baxter's face with caution, strangely disquieted, but proud to be outwardly self-possessed.

"Let's *us* take a walk," she suggested.

"No, I must go to my tent and write!"

"Oh, come now . . don't you be like Mubby! . . that's the way *he* talks."

"All right," I assented, amazed at her directness, "I'll put my work by for the day—though the entire dialogue of the three Galilean fishermen about the miracle of the great draught of fishes is at this very moment burning in my brain."

She laid her hand lightly, but with an electric contact, on the bend of my arm, and off we started, into the inviting fields.

Not far out, we came across a group of romping children. They were shouting and chasing one another about, as happy dogs do when overjoyed with excessive energy.

The example the children set was contagious . . Hildreth and I were soon romping too—when out of the former's sight. We took hands and ran hard down a hill, and half-way up another one opposite, through our own natural impetus.

We changed our mood, strolling slowly and thoughtfully till we came to a small rustic bridge, so pretty it seemed almost like stage-craft, that spanned, at one leap, one of the countryside's innumerable, flashing brooks. We stood looking over into the foaming, speeding water.

"There's one thing sure about Eden .. in spite of the squabbles and disagreements of the elders, the place is a children's paradise."

"That's only because they have all nature for their backyard—no thanks to their elders," Hildreth answered, looking up into my face with a quick smile, "the grown-ups find misery wherever they go."

"Does that mean that you are unhappy?"

"I suppose I should say 'no.' "

"I don't understand what you mean."

"Neither do I, then."

Again that sweet, tantalizing, enigmatic droop of her mouth's corner.

We strolled further .. into the fields again .. with linked comradely hands. It seemed that she and I had been born brother and sister in some impossible pastoral idyll.

.   .   .   .

A change in our spirit again. A fresh desire to romp.

"Let's play just as if we were children, too."

"Tag! You're *it!*" and I touched her arm and ran. She ran after me in that curious loping fashion peculiar to women. I turned and wound like a hare. She stopped, breathless. "That's no fair!" she cried, "you're running too fast."

"Well, then, I'll almost stand still, then see if you can catch me!"

She made at me, shouting, her face flushed with the exercise. I ducked and swerved and doubled.

"You're quite quick and strong," she exclaimed, admiringly, as I caught her by the shoulders.

I stooped over, hunching my back.

"Come on, play leap-frog," I invited. She hesitated, gave a run at me, put both hands on my back, but caught her left leg on my neck. We collapsed in a laughing heap, she on top of me.

Slowly we disentangled ourselves. I reached a hand and helped her up.

"I'm no good at that, either . . let's stop playing . . I'm tired."

We caught sight of a little man crossing a field, trotting like a dog out hunting on his own. He looked back twice as he went.

"—wonder if he saw us?"

"—perhaps—but what matter if he did?"

"Then I hope he's not a fellow Edenite. You have no idea what an undercurrent of gossip runs in this place."

We sank down together on a small knoll under the low-spreading branches of a live oak.' We watched the man who we thought had observed our antics bobbing off down the road, as if running for exercise.

We sat quite apart, at first. Then our hands met in instinctive fondness . . met in the spirit in which we had been romping together.

"You're like a small boy, Johnnie."

"And you haven't acted so very much like a grown woman, have you, Hildreth?" It was the first time I had called her by her first name.

"Can you, or anyone else, tell me just how grown women do act? I myself don't know, yet I'm a woman."

I drew closer to her as if drawn by some attractive power. A stray wisp of her hair lit across my cheek stingingly. Then the wind blew a perfumed strand of it across my lips and over my nostrils.

It made me rub my lips, it tickled so. Hildreth noticed it.

"Wait," she bade playfully, "I'll bet I can make you rub your lips again."

"No, you can't."

"Hold still!" she leaned toward me; I could look down into her bosom. She just touched my lips with her forefinger.

"Now!" she exclaimed triumphantly.

"—think you've tickled me, do you?"

"—just wait!"

I forgot myself. My lips tickled and I rubbed them with the length of a finger . . Hildreth laughed. . .

"Hildreth!"

I leaned toward my friend's wife, calling her again by her first name.

I lay in a half-reclining posture, my head almost against her hip. I was looking up into her face. She glanced down at me with a quick start at the tone of my voice. She looked gravely for a moment into my face. I observed an enigmatic something deep in her eyes . . which sank slowly back as the image of a face does, in water,—as the face itself is withdrawn. She moved apart a little, with a motion of slow deliberation.

"Hildreth!" I heard myself calling again, with a deep voice, a voice that sounded alien in my own ears. . .

"Come, boy!" and she pulled back her hand from my grasp, and catching mine in hers a moment, patted the back of it lightly——" come, don't let's be foolish . . we've had such a happy afternoon together, don't let's spoil it . . now let's start home."

As soon as I was on my feet and away from her, she became playful again. She reached up her hand for me.

"Help me up!"

I brought her to her feet with a strong, quick pull, and against my breast. But I did not dare do what I desired—take her in my arms and try to kiss her. She paused a second, then thrust me back.

"Look, the sun's almost gone down . . and Mubby and Darrie will be home a long time by this time . . and Mubby will be getting fidgety."

The sun's last huge shoulder of red was hulking like a spy behind a distant, bare knoll . . separate blades of grass stood up in microscopic yet giant distinctness, against its crimson background.

Our walk home was a silent, passively happy one that went without incident. . .

.   .   .   .

Penton and Darrie were indeed home before us.

"Where have you two been all this time," Penton asked, a slight touch of querulousness in his voice.

"Oh, Johnnie and I have been out for a walk, too!" replied Hildreth in an even voice.

.   .   .   .

At lunch, the next day,—a day when Penton was called in to Philadelphia on business—while Darrie, Ruth, Hildreth and I sat talking together peacefully about our outdoor board, Hildreth suddenly threw a third of a glass of milk on Darrie's shirt-waist front.

We were astounded.

"Why, Hildreth, what does this mean?" I asked.

"I won't stop to explain," she said, "but from now on I won't stay in the same house with her . . I'm going to move this afternoon, down to Penton's house (meaning the little cottage but a few steps from my tent) . . Ruth rose to intercede. . . "Don't Ruth, don't! I want to be let alone." And Hildreth hurried away.

"What in the world could be the matter with Hildreth?" I asked of Ruth. Darrie had also departed, to the big house, to rub her blouse quickly, so that no stain would remain.

Hildreth's capricious," answered Ruth, "but the plain explanation is downright jealousy."

"Jealousy?"

"Yes . . even though Hildreth no longer loves Penton, she's jealous of him . . the fact is, Hildreth doesn't know what she wants."

"But Darrie—Darrie is her friend?"

"Of course . . and remains her friend. Darrie doesn't want Penton. She only pities him."

I quoted the line about pity being akin to love . . "they do a lot of strolling together."

"Yes. But there's nothing between them . . not even a kiss . . of that I'm certain. Darrie is as cool as a cucumber . . and Penton is as shy with women as—you are!"

I smiled to myself. If Ruth had seen us that preceding afternoon!

"Of course the fault could not all be on Hildreth's side."

"No, they're both a couple of ninnies . . but there's this to be said for Penton, he's trying to get something done for the betterment of humanity . . while Hildreth's only a parasite."

"And Darrie—how about her? What does she do but loaf around in a more conventional manner, talking about her social prestige, the dress of one of her ancestresses in the Boston Museum, her aristocratic affiliations . . how many and how faithful those negro servants of hers are, down South . . between the two, Hildreth has the livest brain, and puts on less."

"Take care! You'll be falling in love with Penton Baxter's wife yet!"

Our talk was halted by Darrie's re-appearance. Hildreth came furtively back, too, from the little cottage, like a guilty child. She apologized to Darrie, and her apology was accepted, and, in a few minutes we were talking ahead as gaily as before. . .

We rehearsed Hildreth in her part as Titania . . for that was the part she was to play in *The Mid-Summer Night's Dream*, that the Actors' Guild of the colony was to put on in their outdoor theatre, a week from that afternoon . . Hildreth insisted on dressing for the part . . in her green, skin tights . . letting her black hair flow free . . wearing even her diadem, as fairy queen. She had a good, musical voice . . a way of speaking with startled shyness that was engaging.

But Hildreth stuck to her original intention of moving to the cottage. She had Mrs. Jones move her things for her.

As I sat in the library of the big house reading Tolstoy's *Anna Karenina*, I overheard Darrie telling Ruth in the bathroom that Hildreth would not have insisted on donning her tights, if she had not been proud of her symmetrical legs, and had not wanted to show them off to me.

Between the three women, nevertheless, Hildreth was easily my choice already . . Darrie was lovely, but talked like a débutante from morning till night. . .

Ruth had too much of the quietist in her, the non-resistent. She had a vast fund of scholarship, knew English poetry from the ground up . . but her bringing that knowledge to me as an attraction was like presenting a peacock's feather to a bird of paradise. . .

However, when Penton came home that night, he found us all in huge good humour. I had just received a check from Derek, and had insisted on spending most of it for a spread for all of us, including a whopping beefsteak.

And we ate and joked and enjoyed ourselves just like the bourgeoisie.

.   .   .   .

If Penton only had had a sense of humour . . but this I never detected in him.

Even at singing classes, which I attended one evening with him . . his whole entourage, in fact. . .

With solemn face he sang high, and always off key, till the three women had to stuff their handkerchiefs in their mouths to keep from laughing at him before his face. . .

After class, we strolled home by a devious path, through the moonlight. This time Ruth walked ahead with little Dan, Hildreth with her husband, Penton,—Darrie with me. . .

"Drag back a little, Johnnie . . Penton and Hildreth are having a private heart-to-heart talk, I can tell by their voices."

We hung back till they disappeared around a bend. We were alone. Darrie began to laugh and laugh and laugh. . . "Oh, it's so funny, I shall die laughing". . .

.   .   .   .

"Why—why, what's the matter!"

For I saw tears streaming down the girl's face in the moonlight.

"It's so awful," replied Darrie, now crying quietly, "—so tragic . . yet I had to laugh . . I'm so sorry for Penton . . for both of them. . .

"Penton *is* such a jackass, Johnnie," she gulped, "and God knows, as I do, he's such an honest, good man . . helping poor people all over the country . . really fighting the fight of the down-trodden and the oppressed."

I put my arm around the girl's waist, and she wept on my shoulder.

Finally she straightened up her head, stopping her crying with difficulty.

"We're all so funny, aren't we?"

"Yes, we're a funny bunch, Darrie . . all so mixed up,—the world wouldn't believe it, would they, if we told them?"

"And you could never make them understand, even if you did tell them. You know, my dear, old Southern daddy—he thinks Penton is a limb of the old Nick himself . . with his theories about life, and the freedom of relations between the sexes, and all that . . even yet he may leave me out of his will for coming up here, though he has all the confidence in the world in me."

And Mary Darfield Malcolm—whom we always called "Darrie" —went quickly to her room when we got back, so the others wouldn't notice that she had been crying. . .

.   .   .   .   .

Quite often, in the afternoons, toward dusk, around a dying fire, the whole community had "sings" out in the woods, near the one large stream that abutted the colony, and gathered into itself, all the little brooks. . .

The old songs were sung; rich, beautiful, old Scotch and English and Irish ballads—which were learnt, by all who wanted to know them, at the singing school . . and the old-fashioned American songs, too.

And the music softened our hearts and fused us into one harmony of feeling. And all the bickerings of the community's various "isms" melted away . . after all, there was not so very much disharmony among us. And, after all, the marvel is that human beings get along together at all.

. . . .

The afternoon before the "circus" the little settlement more than ever took on the appearance of a medieval village . . almost everybody took turns in participating in the "circus" . . almost everybody togged out in costume. But first we had a parade of the "guilds" . . the Actors' Guild, in which Hildreth bore a part; in her pretty tights she looked like a handsome boy page in some early Italian prince's court.

Don Grahame was the son of the leader of the community whom Jones had promised to rake over the coals that night, after the circus.

Don led the Carpenters' Guild, looking like nothing else than a handsome boy Christ. Don, secretly disliking in his heart the free-love doctrines his father and others taught (though he always rose loyally in his father's defence) had gone to the other extreme, he lived an ascetic, virgin life. But it didn't seem to hurt him. He was as handsome as Hildreth was beautiful.

Everybody liked the young fellow. He had sworn that he would maintain his manner of abstinent living till he fell in love with a girl who loved him in return. Then they would live together. . .

That, he maintained, was the true and only meaning of free love. He had no use for varietism nor promiscuity.

The Guilds paraded twice around the Village Green, led by the Guild of Music Masters, who played excellently well.

The Children's Guild was a romping, lovely sight.

. . . .

The circus was held shortly afterward in the huge communal barn, in the centre of its great floor,—the spectators seated about on the sides. . .

There was the trick mule, made up of two men under an ox-hide, the mule fell apart and precipitated Don Grahame in between its two halves . . each half then ran away in opposite directions.

Don rode so well that that was the only way they (I mean the mule) could unseat him. He won much affectionate applause.

Then there was the fearful, great boa-constrictor . . which turned out to be a double-jointed, lithe, acrobatic, boy-like girl whom we knew as Jessie . . Jessie, they whispered, was marked for death by consumption, if she didn't look out and stop smoking so many cigarettes . . she was slender and pretty—but spoke with an adenoidal thickness of speech.

The colony was as merry as if no storm impended.

We adjourned for supper.

After supper, under the evening star we marched back to the barn again, which also served as our town hall. On the way there our talk was subdued and expectant. Many people were disgruntled with Jones.

"Why must he do this?"

"Why can't old Jones let well enough alone? . . no community's perfect, not even our community."

Daniel had been put to bed, angrily objecting.

The five of us joined the flow of people toward the barn. Penton carried a lantern.

"Jones is all right," said Penton to me, "I like his spirit. I'm going to stand by him, if he finds himself seriously pressed, just because the man's spirit is a good one . . nothing mean about him . . but I know he'll place me among the snobs and wealthy of the community."

When all were gathered, as still as at the opening of a prayer meeting, Grahame came in, and, with his son and other friends, took seats opposite Jones. Grahame, who had been master of ceremonies and ring master for the afternoon circus, had not changed his dress of knee-britches and ruffed shirt.

The debate was prolonged and fiery. . .

Jones launched into a gallant attack on Grahame, and was replied to evasively. Don Grahame wanted to punch Jones's head for what he called slurs cast at his father's good name. . .

Penton made a famous speech reconciling, almost, the irreconcilable parties.

And so we adjourned.

Penton and I accompanied Jones home. All the way the latter was arguing against Baxter's plea, that he be more lenient with Grahame. . .

"You look out, Penton," Jones warned with genial firmness . . "Grahame has been trying to persuade people in this community not to bring shoes to me to be mended . . a dirty attempt to starve me out . . Oh, no! . . I haven't the slightest trace of persecution mania. . .

And you'd better look out, Penton, and not play tennis this Sunday, for I'm going to strike back at the tennis-playing snobs here, of whom you're one."

"Jones, what do you mean by that? Surely not a bomb to smear us all over the courts!" Penton joked.

"A bomb, yes . . it will be a bomb of sorts . . but I warn you you shan't play games on Sunday any more. I'll see to that . . not that I've unexpectedly grown religious, but that I mean to strike back as pettily as the way in which I'm being persecuted."

.   .   .   .

"I suppose he means the Blue Laws," Penton commented seriously, "but surely he can get no one to enforce them."

.   .   .   .

But Jones found a facetious officer of the law or so, down in Philadelphia, who were as glad of a chance to molest a radical colony as of an opportunity to put over a good joke. . .

Baxter, Grahame, Bedell, and others of the prominent members of the community were haled in to court . . and, to the surprise of everyone, sentenced to forty-eight hours hard labour on the rock-pile, in the workhouse. . .

And Jones sang triumphant snatches of song and hammered away merrily at shoes in his little shack along the road, while unused hands gathered water blisters making big stones into little ones, with other and heavier hammers.

The newspapers made a great to-do about the matter. The affair was just serio-comic enough to attract nation-wide attention. And the story was a good one—the story of the anarchist-shoemaker who invoked the use of archaic, reactionary laws, in his battle against his less radical antagonists, the Single Taxers and Socialists.

Story after story was also written about our curious little colony. Penton Baxter shared honours with the shoemaker. Reporters

swarmed over his front porch and into his house to interview him, on
the triumphant return of the party when they had served their forty-
eight hours.

Penton gave out interview after interview. And, to his credit
let it be said, though he revelled in the notice accorded him, he also
effected two serious results from what had begun as almost a practical joke . . he started a fight on the absurd Blue Laws by focusing publicity on them . . and he exposed the bad prison conditions
his unknown fellow prisoners lived under, who had *not* gone to the
workhouse in a jocular mood because of resurrected Blue Laws.

Jones was willing to 'let the matter rest, as well as were his other
opponents . . but Baxter kept the fight going as long as he could.
He was accused of loving notoriety. His attitude toward it was
mixed. He did love notoriety . . he enjoyed every clipping about
himself with infinite gusto. But he also used publicity as a lever to
get things done with, that would otherwise never have been noticed.
The others were willing to consider what had happened to them, as a
private affair. Penton gracelessly used that, and every private
adventure for propaganda—turned it sincerely in the way he
thought it might benefit people. . .

He gave the papers a very bad poem—*The Prison Night.*   I
remember but one line of it—

"The convict rasped his vermin-haunted hide."

.   .   .   .

"Come, get into the group; I want the papers to tell the public
about you, too," he urged me, prophetically, as I stood on the outskirts, while three camera men were focusing on him, as he stood,
expectant, blandly smiling, and vain-glorious.

"Boys, I want my friend, the poet, Mr. John Gregory, in the
picture, too."

"Oh, all right!" they assented indifferently, which injured my
egotism. But I was too adroit to show it. I still demurred with
mock modesty. Penton would have been franker.

Finally, at his urgency, they snapped us, our arms about each
other's shoulders.

In the light of subsequent events, they were glad of that picture.

.   .   .   .

Our tennis-playing, Blue-Law martyrs, as I have said, were held
over night in the workhouse . . or maybe two nights, I do not

exactly remember which . . and when they came back they were full of the privations of jail-life, and the degradation of the spirit and mind suffered by prisoners there. To me, their attitude seemed rather tender-foot and callow. It was something that would have been accepted off-handedly by me. I had been in jail often, not for a cause, as I punned wretchedly, but *be-cause*. I did not accord hero-worship to Penton when he returned, as the women of the household did.

For a week it quite reconciled Hildreth with him. . .

.   .   .   .   .   .

But on the first night of his absence Hildreth and I took a stroll together in the moonlight.

Long the three women and myself had sat in the library, while I read aloud from a MSS. volume of my poetry, which I intended submitting to the Macmillans soon. For Ruth knew Mr. Brett and promised to give me an introduction to him. And I was to make a special trip to the city on the money I had saved from my weekly remittances . . for Penton would not permit me to spend a cent for my keep while I visited him. And I had already been with him three weeks. . .

.   .   .   .   .   .

I read them many love poems—those I had written for Vanna. . .

"Why," commented Hildreth, "these verses sound like what a very callow youth would write, who never had experience with women . . I mean by that, intimate knowledge of them."

I flushed and sat silent.

"Some day, when you've lived more," remarked Ruth, "you'll write love-poetry more simple, more direct."

> "Though infinite ways He knows
>   To manifest His power,
> God, when He made your face,
>   Was thinking of a flower!"

I read.

"There again you have an instance of what I mean . . you are only rhetoricising about love; not partaking of its feelings."

"But I wrote all these poems about a real girl," and I told them the story of my distant passion for Vanna.

"No matter—— you're a grown-up man who, as far as knowledge of women is concerned, has the heart of a baby," observed Hildreth.

—"in these days of sex-sophistication a fine thing!" cried Ruth.

"Yes, when out of the mouths of babes and sucklings come quotations from Havelock Ellis and Ellen Key!" cried Darrie.

"Good! Darrie, good!" Hildreth applauded. . .

"—time to go to bed . . here it's almost one o'clock."

"—had no idea it was so late. I have a lot of typing to do to-morrow. Good night, folks!" and Ruth was off to her room upstairs.

"Good-night, Hildréth,—suppose you're going to sleep down in the little house!" It was Darrie who spoke.

"Yes," answered Hildreth, in a simple tone, "I will feel quite safe there . . Johnnie's tent is only a few yards away."

Hildreth and Darrie kissed each other on the mouth tenderly.

"Good night, Johnnie——" and impulsively Darrie stepped up to me, took me by the two shoulders, and kissed me also a kind sisterly kiss . . I responded, abashed and awkward.

A ripple of pleasant laughter at me from both women.

"Johnnie's a dear, innocent boy!" Darrie.

"He makes me feel like a mother to him!" said Hildreth.

Though each of these remarks was made without the slightest colour of irony, I did not like them . . I lowered my head, humiliated under them.

Ever since I had been among them the three women had treated me in the way they act with small boys, preserving scarcely any reserve in my presence. Penton himself had lost all his first disquiet.

Outside—

"I'll take you as far as the cottage . . it's right on the way, you know."

"All right, but where are you going?"

"Into the kitchen to get a lantern."

"The moon is almost as bright as day. We won't need it."

We stepped out into the warm, scented night. In a mad flood of silver the moon reigned high in the sky, dark and bright with the contours and shades of its continents and craters, as if nearer the earth than it had ever been before. . .

"This night reminds me of those lines in Marlowe's *Doctor*

Faustus, the ones that follow after 'Is this the face that launched a thousand ships, and burnt the topless towers of Ilion?' which are, to me, a trifle over-rhetorical . . the ensuing lines are more lovely:

" 'Fair as the evening air—

" 'Clad in the beauty of a thousand stars,' or is it 'ten thousand stars'?"

Hildreth turned her face up to me. Her arm went through mine. She drew my arm close against her body and held it tight in silent response for a quiet interval. . .

"You *are* a poet . . a *real* poet . . and," she dropped her voice, "and, what is more, a real man, too!" there was a world of compassion in her voice. . .

"—You remember Blake's evening star—that 'washed the dusk with silver?' "

"Jesus, how beautiful!" I cried.

We were standing in front of her cottage, that darkled in the trees.

Suddenly, roused by our voices, like some sweet, low, miraculous thing, a little bird sang a few bars of song, sweet and low, in the bushes somewhere, and stopped. . .

"Hildreth, don't let's go to bed yet." I caught her arm in my hands, "it's too beautiful . . to go to bed."

I was trembling all over. . .

"Yes, boy?"

"Let's—let's take a walk."

.   .   .   .

We went through the little sleeping community. She clung to my arm lightly. . .

"You're the first woman I haven't been frightened of, rather, have felt at home with."

"You, who have been a tramp, a worker all over the country . . in big cities . . do you mean to tell me that?——"

"Yes . . yes . . before God, it is true! You don't think I'm a fool, do you—a ninny?"

"No, on the contrary, I think you are a good man . . that it is miraculous . . I—I feel so old beside you . . how old are you, Johnnie?"

"Twenty-six."

"Why, I'm only two years older . . yet I feel like your mother."

. . . .

In the groves adjoining the colony, for a mile on either side, wherever there was a big tree, a circular seat had been built about it. It was on one of these that we sat down, without a word.

I laid my head against Hildreth's shoulder. Soothingly she began stroking my hair. With cool fingers she stroked it.

"What fine hair you have. It's as soft and silky as a girl's."

"I took after my mother in that."

"What a mixture you are . . manly and strong . . an athlete, yet sensitive, so sensitive that sometimes it hurts to look at your face when you talk . . you've suffered a lot, Johnnie."

"In curious ways, yes."

"Tell me about yourself. I won't even whisper it in the dark, when I'm alone."

"I know I can trust you, Hildreth."

"What are you doing, boy?"

"I want to sit at your feet."

"You dear boy."

"I feel quite humble . . I don't want you to see my face when I talk."

She drew my head against her knees. Threw one arm as if protectingly over my shoulder.

"There. Are you comfortable, boy?"

"Yes. Are you?"

"Quite . . don't be ashamed . . I know much about life that you do not know . . tell me all."

. . . .

So I told her all about myself . . my ambition . . my struggles . . my morbidity . . my lack of experience with girls and women. .

"And I must have experience soon . . it's obsessing me . . it can't last this way much longer . . I shall go mad."

And I rehearsed to her a desperate resolve I had made . . to find a woman of the streets, in New York, when I went in, the ensuing week . . and force myself, no matter how I loathed it——

I buried my head in her lap and sobbed hysterically.

Then I apologised—"forgive me if I have been too frank!"

"I am a radical woman . . Penton and I both believe in the theory of free love, though we happen to be married . . what you have told me is all sweet and natural to me . . only—you must not do what you say you'll do—in New York!———"

"I must, or———" and I paused, to go on in a lower, embarrassed voice. . . "Do—do you know what else I thought of—dreamed of———?

"In Paris—I understand—men live with women as a matter of course———

"You see———" I was hot with shame to the very ears, "you see— there, you know,—I thought if I went there I would find some pretty little French girl that I would take to live with me . . in some romantic attic in the Montmartre district . . and we would be happy together . . and I would be grateful, so grateful, to her!"

"Why you're the Saint Francis of the Radicals," Hildreth exclaimed.

"Please don't make fun of me . . I suppose you think me very foolish."

"Foolish? . . No, I think you have a very beautiful soul. I wish every man had a soul like that."

She took my head in her hands and kissed me on the brow.

"Hildreth, only tell me what I am to do?"

"I do not know . . theoretically I believe in freedom in sex . . I wish to God I could help you."

"Why can't you?"

"Hush, you do not know what you're asking!"

"By the living Christ, I only know that I would crawl after you, and kiss your holiest feet before all the world, if you helped me."

"Now I understand what Lecky meant when he spoke of the sacrificial office of a certain type of women . . I only wish . . but come, we must go."

I was on my feet beside her, as she rose.

"Yes, we had better go home," I spoke quietly, though my heart pumped as if I had taken strychnine.

I put my arms about her, to steady her going, for she stumbled.

"Why, Hildreth, dearest woman, you're trembling all over, what's the matter? . . have I—I frightened you with my wild talk?"

"Never mind . . no, take your arm away . . Let me walk alone a minute and I'll be all right . . I'll be all right in a minute . . it's just turned a trifle chilly, that's all."

.   .   .   .

"Hush!" going down the path by the big house, Hildreth stopped, hesitated. "I'm—I'm not going to the little cottage to-night."

"Then I'll say good-night!"

"No, come on in and we'll sneak out to the kitchen and find something to eat . . aren't you hungry?"

"A little bit. But I'm afraid we might wake Ruth and Darrie up."

We tip-toed in. Hildreth searching for the matches, knocked the wash-basin to the floor. We stood hushed like mice.

"Who's down there?" asked Darrie's voice, with a dash of hysteria in it . . of hysteria and fright.

"Damn it, there's Darrie waked up."

"Such a clatter would wake anyone up!"

"Who's there, I say!"

"It's only me, Darrie . . I got hungry in the night and came up to the house to snatch a bite to eat."

"Oh . . I'm coming down to join you, then."

We saw Darrie standing at the top of the stairs, her eyes luminous and wide with emotion.

She stood, rosy-bodied, in her night-dress, which was transparent in the light of the lamp she carried. . .

"Johnnie's here, too!" warned Hildreth.

"Oh!" cried Darrie, and turned back, to re-appear in her kimono.

"I'm sorry we waked you up. But I knocked that infernal basin down off the sink."

"You didn't wake me. I was awake already. I haven't slept a wink."

"Neither have we!" I responded.

"What?" Darrie asked me in so startled, impulsive a manner that Hildreth and I laughed . . and she laughed a little, too . . and then grew grave again. . .

"It was such a beautiful night, Johnnie and I took a walk in the moonlight."

Darrie looked from one to the other of us with a wide, staring look.

"You needn't look that way, Darrie!"

"Please, please, Hildreth!"

"You and Penton have taken walks in the moonlight."

"Hildreth, dear, I'm not rebuking you . . and you know my walks with Penton are all right, are harmless."

"Yes, I know they are . . but you mustn't rebuke me, either."

"I wasn't rebuking either you or Johnnie . . it isn't that I'm thinking of at all . . but everything has been so uncanny here to-night . . I could not sleep . . every little rustle of curtains, every creak or motion in the whole house vibrated through me . . something's going to happen to someone."

"You're only upset because Penton's in jail," I explained.

"No, that's not it . . that's nothing compared to this feeling . . this premonition——"

"Come on, let's make some coffee . . in the percolator."

"You girls sit down and I'll make it. I've been a cook several times in my career."

Someone was knocking about in the dark, upstairs. We heard a match struck. . .

"There, we've waked Ruth, too."

"What's the matter down there?" Ruth was calling.

"Come on down and join us, Ruth,—we're having a cup of coffee a-piece."

"It's only two o'clock . . what's everybody doing up so early? Has Penton come back?"

"No . . but do come down and join us," I replied.

.   .   .   .

"I tell you, I thought it was burglars at first, and I was going to the drawer in Penton's room and get out his six-shooter."

"Does Penton keep a gun?" I asked.

"Yes . . it's the one he bought to shoot the mongrel dog with."

.   .   .   .

We ate some cold roast beef sandwiches and drank our coffee.

Hildreth stayed in the big house, not going down the path with me.

I went silently to my tent. It was blowing a little now. The moon was surging along behind little, grey, running clouds. It would rain before daylight. A haunted shiver swept through my back as I stole along the path. I repeated poetry rapidly aloud to crowd out uncanny imaginings. I had a silly, sick impulse to run back to the big house and sleep on the couch in the library.

But I forced myself on. "If you're ever going to be a man, you'd better begin now," I muttered to myself, as if talking to another person.

In my tent . . I lit the lamp. I removed all hanging objects because their lurching shadows sent shivers of apprehension through me. . .

"That damned coffee—wish I hadn't drunk it."

.   .   .   .

The wind and rain came up like a phantom army. It sang in the trees, it drummed musically on my tent. It comforted me.

The floodgates of my mind, my inspiration, broke loose. I rose to my super-self. And now if a horrible thing had stood grey at my elbow, unmoved, I would have looked it unflinchingly in the sightless visage. . .

My pencil raced over paper . . raced and raced.

"Here it comes . . just like your good rain, so kind to earth . . Oh, beautiful God, I thank Thee for making me a poet," I prayed, tears streaming down my face.

.   .   .   .

The second act of *Judas* stood complete, as if it had written itself.

I rose. It seemed hardly an hour had passed.

It took me a few minutes to work the numbness out of my legs. How they ached! I stepped out of the tent-door like a drunken man . . fell on my face in some bushes and bled from several scratches. The blare of what was full daylight hurt my eyes. I had been writing on, entranced, by unneeded lamp, when unheeded day burned about me.

Stepping inside again, I saw by my Ingersoll that it was twelve o'clock. I fell into a deep sleep, still dressed . . I was so exhausted. Usually I slept absolutely naked.

.   .   .   .

These were the things that happened while Penton was in jail because he played tennis on Sunday.

.   .   .   .

Now I was part and parcel of the household, no longer a stranger-friend on a visit. Though Penton's jail-experience did not thrill me, the continued thronging of reporters did, as did Baxter's raging desire to do good for the poor ordinary prisoners in jail. He had got at several of them who had received a raw deal in the courts, and was moving heaven and earth to bring redress to them.

He gave interviews, dictated articles . . the State officials were furious. "What's the matter with the fellow? What's he bother about the other fellows for, he ought to be glad he's not in their shoes!". .

In agitations for the public good, in humanitarian projects, Baxter was indeed a great man . . I loomed like a pigmy beside him.

.   .   .   .

Darrie and I in dialogue:

She met me on the path, as I was proceeding toward the big house. She carried Carpenter's *Love's Coming of Age* in her hand. She was dressed daintily. Her brown eyes smiled at me, and a rich dimple broke in her cheek.

But Darrie was taller than Hildreth, and I like small women best; perhaps because I am myself so big.

"Don't go up to the house, Johnnie."

"I want a book from the library."

"Hildreth and Penton are there. Hildreth is having a soul-state."

"A what?" I laughed.

"Oh, she thinks something is the matter with her soul, and, for the three hundredth time since I've known them, Penton and she are discussing their lives together."

"I don't see anything to jest about in that."

"I'm tiring of it . . if Hildreth has a tooth-ache, or anything that the rest of us women accept as a matter of course, she runs to Mubby, as she calls him . . and, as if it were some abstruse, philosophical problem, they talk on, hour after hour . . like German metaphysics, there's no end to it. They've been at it since ten and they'll go on till four, if they follow precedents . . Penton takes Hildreth too seriously."

"You talk as if you, you were jealous of Hildreth and in love with Penton."

"It's neither the one nor the other. I love them both, and I want to see them happy together."

"You see, Darrie, neither you nor I are married, and neither of us knows anything about sex, except in the theory of the books we've read—how can *we judge* the troubles of a man and woman who are married?"

"There's a lot in what you say."

"I believe it would be better if we both cleared out and left them to fight this out alone."

"Perhaps it would."

.   .   .   .

"Darrie, Oh, Darrie!—want to come for a walk with Hildreth and me?"

So the three set off together, leaving me and Ruth alone.

.   .   .   .

Ruth and I had just settled down to a discussion of the writing of narrative poetry, how it was done, and the reason why it was no longer customary with the poets to write longer stories out of real life, like Chaucer's *Canterbury Tales*,—when we heard a rustling as of some wild thing in the bushes beside the house, and here came Hildreth breaking through, her eyes blazing, her hair down, her light walking skirt that she had slipped on over her bloomers torn by catching on thorns.

She staggered into the open, swept us with a blazing glance as if we had done something to her, and hurried on down the path toward the little house where Penton had written in quiet till she had strangely routed him out and taken its occupancy for herself.

"Hildreth!" I leaped to my feet, starting after her, "Hildreth what's the matter?"

I had put all thought of narrative poetry out of my head.

"Don't follow her," advised Ruth, in a low, controlled voice, "it's best to let her alone when she acts like that . . she'll have it out, and come back, smiling, in an hour or so."

I plunged on. Ruth ran after me, catching me by the shoulder from behind.

"Listen to me. Take my advice and keep out of this—Johnnie!" she called my name with a tender drop in her voice.

If it had not been for her tell-tale pronouncement of my name I might have listened to her . . but that made me angry, and it ran through my mind how she and Penton had fatuously arranged my marrying her. . .

I ran after Hildreth. She slammed the door when I was so close upon her that the wind of its shutting went against my face like a blow.

I found myself on my knees by the door.

"Let me in," I said through the key-hole, for the door was locked; she had thrown the bolt on the inside.

"Go away, Johnnie, I want to be alone."

"Hildreth, dearest woman, do let me in. It hurts my heart to see you so suffer so."

"I don't want to see anybody. I want to die."

"I'll come in the window."

I was at the window madly. I caught it. It was locked. But I pulled it up like a maniac. The lock, rusty, flew off with a zing! The window crashed up. I tumbled in at one leap.

My whole life was saying, "this is your woman, your first and only woman—go where she is and take her to yourself!"

That avalanche of me bursting in without denial, struck little Hildreth Baxter dumb with interest. She had been kneeling by her bed, sobbing. Now she rose and was sitting on it.

"Well?" and she smiled wanly, looking at me with fear and a twinkle of amusement, and intrigued interest, all at one and the same time, on her face——

"I couldn't stand seeing you suffer, Hildreth. I had to come in. And you wouldn't unlock the door .. what has gone wrong?"

"It's Darrie!—"

"But you all three started on your hike like such a happy family, and——"

"For God's sake don't think I'm jealous of Darrie .. I'm only wild about the way she encourages Mubby to talk over his troubles with her—and tell her about him and me, asking *her* advice .. as if *she* could give any advice worth while——

"They began to talk and talk about me just as if I were a laboratory specimen. . .

"Damn this laboratory marriage! damn this laboratory love!

"Penton experiments, and Penton experiments . . on his cat, his dog, himself, me—you, if you'd let him .. everybody! let him marry Humanity if he loves it so much."

"But what did you do?"

"I caught myself running away from them, and sobbing."

"And what did they do?"

" 'Hildreth, for God's sake!' Mubby called, 'what's the matter now?' in that bland, exasperating tone of his,—that injured, self-righteous, I'm-sacrificing-myself-for-mankind tone——"

—I had to laugh at her exact mimicry. . .

I stroked her hair. . .

"   •   •   ,   •   •   •

"I'm glad you came to Eden, John Gregory. You might be a poet, but you have some human sense in you, too. . .

"Oh, you don't know what I've been through," then, femininely, "poor, poor Mubby, he's been through a lot, too."

Her tears began to flow again. I sat beside her on the bed. I put my arm about her and drew her to me. I kissed her tear-wet mouth. The taste of her ripe sweet mouth with the salt of her tears wet on her lips was very good to me. . .

In a minute unexpectedly she began returning my kisses . . hungrily . . her eyes closed . . breathing deeply like one in a trance. . .

.   .   .   , ...

"Go up to the house now, Johnnie, my love . . go, so Mubby won't be suspicious of us . . I want to stay here . . leave the blinds drawn as they are. . .

"You have been so gentle, so sweet."

"Hildreth . . listen to me . . this has been the greatest day in my life, will always be! If I died now, I would go to death, singing. . .

"You're the most wonderful woman in the world. . .

"I want you to be mine forever. . .

"I know what it all means now. . . .

"It's like Niagara, sweetheart . . one hears so much of it . . expects so much . . that it seems disappointing, the first actuality. . .

"Then afterward, it's more than any dream ever dreamed of what it would be!

"I want to work for you. . .

"I want to let you walk all over me with your little feet. . .

"I want you to kill me, sweetheart. . .

"I want to die for you. . .

"Hildreth, I love you!

"I'll tell Penton . . I'll tell everybody— 'I love Hildreth! I love Hildreth!' "

.   .   .   .

"Johnnie, my own sweet darling, my own dear, pure-hearted, mad, young poet. . .

"Don't talk that way. . .

"Come to me again. . .

.   .   .   .   .   .

"Penton must not know. Not yet. You must let *me* tell him.

"It is my place to tell him, sweetest of men, my darling boy. . .

.   .   .   .

"Go to your tent.
"He'd see it in your eyes now."
"No, I won't go to my tent. I'll go right up to the house.

.   .   .   .

"If he says anything to me I'll kill him.
"I'm a man now.
"I'll fight him or anybody you want me to."

.   .   .   .

These were the words we said, or left unsaid. I am even yet too confused to remember the exact details of that memorable time.

For I was re-born then, into another life.

Is there anyone who can remember his birth?

I returned to my tent in a blissful daze.

I had not the least feeling of having betrayed a friend.

The only problem that now confronted us was divorce! I would ask Penton to divorce Hildreth, and then Hildreth and I would marry.

But why even that? Was not this the greatest opportunity in the world for Hildreth and me to put to practical test our theories . . proclaim ourselves for Free Love,—as Mary Wollstonecraft and the philosopher Godwin had done, a century or so before us?

.   .   .   .

The following day Ruth and I ate breakfast together, alone. I had behaved with unusual sedateness, had showed an aplomb I had never before evidenced. Full manhood, belated, had at last come to me.

With more than usual satisfaction I drank my coffee, holding the cup with my hands around it like a child . . warming my fingers, which are nearly always cold in the morning. . .

Then, while Ruth sat opposite me, eyeing me curiously, I began to sing, half-aloud, to myself.

A silence fell. We exchanged very few words.

And it was our custom, when together, Ruth and I, to hold long discussions concerning the methods and technique of the English poets, especially the earlier ones.

This morning Baxter's secretary rose and left part of her breakfast uneaten, hurrying into the house as if to avoid something which she had seen and dreaded.

.   .   .   .

I ate a long time, dreaming.

Darrie came out, followed immediately by Daniel. Daniel was in an obstreperous mood . . he cried out that I must be his "telegraph pole," that he would be a lineman, and climb me. I felt an affection for him that I had not known before. I played with him, letting him climb up my leg.

He finished, a-straddle my shoulders. I reached up and sat him still higher, on my head. And he waved his arms and shouted, as if making signals to someone far off.

Darrie laughed.

"Which would you rather have, a son or a daughter?" she asked me.

"I don't know," I replied, letting Daniel slide down, "but I think I'd rather have a daughter . . the next generation will see a great age of freedom for women . . feminism. . .

"Then it would be a grand thing, too, to have a beautiful daughter to go about with . . and I would be old and silver-haired and benignant-looking . . and people would say, as they saw the two of us:

" 'There goes the poet, John Gregory, and his daughter . . isn't she a beautiful girl!'

"And she would be a great actress."

.   .   .   .

Penton came forth from the big house . . he poised tentatively like a queer bird on the verge of a long flight . . then he wavered rapidly down the steps.

"—slept late! . . has the mail come yet? . . where's Ruth?"

"Isn't she in the house?" I queried.

"I saw her stepping out at the back door a minute ago" . . said Darrie.

"We had breakfast together . . I . . ."

"I hope she doesn't stay away long . . I have an article on Blue Laws as a Reactionary Weapon, that I want to dictate for a magazine . . —one of her moods, I suppose!"

I looked the little, large-browed man over almost impersonally. I saw him as from far away. He came out very clear to me.

I found a profound pity for him waking in my heart, together with a sort of contempt.

"And where's Hildreth?"

"Not up yet I presume," replied Darrie.

. . . .

I excused myself and hurried back to my tent . . where, instead of settling down to work on the third act of my play, I lay prone on my cot, day-dreaming of the future. How beautiful it would be, now that I had at last found my life-mate!

I thanked God that nothing trivial was in my heart to mar the stupendousness of my love, my first real passion for a woman!

. . . .

"Johnnie!"

I leaped alert. It was Hildreth, at my tent door. . .

"Get up, you lazy boy . . surely you haven't been sleeping all this time?"

"No, darling."

"I ate my breakfast all alone," she remarked, in an aggrieved tone, "where's Darrie and Mubby and Ruth?"

"God knows! I don't—and I don't care!"

"You needn't be peevish!"

"Peevish? —as long as you are with me I don't care if all the rest of humanity are dead."

I stepped out beside her. We stood locked in a long embrace.

She drew back, with belated thoughtfulness. . .

"We ought to be more careful . . so near the house."

"I'm so glad you're in the little house near my tent, Hildreth."

"But we can't be together there much . . it's too near the big house."

"What shall we do, then?"

"There's the fields and the woods . . miles of them . . the whole outside world for us."

"I don't see why *we* shouldn't go strolling together . . the rest are all abroad somewhere, too . . but we must be careful, Johnnie, very careful."

"Careful—why?"

"Because of Mubby."

"But he doesn't love you any more?"

"I'm not so sure about that .. I'm not so sure about anything."

.   .   .   .

I never saw the world so beautiful as on that day. I was translated to the veritable garden of Eden. The community had been
named rightly. I was Adam and Hildreth was my Eve.

And so it went on for two blissful weeks. . .

If the Voice of God had met us, going abroad beneath the trees,
I would not have been surprised.

Hildreth took her volume of Blake with her on our rambles ..
and we revelled in his "Songs of Experience" as well as "Songs of
Innocence"; and we were moved deeply by the huge, cloudy gran-
deur of his prophetic books. . .

Why could it not go on forever thus? eternal summer, everlasting
love in its first rosy flush? . .

Hildreth was very wise and very patient with one who was as
yet a mere acolyte in love's ways and uses .. she taught me many
things, and I adored her for it—as little by little, day by day, she
brought me to the full stature of my manhood. . .

.   .   .   .

Of course the two other women of the household immediately
sensed what was happening. But Penton remained pathetically
blind. . .

What an incredible man! A mole would have gotten a glimmer
of the gradually developing change.

With bravado I acted my part of the triangular drama .. but
Hildreth carried off her part with an easiness, a femininely delicate
boldness, that compelled my utmost admiration .. she even threw
suspicious Ruth and Darrie off the scent—at times.

.   .   .   .   .

The night of the performance of *A Midsummer Night's Dream* I
shall never forget .. Hildreth as Titania in her green tights .. I
sat in the back (she would not allow me in the front because it
might fluster her, she pleaded) and enjoyed a sense of blissful ownership in her, as she glided about, through the Shakespearean scenes ..
—such a sense of ownership that it ran through my veins with a
full feeling, possessed my entire body. . .

Who was this little, alien man, Penton Baxter, who also dared
claim her possession! . .

Nonchalantly and with an emotion of inner triumph I let him

walk homeward with Hildreth, while I paced along with Ruth and Darrie.

Let him congratulate her now on her triumph . . that she had had, as Titania, there under the wide heaven of stars, in our outdoor theatre . . in the midst of the Chinese lanterns that swayed in the slight breaths of summer air. . .

Later on, when she was warm in my arms, *I* would congratulate her . . —tell her she was greater than Bernhardt . . than Duse herself! . . tell her every incredible thing that lovers hold as mere, commonplace truths.

.   .   .   .

Jones had acquitted himself wonderfully as Bottom . . roaring like any suckling dove . . putting real philosophic comedy in his part . . to the applause of even the elder Grahame, who, to do him credit, was not such a bad sport, after all.

.   .   .   .

"Johnnie, we are having a sing to-night . . there'll be a full moon up. I have informed the committee that you will read a few of your poems by the camp-fire."

"—the first time I ever heard of it," I replied, concealing my pride in the invitation, under show of being disgruntled. . .

That was Penton's way, arranging things first, telling you afterward.

"But you will do it? I have said you would!"

"Yes, Penton, if you wish me to!"

.   .   .   .

Hildreth was always insistent on my strength . . my greyhound length of limb, my huge chest . . she stood up and pounded on my chest once. . .

"Oh, why do I pick out a poor poet, and not a millionaire, for a lover!"

.   .   .   .

There grew up between us a myth . . we were living in cave-days . . she was my cave-woman . . I was her cave-man. . .

As I came to her in my bath-robe (for now, bolder with seeming immunity, we threw caution aside, and met often in the little house)——

As I came to her in my bath-robe, unshaven, once . . she called me her Paphnutius . . and she was my Thaïs . . and she told me Anatole France's story of *Thaïs*.

But the cave-legend of our love . . in a previous incarnation . . was what spelled her most . . she doted on strength . . cruel, sheer, brute strength. . .

That I could carry her, lift her high up with ease, toss her about, rejoiced her to the utmost. . .

I caught her up in my arms, pleasing this humour, tossing her like a ball . . till my muscles were as sore as if I had fought through the two halves of a foot-ball game. . .

Out of all this play between us there grew a series of Cave Poems. One of them I set aside to read at the sing, beside the camp-fire.

.   .   .   .

They had chorused *Up With the Bonnet for Bonny Dundee* and *You Take the Highway* . .

There ran a ripple of talk while they waited for me.

In the red glow of the camp-fire I towered over the stocky little husband as he introduced me.   Hildreth was sitting there . . I must make a good impression before my mate.   All I saw was she— too patently, I fear.

I went through poem after poem, entranced with the melody of my verse . . mostly delicate, evanescent stuff . . like this one. . .

"THE EMPEROR TO HIS LOVE

"I've a green garden with a grey wall 'round
  Where even the wind's foot-fall makes no sound;
  There let us go and from ambition flee,
  Accepting love's brief immortality.
  Let other rulers hugely labour still
  Beneath the burden of ambition's ill
  Like caryatids heaving up the strain
  Of mammoth chambers, till they stoop again. . .
  Your face has changed my days to splendid dreams
  And baubled trumpets, traffics, and trirèmes;
  One swift touch of your passion-parted lips
  Is worth five armies and ten seas of ships."

Hildreth's applause was sweet. My heart almost burst with happiness within me, as those tiny hands, that had run through my hair and been so wonderful with me . . hands that I had kissed and fondled in secret—joined in unison with Penton's and Darrie's and Ruth's hand-claps.

"And now I will finish with the *Song of Kaa, the Cave-Man*," I announced . . it seemed that the poem was not, after all, in the bunch of MSS. I had brought along with me. . .

At last I found it—and read:

"THE SONG OF KAA

"Beat with thy club on a hollow tree
  While I chant the song of Kaa for thee:
  I lived in a cave, alone, at first,
  Till into a neighbouring valley I burst
  Wild and bearded and seeking prey,
  And I came on Naa, and bore her away. . .
  Away to my hole in the crest of the hill,
  Where I broke her body to my fierce will. . .

·   ·   ·   ·   ·

"My fellow cave-men, fell in a rage:
  'What hast thou done?' cried Singh, the Sage,
  'For I hear far off a battle-song,
  And the tree-men come, a hundred strong. . .'
  Long the battle and dread the fight;
  We hurled rocks down from our mountain height"——

I copy this from memory alone . . Hildreth has all my cave-poems.
I gave them to her, holding no transcripts of them——
The upshot——

"All of our tribe were slain . . Naa and I alone escaped—
     going far off——
  To start another people and clan:
  She, the woman, and I, the man!"

In my love-drunkenness, I looked directly at Hildreth as I read

the last lines . . she lowered her head and picked at her sandal. . .
The applause was tumultuous. . .
Penton Baxter rose to his feet, as chairman of the occasion. . .
"I'm sure we all thank Mr. Gregory——"

    •   •   •   •   •   •   •

Events trod rapidly on one another's heels. Though Penton
had gone on frequent walks with Darrie, after his day's work,—
chiefly because Hildreth had not wanted to go on walks with him
herself, or had not wanted to accompany them both—yet she and
I seized on the precedent Penton and Darrie had set, and we were
abroad most of the time . . roaming idyllically in the fields, the
woods . . passionate . . mad with the new love that had come to us . .
unseeing, in our absorption in each other's arms . . praying with
devout lover's prayers that we were as unseen as unseeing. . .
We were abroad in the fields so much that even Penton himself
must notice it. . .
So we developed the flimsiest of all flimsy pretexts . . pretended
to be engrossed, together, in of all things, the study of—toadstools
and mushrooms . . taking with us Neltje Blanchan's book on *Mushrooms and Toadstools,* with its beautiful coloured illustrations . .
and we did learn a lot about these queer vegetations that grow
without the need of chlorophyll . . entering into a world of new
colours in the vegetable kingdom . . exquisite pinks and mauves
and greys . . blues . . purples . . reds . . russets . . in the darkest
spots of the woods we sought and found strange species of these
marvellous growths . . that grow more readily in the dark and
obscurity, the twilights of nature, than in the open sunlight of
green summer days. . .

    •   •   •   •   •   •   •

Down vistas of forest we often pursued each other . . often got
lost so that it took hours for re-orientation . . once, for awhile, to
our great fright, we could not re-discover our clothes, that we had
lightly tossed aside on the bank of a brook lost and remote,—that
had never before laved a human body in its singing recesses of
forest foliage . . for I had been playing satyr to her nymph, pursuing her. . .

    •   •   •   •   •   •   •

And each day saw us a little more reckless, more bold and open in our love, our passion, for each other.

.   .   .   .   .   .

"How handsome love is making you, my Paphnutius!"

I was wearing my bath-robe, had stopped at her cottage a moment, in the morning, where she sat, in an easy chair, reading peacefully. . . I was on my way for my morning dip in a nearby brook. . .

My bath-robe, that made me, somehow, feel so aristocratic, so like a member of the leisure class . . I forgot to tell how I had brought it all the way from Kansas, together with my MSS.

.   .   .   .   .   .

As I swam about in the brook, not over four feet deep, I sang and shouted. I had never been so happy in my life. . .

I dried myself in the sun, using its morning heat for a towel. . .

As I sat there on a rock, I heard a crackling of twigs, and Penton thrust his way through the intervening branches to my bare rock and my bare self . . I hastily, I do not know why, put on my bath-robe. . .

"Hello, Penton."

"Good morning, Johnnie. I felt you'd be down here for your morning bath . . I came to have a serious talk with you."

"Yes?"

"I want you to take calmly what I am about to say!"

Penton was much impressed with my stories of tramp days and tales of adventure on land and sea, which you may be sure my sense of the dramatic had encouraged me to lay on thick—and he, plainly, did not desire any heat in the discussion which was to follow. . .

"Recently it has come to my attention that there has been a lot of gossip about you and Hildreth . . your conduct together." He drew his lips together tightly, settled himself for a long siege. . .

"Why, Penton," I began, protestingly and hypocritically,—I had planned far other and franker conduct in such an emergency—but here I was, deprecating the truth——

"Why, Penton, God knows——"

"Never mind . . if it is true, I am very sorry for you—for Hildreth's sake, for yours, for mine . . but I want to warn you, if it is not true, to look out . . you, as a friend, owe me some obligations . . I have taken you in here, accepted you as one almost of my family, and——"

"But, Penton, this is unfair," I lied, "unfair even to suspect me——"

"If it had been anybody but you, Johnnie, I would have been suspicious weeks ago . . Oh, I know, Hildreth . . she is giving all the manifestations . . how her face shines, how beautiful she has grown, as she does, with a new heart interest! . . and her taking my little cottage . . ousting me from it. . .

"If it was anyone else," and he fetched a deep sigh, with tears standing in his eyes, leaving the sentence incomplete.

At that moment I was impelled almost to cast myself at his feet, to confess, and beg forgiveness. . .

"I want to warn you," he went on, "of Hildreth . . once before this has happened . . she is a varietist by nature, as I am essentially a monogamist."

"—and the free love idea, it was you who taught her this, brought her into contact with Havelock Ellis, Ellen Key, Rosa Von Mayerreder?"

"I deny that. I believe in human freedom . . divorce . . remarriage . . but not in extreme sex-radicalism . . Hildreth has misinterpreted me . . the people you mention are great idealists, but in many ways they go too far . . true—I brought Hildreth into contact with these books; but only that she might use her own judgment, not accept them wholly and blindly, as she has done. . ."

I looked at the man. He was sincere. An incredible, naïve, almost idiotic purity shone in his face. . .

Again I was impelled to confess. Again I held my tongue. Again I lied.

"Penton, what you have just said about you and Hildreth and your lives together, I shall consider as sacred between us."

He gave me his hand.

"Promise me one thing, that you will not take Hildreth as your sweetheart . . be true to our friendship first, Johnnie."

"Penton, I am only flesh and blood; I will promise, if anything happens, to tell you, ultimately, the truth."

He looked at me with close scrutiny again, at this ambiguous speech.

"Johnnie, *have* you told me the absolute truth?"

"Yes!" evading his eyes.

"—because there is a wild strain in Hildreth that only needs a little rousing——" He paused.

.   .   .   .

"Johnnie," as we walked away, "don't you think you had better pack up and leave? *The next time* I am going to sue for a divorce."

.   .   .   .

We walked home arm in arm. I simulated so well that it was Baxter who begged pardon for even suspecting me.

But I felt like a dog. I, for my part, determined to bid farewell to Hildreth that very evening, before she retired for the night, in her cottage—take train to New York, and so to Paris, without first finishing my *Judas*, as I had intended.

We would bury forever in the secret places of our hearts what had already happened between us .. this was my first impulse. ..

My next was—that we should up and run away together, and defy Penton Baxter and the world.

.   .   .   .

Hildreth could see by the strangeness in my behaviour, as I came into the cottage, to kiss her good-night .. and stay a little while—a new custom of ours, as we grew bolder—could see that I had something on my mind.

I related to her all that had taken place between me and Penton that morning. ..

"The cad," she cried, "the nasty cad, to talk to you so about me. .. I would have told you myself because you are my lover .. but he had no right to tell you .. as far as he has proof positive, you are merely a mutual friend. ..

"But that's the way with him. He has mixed his own life up so that it is all public, to him.

"Yes," she cried impetuously and passionately .. "it's true .. I have not been faithful to him before. .."

"—and you returned to him? wasn't that weak?"

I took her hands in mine, with mind and soul made up at last. ..

"This time you can go through with it. Here's a man who will stand by you forever. I can earn a living for both of us, and——"

"Don't let's discuss the horrid old subject any more to-night. .. I'm tired of discussing .. as you love me, read some poetry to me .. or I shall scream!"

"Have you ever read the sonnets of George Santayana? .. I know most of them by heart .. let me quote you his best. . .

> 'O world, thou choosest not the better part!
> It is not wisdom to be only wise,
> And on the inward vision close the eyes,
> But it is wisdom to believe the heart.
> Columbus found a world, and had no chart
> Save one that faith deciphered in the skies
> To trust the soul's invincible surmise
> Was all his science and his only art.
> Our knowledge is a torch of smoky pine
> That lights the pathway but one step ahead
> Across a void of mystery and dread.
> Bid, then, the tender light of faith to shine
> By which alone the mortal heart is led
> Unto the thinking of the thought divine!'

 · · · · ·

"I wish I had written that!" I said, in a hushed, awed voice, after a moment's silence. . .

 · · · · · ·

"Now kiss me good-night and go to your tent .. I feel restless troubled in spirit, to-night," she said, continuing:

"Perhaps I have been too harsh with Penton. . .

"He is steering on a chartless sea with no compass. . .

"No wonder he, and all radicals and pioneers in human thought, blunder ridiculously. . .

"The conservative world has its charts, its course well mapped out. . .

"I suppose I am not strong enough, big enough, for him."

"Hush! now it is you who're just talking!" I replied.

"You're jealous!"

"By God, yes. I *am* jealous, though I suppose I ought to be ashamed of it."

 · · · · · ·

She sat in bed, propped up with pillows. She had been reading Shakespeare's sonnets aloud to me. The big green-shaded reading lamp cast a dim light that pervaded the room.

She reached out both arms to me, the wide sleeves falling back
from them, and showing their feminine whiteness. . .

I sat down beside her, caught her to me, kissed her till she was
breathless. . .

"There . . there . . please! *Please!*"

"What! you're not tiring of my kisses?"

"No, dearest boy, but I have a curious feeling, I tell you . .
maybe we're being watched. . ."

"Nonsense . . he believes I told him the truth."

And I caught her in my arms again, half-reclining on the bed.

"Sh!" she flung me off with a sudden impulse of frightened
strength, "I hear someone."

"It's only the wind."

"Quick! . . my God!"——

.   .   .   .

I snatched up a volume of Keats. It fell open at "St. Agnes
Eve." I hurled myself into a chair . . gathering my breath I began
aloud, as naturally as I could——

> "St. Agnes' Eve! ah, bitter chill it was;
>   The owl, for all his feathers, was a-cold——"

At that very instant, Penton burst in at the door.

He paused a dramatic moment, his back to it, facing us.

I stopped reading, in pretended astonishment.

"Well, Penton?" acted Hildreth languidly. . .

The look of defeat and bewilderment on the husband's face would
have been comic if it had not been pitiable.

I rose, laying the book down carefully.

"I think I'll go now, Hildreth . . you wish to see Penton alone."
I put all the calm casual deference in my voice possible. I started
to walk easily to the door.

"No! stop! I wish you to stay here, John Gregory . . since you've
got yourself into this——"

"I'd like to know what you mean by 'got yourself into this'?"

"Oh, Gregory, let's not talk nonsense any longer."

"You don't believe what I assured you this morning?"

"Johnnie, it's not human . . I can't make myself, and I've tried
and tried, God knows!"

"I'd like to know, for my part, just what you mean, Penton Baxter, spying on me this way—bursting in on poor Johnnie Gregory and me like a maniac, while we were only reading poetry together."

"—reading poetry together!" he echoed bitterly, almost collapsing, as he went into a chair.

Again I tried to make my exit.

"Johnnie, I want you to stay. I want to have all this out right here and now," snapped Baxter decisively.

"Very well . . if you put it that way."

"—a nice way to treat your guest," Hildreth interposed, "the way you've been raving about him, too. 'Johnnie Gregory' this, and 'Johnnie Gregory' that!—and the minute he arrives, first you try to make him put up at the community inn; and now you accuse him of—of——"

Hildreth began to weep softly. . .

And then began a performance at which I stood aside, mentally, in admiration . . the way that little woman handled her husband! She wept, she laughed, she upbraided, she cajoled . . at one moment swore she wanted nothing better than to die, at the other, vowed eternal fidelity till old age overtook them both. . .

.   .   .   .

"I *must* go," I cried, quite ashamed of myself in my heart. Baxter's credulity had expanded again, in the sun of Hildreth's *forgiveness* of him for his unjust suspicions! . .

For the first time in my life I perceived how a desperate woman can twist a man any way she wants.

"No, you must not go! it is I who am going—to show that I trust you."

"Good God!" I protested—this was too much! "no, no . . good-night, both of you . . good-night, Penton! good-night, Hildreth!"

Penton Baxter stepped in my way, took hold of one of my hands in both of his. . .

"Please, Johnnie, please, dear friend . . I wish you to stay while I myself go. Finish reading the poem to Hildreth . . I think I have been too harsh in my judgment of both of you . . only please do be more discreet, if only for appearance's sake, in the future. . .

"Sit down where you were. I wish to show that I trust you both. . .

"Good-night, Hildreth!" and he kissed his wife in fond contrition.

"Good-night, Johnnie . . forgive me!"

And he wavered out at the door, his face set in pain.

. . . .

As soon as he had gone I rose swiftly.

"And now I must go."

"If you men aren't the funniest things!" she caught me by the hand, detaining me . . "not yet . . wait a minute. Read more of that poem you began, if only for a blind."

I picked up the book, started reading again . . strangely a rush of tears flooded my eyes and blurred the type. . .

I began to sob, heart-sick. I did love the absurd little man. My heart ached, broken over my lies. . .

"Oh! Oh!" I sobbed, "Hildreth, my woman, my sweetheart—he trusted me, Hildreth . . he trusted me!"

I knelt by the bed, thrusting my head into the lap of my First Woman.

She kissed me on top of the head.

"You're both two big, silly babies, that's all you are."

. . . .

It was dawn when I returned to my tent, pulled the flap aside, fell, exhausted, on my cot in dreamless sleep. . .

. . . .

How was it all going to end?

It seemed to me that I had tapped violent, subterranean currents in life and passion, that I had not hitherto known existed. . .

Free Love, Marriage, Polygamy, Polyandry, Varietism, Promiscuity—these were but tossing chips of nomenclature, bits of verbal welter, upborne by deep terrible human currents that appalled the imagination!

The man who prated glibly of any ready solution, orthodox or heterodox, radical or conventional, of the problem of the relationships between men and women was worse than a fool, he was a dangerous madman!

. . . .

Hildreth and I, a-field, had found a bed of that exceptionally poisonous mushroom named *Pallida* something or other . . the book said its poison was kin to that of the poison in the rattlesnake's bite.

My eyes met with Hildreth's . . we needed say no word, both thinking
the same thought that frightened us! . . "how easy it would be—!"

. . . .

Now we were plumbing the darker side of passion. Something
that Carpenter does not write of in his *Love's Coming of Age.*

. . . .

A night of wind, shifting into rain. Hildreth I knew would be
afraid, alone.

I stepped into her cottage, in my bath-robe. She almost screamed
at my sudden appearance. For I came in at the door like a shadow,
the wind and rain making such a tumult that a running horse would
not have been heard.

"Dearest . . you're all wringing wet . . you're dripping all over
the floor. Throw off that robe. Dry yourself—there's a towel
there!"

She flung me her kimono. "Here, put this on, till you're comfortable again."

I came out in her kimono, which I was bursting through . . my
arms sticking out to my elbow.

She laughed herself almost into hysteria at my funny appearance.

. . . .

"It will be quite safe to-night. I don't think he'd venture out.
This is a hurricane, not a rainstorm . . besides, I believe he's a little
afraid of you, Johnnie . . I was watching him rather closely, while
I handled him, the other night . . he kept an uneasy eye on you all
the time."

"God, but you were superb, Hildreth . . if you could only act
that way on the stage!—"

"I *could* act that way on the stage," she replied unexpectedly, a
trifle put out. . .

Then——

"A woman has to do many things to save herself——"

"Oh, I swear that you are the most marvellous, the most beautiful
woman in the world . . I love you . . I adore you . . I'd die for you . .
right here . . now!"

. . . .

As we lay there in the dark the storm pulled and tugged and
battered as if with great, sinister hands, striving to get in at us.

Hildreth trembled in my arms, shaking afresh at each shock of the wind and the rain.

"Don't be afraid, my little woman!"

"I wonder if he'd dare come down to-night?"

"If he did, and caught us, I'd kill him."

"He knows that, if he knows anything, I'm sure . . that's why I think we're all right!"

And she came up closer into my arms with a sigh of content.

.   .   .   .

I had been asleep. . .

The sudden madness and saturnalia of love into which I had these few weeks been plunged tapped, it seemed, my subliminal consciousness, maybe my memory of former incarnations. . .

I never had such a vision in my life. . .

I was fully aware of my surroundings, yet through them shone another, a far reality that belonged to me, too.

I described it to Hildreth, as she lay, thrilled, beside me.

A cave . . high up on the hill-crest . . our cave, that we had imagined, now come true. . .

I was a huge chap, with a girdle of leaves about my waist . . strange, tropic leaves . . there was black hair all over my body . . there was a little, red fire back in the cave's obscurity. . .

I had come in, casting a dead fawn down from my shoulder. . .

Hildreth came forward . . it was plainly she . . though with fine red hair like down on her legs. . .

"But your name is Naa . . my name is Kaa, the hunter, the slayer of good, red meat."

"Johnnie, do you really see that,—*all* that!"

She was enthralled like a child, as I described the landscape that lay, spread immense, beneath us . and the wide ocean, great and blue, that tossed to the east.

Though I was genuinely possessed by this strange vision, though it was no make-believe, I could not help injecting a little Kansas horse-play into it. . .

I sank my teeth in "Naa's" shoulder, till she cried aloud. I seized her by the hair and dragged her till she lay prone on the floor.

I stood over her, making guttural noises, which I did so realistically that it made shivers run up and down my back while doing it. . .

I was almost as frightened as she was.

Before I knew it, she was thinking I had suddenly gone mad. She was shouting "Mubby" for help—her husband's pet name. . .

The little fool! I caught her over the mouth with a grim hand.

"Don't do that . . can't a fellow play once in a while?"

"But it wasn't *all* play, was it?"

"No, I really saw the cave, and the primeval landscape.

"Shall I tell you some more?"

"No, it frightens me too much . . it seems too real. And you've bruised me, and my head feels as if you've torn half my hair out."

"Why did you call out your husband's pet name?"

"I don't know . . did I?"

"Yes!"

"After a pause in the dark.

"Tell me, was he . . was Mubby . . back there, in our former life?"

"O yes, he was there."

"And Darrie, too?"

"Yes, Darrie, too!"

"If my name was Naa and your name was Kaa, what were their names?"

"Mubby was named Baa and Darrie was Blaa!"

This convulsed Hildreth.

"You great, big, sweet fool of a poet, I do love you, I really do!"

.   .   .   .

"We were made for each other in every way . . my head just fits your shoulder," she observed quaintly.

.   .   .   .

"Mubby came down to me this morning," said Hildreth one evening, "and pleaded to be taken back again . . as husband. . ."

"And what?—"

"What did I do? . . when I love you? . . the mere idea made me sick to think of. I couldn't endure him again."

.   .   .   .

One afternoon Penton and Hildreth were closeted together from lunch to dark. It was my turn to cry out in my heart, and suffer agonies of imagination.

.   .   .   .

The next morning Hildreth began packing up, with the aid of

Mrs. Jones. I came upon her, in the library, where I had gone to get a book. My face fell dismally.

"I can't endure it any longer, Johnnie, I'm going back home, to New York . . my father will take me in."

"And how about me?"

"—wait patiently a few days then, if you still feel the same about me, follow me! . . and, until you come to join me, write me at least three times a day."

"I'll do it . ." then I couldn't help being playful again, "I'll write you entirely in cave-fashion."

"I am taking a big step, Johnnie, I'm through with Penton Baxter forever—but I wonder if my new life is to be with you . . you are such an irresponsible, delightful madman at times. . .

"You're wonderful as a lover . . but as a man with a woman to take care of——!"

"Don't worry about that! just give me a chance, and I'll show you I can be practical too."

.   .   .   .

Hildreth had gone. With her going the bottom seemed to drop out of my existence, leaving a black hole where it had fallen through. I walked about, looking so truly miserable, that even Baxter spoke with gentle consideration to me.

"Poor Johnnie, to think you'd run into a proposition like this, the first pop out of the box."

"No, it isn't what you think . . I'm getting malaria, I believe."

.   .   .   .   .   .

But to be deprived of her, my first love. No longer to be in her presence, no longer to watch her quiet smile, the lovely droop of her mouth's corner . . to feed on the kisses no more that had become as necessary as daily bread itself to me——

I began to lose weight . . to start up in the night, after a brief fit of false slumber, hearing myself, as if it were an alien voice, crying her name aloud. . .

I whispered and talked tender, whimsical, silly things to my pillow, holding it in my arms, as if it were she. . .

.   .   .   .   .   .

Each day I sent her four, five letters . . letters full of madness, absurdity, love, despair, wild expressions of intimacy that I would have died to know anybody else ever saw.

Her first letter in return burned me alive with happiness. . .

.   .   .   .

"—you know why she went to the city," Penton teased, "it's because 'Gene Mallows, the California poet, is up there. He and she got on pretty well when we were on the coast."

"You lie!" I bellowed, beside myself, "Hildreth will be faithful to me . . she has promised."

Penton Baxter looked me up and down, courageously, coolly, for a long time. Slowly I realised what I had just said.

"That's all I wanted to know, John Gregory! I've got it out of you at last!"

He turned on his heel.

Changing his mind, he faced me again. This time there was a despairful agony of kindness in his face.

"Dear boy, I'm sorry for all this thing that has come between us. But there is yet time for you to keep out of it. Hildreth and I are done with each other forever . . but you needn't be mixed up in this affair. . .

"Johnnie, let her stay in New York, and, no matter how much she wants you, don't go up there to join her."

"I love her. I adore her. I want to be where she is. Now the whole truth is out."

"My poor friend!"

"Don't call me your friend—you——"

He tightened his lips. . .

"If you go up there to join her, remember that I gave you fair warning."

.   .   .   .

I could endure it no longer, the torment of not seeing her, of not being with her. . .

As her favourite sonneteer, Santayana, writes—lines she often quoted—

> "Love leads me on, no end of love appears.
> Is this the heaven, poets, that ye paint?
> Oh then, how like damnation to be blessed!"

.   .   .   .

I informed Ruth, Darrie, Penton that I was going to New York in the morning. . .

Penton immediately whisked out of my sight, full of uncontrollable emotion. . .

Darrie and Ruth almost fell upon me, trying to persuade me not to rejoin Hildreth. I evaded by saying that I was now on my way to Europe, that possibly I might see her before I went, but——

.   .   .   .

I had an hour till train time. My MSS. was packed again, my Josephus, my Homer, my Shakespeare, my Keats, my bath robe.

I thought I would escape without saying good-bye.

Put Penton came down the front porch, stood in my path.

"Johnnie, a last warning."

"I want none of your last warnings."

"Are you going to Hildreth?"

"I'm tired of being a liar. I've never lied so much in my life . . yes, I'm going to Hildreth . . and I'm going to persuade her to live with me, and defy the whole damned world — the world of fake radicals that talk about divorces when the shoe pinches them, as well as the world of conservatives," I announced harshly.

"I've done all I could!" he responded wearily, "I see you won't come to your senses—wait a minute!" and he turned on his heel. He had asked me to wait with such solemnity that I stuck still in my tracks, waiting.

He disappeared into the big house, to re-emerge with, of all things, *the coffee percolator!*

"Here!" he exclaimed, holding out the object to me ceremoniously and seriously, "you can take this to your goddess, this poison-machine, and lay it on her altar. Tell her I offered this to you. Tell her that it is a symbol of her never coming back here again."

Here was where I too lacked a sense of humour. I struck the coffee percolator out of his hands. I stalked off.

.   .   .   .

On the way to New York I built the full dream of what Hildreth and I were to effect for the world—a practical example, in our life as we lived it together, of the rightness of free love. . .

We would test it out, would rent a cottage somewhere, preferably on the Jersey coast near the sea shore . . autumn was coming on, and there would be lovely, crystal-clear weather . . and the scent of pines in the good air.

.   .   .   .

Perhaps Penton, Hildreth and I could all three join in amicable accord, over the solution of our difficulty, along radical and idealistic lines.

.   .   .   .

I hurried to the address given me by Hildreth. She was not in, but her mother was . . a plump, rather good looking, fashionably dressed woman. Evidently the mother did not know of the relationship between me and her daughter.

"So you are the poet Hildreth has told me about?" after we had discoursed for upwards of an hour——

"I can easily see how Hildreth has grown so fond of you," and she patted me on the head as if I were a schoolboy, in motherly fashion.

.   .   .   .

"Mother's rather stupid and old-fashioned . . there'd be no use trying to explain the situation to her. The best thing we can do is to persuade her that Daniel needs her, down in Eden . . that will remove her from the flat, so we can have it all to ourselves for a few days, in order to plan what is to be done next."

Next morning Mrs. Deuell, Hildreth's mother, as innocent as a new-born lamb as to what was up, permitted herself to be shipped off to Eden, to take care of Daniel.

.   .   .   .

Instead of planning, however, and marshalling our resources, Hildreth and I abandoned ourselves to the mutual happiness and endearments of two love-drunk, emotion-crazed beings on a honeymoon. . .

.   .   .   .

The bell rang. In walked Darrie.

"Well, Darrie!" and Hildreth embraced her friend. And I was glad to see her, too. I knew that, in spite of the high pressure we had lived under during the past summer, Darrie was trying hard to be just, to be friend to all of us. . .

She laughed at the disorder of the place . . dishes unwashed . . food scattered about on the table. . .

"What a pair of love-birds you two are."

"And has Penton accepted the situation?"

"I came up to tell you that he has . . it has made him quite sick, though!"

"Poor Mubby!" Hildreth ejaculated.

"—but he has sent me to tell you that you can go away together wherever you please, that he won't molest you in the least."

"It's too incredible!" cried Hildreth, almost disappointed, "you don't know him . . he's changed his mind, I am sure, since you left."

"He said he would follow me by Saturday (it was Wednesday) leaving your mother in care of Daniel."

"Does mother suspect?——"

"No . . not at all."

"If the entire world fell about mother's ears, she wouldn't know."

"What do you two lovers purpose doing?"

I unfolded my scheme of living with Hildreth in a Jersey bungalow. . . Derek's income to me would go on a while yet . . I could sell stories and poems to the New Yorw magazines. . . Hildreth could write a book as well as I . . we would become to the modern world an example of the radical love-life . . the Godwin and Wollstonecraft of the age.

.   .   .   .

We ate supper together, the three of us, in the flat. It was so cosy. Darrie and Hildreth joined in cleaning the house that afternoon.

But a bomb was to be hurled among us.

At twelve o'clock of the next day the 'phone rang.

Darrie answered it. After a few words she came for me, her face as white as a sheet. . .

"My God, Penton is in town!"

"—this is only Thursday . . he was not coming till Saturday!" I exclaimed, full of forboding.

"I knew, I knew he wouldn't keep his original mind!" exclaimed Hildreth.

"He's holding the wire . . wants to say something to you, Johnnie."

.   .   .   .

"Yes, Penton, what is it?"

"Only this," his voice replied, as if rehearsing a set speech, "yesterday afternoon I sent a telegram to my lawyer to institute proceedings for a divorce, and I mentioned you as co-respondent. . ."

"Damn you to hell . . I thought we were going to settle this in the radical way?"

"It's the only way out that I can see. I've stood this business till it's almost killing me."

"Well, is that all?"

"No . . somehow—how, I do not know, the *New York Journal* has gotten hold of my wire . . it will be in all the papers to-night or to-morrow . . so I advise you and Hildreth to disappear quietly some-where, if you don't want to see the reporters,—who will all presently be on the way to the flat."

"Damn you, Penton . . needn't tell *me* about the news leaking out . . you've done it yourself . . now I want you to promise me only one thing, that you'll hold the reporters off for a couple of hours, till we have a good start."

"I'll do my best," answered he, "but please believe me. How they got the contents of the telegram I do not know, but on my honour I did not give it out nor did I tell the reporters where you are."

. . . .

Hildreth was so angry she could hardly speak.

"This is a fine to-do," exclaimed Darrie, "Penton distinctly prom-ised me——"

"I'd like to get a good crack at him!" I boasted, at the same time enjoying the excitement.

. . . .

Hildreth began packing her clothes in a large suitcase . . as we later found she cast all her clean clothes aside, and in her excitement included all her soiled linen and lingerie. . .

We had our last meal together. I brought in a large bottle of white wine. All of us grew rather hilarious and made a merry joke of the adventure. We poked fun at Penton.

We sallied forth at the front door, Darrie to go to the Martha Washington. "I don't want to be mixed up in the coming uproar and scandal," she exclaimed . . "so far, I'm clear of all blame, and I know only too well what the papers would insinuate."

Hildreth and I took train for New Jersey . . two tickets for—anywhere . . in our excited condition we ran off first to Elizabeth. We had with us exactly one hundred dollars, which I had borrowed of Darrie before we parted on our several ways.

I registered for Hildreth and myself as "Mr. Arthur Mallory and wife," in the register of an obscure hotel near the noise and clatter of a hundred trains drawing continually out and in.

It made me happy and important to sign her name on the register as something belonging to me.

Once alone in the room, Hildreth, to my consternation, could talk of nothing else but Penton.

"—to think that he would do such a thing to me, only to think of it!" she cried vehemently, again and again.

"If he believes in freedom for men and women, why was all this necessary? the sordidness of the public clamour? the divorce court? . . oh, my poor, dear, sweet, wild poet-boy, you're in for it! Don't you wish you were well out of all this and back in Kansas again?"

"No; I am glad. As long as I am with you I don't care what happens. I love you, Hildreth!"

.   .   .   .

In the night she woke, screaming, from a nightmare. I could hardly stop her.

"Hush, dearest . . darling . . sweetheart. . . I am with you; everything is all right" . . then, as she kept it up, "for God's sake . . Hildreth, do be quiet . . you're all right . . the man you love is here, close by you . . no harm shall come to you."

"Oh, Johnnie," clutching me, quivering, "I've just had such a horrible dream," sobbing as I took her tenderly in my arms. . .

"There, there, darling!"

She was quiet now.

"In a few minutes we would have had the whole hotel breaking in at the door . . thinking I was killing you."

.   .   .   .

She woke up again, and woke me up.

"Johnnie, find me some ink and a pen. I'm going to write that cad a letter that will shrivel him up like acid."

"Can't you wait till morning, Hildreth?" sleepily.

"No . . I *must* write it now."

I dressed. I went down to the hotel writing-room and came back with pen and ink.

She sat up in bed and wrote the letter. She then read it aloud to me. She was immensely pleased with her effort.

With a final gesticulation of vindictive, feminine joy, she succeeded in spilling the whole bottle of ink on the white bed-spread.

"Now you've done it."

"We'll have to clear out early before the chambermaid comes in . . we're only staying here for one night and can't waste our money paying for the damage."

In the morning I bought the papers.

The *American* had made a scoop. There it was, the story of the whole thing on the front page.

"PENTON BAXTER SUES FOR DIVORCE

NAMES VAGABOND-POET AS CO-RESPONDENT"

There it stood, in big head-lines.

The actuality stared us in the face. We belonged to each other now. It was no longer a summer idyll, but a practical reality.

As we took the train for Long Branch we realised that we had plunged midmost into the action that would put all our theories to the test. . .

I looked at my woman with a sidelong glance, as she sat beside me on the train seat. . . She was so pretty, so frail, so feminine that I pitied her, while at the same time my heart swelled with tenderness for her, and with pride of possession. For she was mine now without dispute. She, for her part, spoke but little, except illogically to upbraid Penton Baxter, as if he had perpetrated an ill on two people thoroughly innocent.

I was angry with him on other grounds . . he was not playing the radical game, but taking advantage of the rules of the conventional world.

With a fugitive sense of pursuit, we hired a cabby to drive us to a summer boarding house at Long Branch . . where Hildreth and I rented a single large room for both of us. . .

And there Hildreth immediately went into hysterics, and did nothing but weep. While I waited on her hand and foot, bringing up food to her because she was sensitive about the probability of people recognising her.

We stayed there a week. Each day the papers were full of our mysterious disappearance . . reporters were combing the country to find us. Reports of our being in various places were sent in by enterprising local correspondents. . .

Again we entrained . . for Sea Girt.

An old cabman who drove a dilapidated rig hailed us with uplifted whip.

"We are looking for a place to board."

"I'll take you to a nice, quiet place, just suited to two home-loving folks like you," he replied, thinking he had paid us a compliment, and whipping up his ancient nag.

Hildreth gave me a nudge and a merry look and it pleased me to see she still had her sense of humour left.

That night, as I held her in my arms, "Don't let these little, trivial inconveniences and incidents—the petty persecutions we are undergoing, have any effect on our great love," I pleaded.

"That's all very well, darling Johnnie, but where are we going to?"

"We'll find a cottage somewhere . . a pretty little cottage within our means," I replied, visioning a vine-trellised place such as poets and their brides must live in.

"Our money is giving out . . soon we'll have—to turn back to New York!"

"If we do, that need not part us . . I'll get a job on some newspaper or magazine and take care of you."

.   .   .   .

When I called for my mail at the Sea Girt post office, sure of hearing from Darrie, anyhow,—who promised us she would keep us posted, I found no letter. And the man at the window was certain he had handed over several letters addressed to me to someone else who had called for them, giving my name as his.

A wave of hot anger suffused my face. How stupid of me not to have noticed it before. Now I remembered the men who had followed us.

Our mail was being intercepted. How was Baxter to procure his divorce without gaining evidence in just such a way?

.   .   .   .

One night I started on a long walk alone. I walked along the beach. In the dark I took off my clothes and plunged for a swim into the chilly surf . . a high sea was thundering in. I was caught in the undertow, swept off my feet, and dragged beyond by depth . . for a moment I was of a heart to let go, to permit myself to be drowned . . I was even intrigued, for the moment, by the thought of what the newspapers would say about my passing over in such a romantic way.

But the will to live rose up in me. And I fought my way,—and it was a bitter fight,—back to shallow water. I flung myself prone on the beach, exhausted.

When I reached our room again, I related my adventure to Hildreth.

It was she who took care of me now. I lay all night in a high fever . . but I was so happy, for the woman of my heart sat close by me, holding my hand, speaking soft terms of endearment to me, tending to all my wants.

This tenderness, this solicitude and companionship seemed for the first time better to me than the maddest transports of passion that swept us into one.

. . . .

In the morning mail came a letter, general delivery, from Penton . . Now I was sure he was having our every step watched. A blind passion against him rose in me . . the little bounder!

In the letter he asked me to meet him at the Sea Girt railway station at four o'clock. I made it by the time indicated, by a brisk walk.

There he was, dropping off the train as it came to a stop. Another scene flashed through my mind, a visual remembrance of the day he had dropped off to visit me at Laurel.

Then we had rushed toward each other, hands extended in warm, affectionate greeting . . now . . I slowly sauntered up to him.

"Yes, Penton, what do you want; how much longer are you going to torture your wife?"

"—yours now, Johnnie; mine no longer!" grimly.

"If she were wholly mine, I'd knock you flat . . but you still have a sort of right in her that protects you from what I otherwise might do to you."

"For heaven's sake, let's be calm."

"Calm—when you say in your letter, 'you need not be afraid, I meditate no harm?'—do you mean to imply that, under any circumstance, I would be afraid of you?"

"Johnnie, there is only one way to settle this . . I'm set on getting the complete evidence for a divorce . . exactly where is Hildreth now?"

"None of your damned business . . all I can say is that she is somewhere near here . . and she's sick and hysterical through your persecutions . . and if you don't call off your snooping detectives, by the Lord God, if I run into any of·them, I'll try to kill them."

"Johnnie, it's the best thing to deliver the legal evidence and have it over with. Let me accompany you to where Hildreth is, and——"

"If she set eyes on you," I replied, "she'd fly at you and scratch your eyes out—in her present mood."

"Only *show* me where she is, then—point out the place."

"If I find you snooping around, you'll need hospital attention for a long time."

"Then you won't help facilitate the proceedings, secretly?"

"No, since you've begun this game, find out what you can yourself. What do you think I am?"

"A very foolish young man to treat me so when I am still your best friend."

"Here comes the north-bound train. You hop aboard and go on back to New York."

Seething with rage, I caught Penton Baxter by the arm and thrust him up the steps. . .

.   .   .   .

Next morning came a letter from Darrie, from the Martha Washington. We were the talk of the town, she told us.

She had tried to keep Penton from employing detectives to follow us. She advised us to return to New York—we must be out of money by this time. . .

Hildreth could stay at her mother's and father's flat till we made further arrangements for going off some place together.

.   .   .   .

"Darling, if we return from what has proven to be a wild-goose chase, will you promise me not to become disheartened, to lose faith in me?"

"Of course not, Johnnie . . I think Darrie offered very good advice," she sighed.

Back we turned, by the next day's train, full of a sense of frustration; what an involved, unromantic, practical world we lived in!

.   .   .   .

Hildreth heaved a sigh of content as we walked into her mother's flat again. Her mother was still at Eden . . alone . . taking care of Daniel, for whom she had a great love.

We had Darrie over the telephone, and soon she was with us, giving us the latest news of the uproar.

The papers were at us pro and con, mostly con.

Dorothy Dix had written a nasty attack on me, saying that I was climbing to fame over a woman's prostrate body . . that, in my own West, instead of a judge and a divorce court, a shotgun would have presided in my case. . .

The *Globe* was running a forum, suddenly stopped, as to whether people of genius and artistic temperament should be allowed more latitude than ordinary folk. . .

As Hildreth and I rode down Broadway together, side by side, unrecognised, on a street car, we saw plastered everywhere, "Stop That Affinity Hunt," a play of that name to be shown at Maxime Elliott's Theatre. . .

I must admit that I was pleased with the sudden notoriety that had come to me . . years of writing poetry had made my name known but moderately, here and there . . but having run away with a famous man's wife, my name was cabled everywhere . . even appeared in Japanese, Russian, and Chinese newspapers. . .

.   .   .   .

But this was not what I wanted of the papers . . I must use this space offered me to propagandise my ideas of free love. . .

So I arranged to meet Penton privately in the lobby of the Martinique.

.   .   .   .

Hildreth and I were there, waiting, before Penton came the next day. Appearing, he wore the old, bland, childlike smile, and he shook hands with us as if nothing untoward had ever taken place.

Someone had tipped off the reporters and they were on time, too, crowding about us eagerly. One young fellow from the *Sun*, looking like a graduate from a school of divinity, asked a special interview of me alone, which I gave . . afterward . . in a corner.

That *Sun* reporter gave me the fairest deal I ever received. He talked with me over an hour, without ever setting pencil to paper . . the other interviews were long over, Penton had left, Hildreth sat chafing. . .

"Come over and join us, Hildreth."

She sat listening in silence while I continued rehearsing all my
ideas on marriage, love, divorce . . how love should be all . . how
there should, ideally, be no marriage ceremony . . but if any at all,
only after the first child had been born . . how the state should have
nothing to do with the private love-relations of the individual . .

The reporter from the *Sun* shook hands good-bye.

"But you haven't taken a single note!" I protested.

"I have it all here, in my head."

"But how can you report me accurately?"

"See to-morrow's *Sun*."

. . . .

The interview with me was a marvel in two ways: it represented
to a hair's breadth everything I had pronounced, transmuted into
the reporter's own style of writing . . it curtailed my conversation
where I had repeated myself or wandered off into trivial detail.

. . . .

"I wonder what they'll say back in Kansas!" I had exclaimed
to Hildreth, in the hearing of the reporters.

"Oh, bother Kansas!" replied Hildreth humorously.

For a month "I wonder what they'll say back in Kansas" was a
catch-word for Broadway and the town.

When the *Evening Journal* put us in their "Dingbat Family" I
enjoyed the humour of it. But Hildreth was angry and aggrieved.

"You and Penton," remarked she, "for men of culture and sensi-
bility, have bigger blind spots than ordinary in your make-up. Why,
Johnnie, I believe you enjoy the comic pictures about this business! . .

"The only way to conduct propaganda for a cause is through
the dignified medium of books, I am rapidly becoming convinced—
not through newspaper interviews; which, when they are not silly,
are insulting."

. . . .

Baxter's lawyer soon put a stop to our public amicability . .
"collusion," he warned Penton; "they'll call it collusion and you
won't get your final decree."

Tad drew cartoons of us . . a cluster of them . . "*Silk Hat
Harry's Divorce Suit*" . . with dogs' heads on all of us . . Hildreth,
with the head of a hound dog, long hound-ears flopping, with black
jade ear-rings in them . . Penton, a woe-begone little pug. . .

A box car loomed in the centre of the main picture, *"The Affinity Nest of the Hobo Poet,"* I think it was legended . . then I was drawn standing, one leg crossed over the other, the peak of the toe jauntily resting on the ground, hand-in-breast like an old-fashioned picture. There was a tin can thrown over the shoulder of the tattered bulldog that represented me . . one of my ears went through my hat . . beneath, a rhyme ran:

> "I am the hobo poet,
>   I lead a merry life:
> One day I woo the Muse, the next,
>   Another fellow's wife!"

    •   •   •   •   •   •

I brought this up to the cottage we had now procured, down in West Grove, N. J., where we had gone finally to escape the city, and the swarm of reporters that seemed never to cease pursuing us . . for, when we found out that they did not want propaganda, we sought to hide away from them. . .

Hildreth had been rather gloomy at breakfast that morning, and I thought she would join in a laugh with me over Tad's horse-play. There is a streak in me that makes me enjoy the grotesque slap-stick of the comic artists.

When Hildreth saw the cartoons, she laughed a little, at first; then she wept violently.

Then she wrote a savage letter to Tad, letting him know what she thought of his vulgarity.

    •   •   •   •   •   •

"There is one thing in you which I shall never quite compass with my understanding," she almost moaned, "you express the most exquisite thoughts in the loveliest language . . you enter into the very soul of beauty . . and then you come out with some bit of horse-play, some grotesquerie of speech or action that spoils it all."

Nevertheless, it was the humanness in me that brought all the reporters who came to interview us to sympathise with Hildreth and me, instead of with Penton.

    •   •   •   •   •   •

Yes, we had found our dream-cottage . . back in the lovely pines, near West Grove. At a nominal sum of fifteen dollars a month; the actress who owned it, sympathising with our fight, had rented it to me for the fall and winter . . if we could stand the bitter cold in a summer cottage. . .

There Hildreth stayed, seemingly alone, with Darrie, who had come down to chaperon her. To the reporters who sought her out when her place of retreat became known, she averred that she had no idea of my whereabouts. In the meantime, under the name of Mallory, I was living near by, was renting a room in the house of a Mrs. Rond, whose husband was an artist.

I came and went to and from my cottage by a bye-path through the pines that led to the back door.

Darrie, as we called her, performed the most difficult task of all —the task of remaining friends to all parties concerned.

The strain was beginning to tell on Penton. A strange, new, unsuspected thing was welling up in his heart, Darrie averred . . his love for his repudiated wife was reviving so strongly that now he dared not see her, it would hurt him too deeply. . .

His friends, the Stotesburies, a wealthy radical couple, had let him have a cottage of theirs up in Connecticut, and he was staying in it all by himself, doing his own cooking and hurrying with a new book in order to get enough money to defray the enormous expenses he had incurred by initiating and prosecuting his divorce suit. . .

And now Daniel joined us. Daniel and I agreed with each other famously. For he liked me. He took walks with me, and we went bathing together after I had done my morning's writing. We crabbed in the Manasquan River, and fished.

Once, when I was galloping along the road in imitation of a horse, with him perched on my shoulders——

"Say, Johnnie, I like you . . I won't call you buzzer any more!"

"I like you, too, Daniel, but don't squeeze me so hard about the neck . . it's choking my wind off."

.   .   .   .

That was a happy month . . that month of fine, fairly warm fall weather that Darrie, Hildreth, Daniel and I spent together in the little cottage back in the woods, secluded from the road.

The newspapers had begun to let up on us a little. It had grown a bit galling and monotonous, the continual misrepresentations of ourselves and what Hildreth and I were trying to stand for.

    .   .   .   .

Now that I was playing the conventional game of evasion and hypocritic subterfuge, holding a nominal lodging at Mrs. Rond's as one Mr. Arthur Mallory, and explaining my being seen with Mrs. Baxter by the statement that I was a writer sent down by a publishing house for the purpose of helping her with a book she was engaged in writing——

Though everybody knew well who I was, it assuaged the American passion for outward "respectability," and we were left, comparatively speaking, alone to do as we wished. . .

    .   .   .   .

Hildreth was a spoiled, willful little rogue . . once or twice she tried a "soul-state" on me. . .

Walking through the pines one day, suddenly she sat down in her tracks, began crying, and affirmed in a tragic voice, that she couldn't stand the strain of what she had been through any longer, that she believed she was going crazy.

I immediately plumped down on all fours and began running up and down through the crashing underbrush, growling and making a great racket. Startled, intrigued, she watched me.

"Johnnie, don't be such a damn fool! What *are* you doing?"

"I'm going crazy, too, I'm suffering the hallucination that I'm a big brown bear, and you're so sweet that I'm going to eat you all up."

I ran at her. She leaped up, pealing laughter. I began biting at her ankles . . at the calves of her legs . . "oof! oof! I'm going crazy too!" She squealed, delighted, her mind taken off her troubles . . she struck me on the head with her open hands, to keep me off . . I bowled her over with a swift, upward jump . . I picked her up and carried her off, kissing her.

    .   .   .   .

"My darling big rascal . . my own Johnnie Gregory!" She caught me fondly by the hair, "I can't do anything with you at all!"

Once again, waking me up in the middle of the night:

"Johnnie, I—I have a dreadful impulse, an impulse to hit you . . I just can't help it, Johnnie dear! I must do it!" and she fetched me a very neat blow in the face.

"You don't mind, do you . . having your own little girl hit you?"

Now, poor Penton would have spent the remainder of the night
taking this "impulse" and the act which followed it as a serious
problem in aesthetics, economics, feminism, and what-not . . and
the two would have talked and discussed, their voices sounding and
sounding in philosophic disquisition . . and, before the end, Hildreth,
persuaded to take the situation seriously and enjoying the morbid
attention given her, Hildreth would have gone off several times
into hysterics. . .

My procedure was a different one:

"—of course I don't mind you following your impulses . . you
should . . but also I have just as imperative an impulse—now that
you suggest it—to hit you."

And I was not chary of the vigorous blows I dealt her, a tattoo of
them on her back. . .

"Why, Johnnie," she gasped, "you—hit—me!" and her big eyes,
wide with hurt, filled with tears. And she cried a little. . .

"There, there, dear!" I soothed. Then, with a solemn look in my
face, "I couldn't resist my impulse, either."

"You mustn't do that any more, Johnnie . . but,—you must
let *me* hit *you* whenever I want to."

But she never had that "impulse" again.

　　　・　　　・　　　・　　　・　　　・　　　・

But, though we romped a lot, Darrie, Hildreth, Daniel, and I,—
and though Hildreth called me her "Bearcat" (the only thing she
took from the papers, whose title for me was "The Kansas Bearcat") don't think that this made up all our life in our cottage. . .

In the morning, after breakfast, which Daniel and I usually ate
together alone, we being the early risers of the household—I repaired to the large attic and wrote on my play. Then frequently
I read and studied till four, keeping up my Latin and Greek and
German, and my other studies.

Darrie also wrote and studied in her room . . Daniel led the
normal life of the happy American boy, going where the other boys
were, and playing with them—when he and I didn't go off, as I have
said, for the afternoon, together, crabbing and fishing.

Hildreth, of course, was working hard at *her* book—a novel of
radical love. . .

After four was strolling time, for all of us . . along the river, by the ocean beach, further away . . or among the pines that reached up into our very backyard.

When the grocer boy or the butcher boy came, I (for the sake of outward appearances) stepped out of sight, though it irked me, still to resort to subterfuge, when we had launched forth with such a fanfare of publicity. . .

"Wait till Penton wins the decree, then we can come out into the open and live in a Free Union together—or *marry!*" Hildreth begged of me . . and I acquiesced, for the time. . .

.   .   .   .

Each evening, by the open fire, I read aloud from the poets . . or Darrie or Hildreth did . . happy evenings by fire-light, that shall always live pleasantly in my memory. . .

We had but few disagreements, and those trifling ones.

Darrie was herself in the midst of a romantic courtship. 'Gene Mallows, the Californian poet, had fallen madly in love with her, having met her during his brief visit to New York. . .

Every day Darrie received her two, three, even four letters from him, couched in the most beautiful literary phraseology . . and each letter invariably held a sonnet . . and that, too, of an amazingly high standard of poetic excellence, considering the number Mallows was dashing off every day . . many of them were quite lovely with memorable phrase, deft turn of fancy or thought.

.   .   .   .

Penton recalled Daniel to the city. . . Afraid now that the papers might locate him with us. . .

We had a few warm mid-days of glorious sunshine still, and I often persuaded Darrie and Hildreth to take nude sunbaths with me back of the house . . which we enjoyed on outspread blankets, ever keeping a weather eye for intruders. . .

As we lay in the sun we read poetry aloud. And I read aloud much of a book that amounted to our Bible, Havelock Ellis's *Sex in Its Relation to Society.*

I might add, for the sake of the reader who may be prone to misinterpret, that our behaviour was quite innocent, as we lay about in that manner. . .

.   .   .   .

Our best friend was the artist's wife, Mrs. Rond . . she was, in her way, herself a character . . the poverty of her family was extreme. She had a numerous menage of daughters; and a horde of cats as pets. Whenever she walked away from her house the cats followed her in a long line, their tails gaily in the air, like little ships sailing.

Mrs. Rond smoked incessantly, rolling her own cigarettes, from packages of Plowboy tobacco. . .

Her conversation was crisp, nervous, keen. An intellectual woman of the highest type; with all her poverty, she preserved around her an atmosphere of aristocratic fineness (even if she did smoke Plowboy) which bespoke happier days, in an economic and social sense.

She was thoroughly radical, but quiet and unostentatious about it. She looked on me and Hildreth as play-children of the feminist movement.

I think it was the exaggerated maternal instinct in her that moved her to foster and champion Hildreth and me . . an instinct that made her gather in every stray cat she found on the road . . she is the only person I have ever known who could break through the reserve of the cat's nature, and make it as fond and sentimental as a dog is toward its master.

Mrs. Rond knew all the classics, and, in her library, which she never let go, when their economic crash came, were most of the English poets and essayists and novelists from Malory and Chaucer down to William Watson and W. L. George. . .

She made us welcome at her home. We formed a pleasant group together, the occupants of my little cottage back in the pines, and she, her valitudinarian husband, and her four daughters, the eldest of whom, Editha, was of an exquisite type of frail, fair beauty . . all her daughters had inherited their mother's keen-mindedness . . she had brought them up on the best in the thought, art, and literature of the world. . .

The relationship between mother and daughters was one more of delightful, understanding comradeship than anything else . . in spite of the fact of Mrs. Rond's over-developed maternal instincts . . a favourite trick of the two youngest daughters being to hide away upstairs and then call out in mock tones of agony, in order to enjoy the sight of their mother, running breathless, up from the kitchen or in from the yard, and up the stairs, pale with premonition of some accident or ill, and crying, "what's the matter? children, what's the matter?"

"Oh, nothing, mother . . we're only playing."

And her relief would be so great that she would forget to scold them for their childlike, unthinking cruelty.

*   *   *   *   *   *   *

Just before I had left Kansas to come East on my projected trip to Europe, the magazines had begun to buy my poems, the best of them—Now every poem of mine was sent hurriedly back with an accompanying rejection slip.

Yet I was sure that I was writing better than ever before.

Simonds, of the *Coming Nation,* and the editor of the Kansas City *Star* were about the only editors who now took my work. I inferred rightly that my notoriety was what was tabooing me. I determined to run up to New York and find out for myself if this was true!

As I rode north along the flashes of sea, marsh, and town, I thought of my little flock that I had left behind for a day, with intense satisfaction and content. They were mine. Hildreth was my woman, Daniel had been my child for the space he was with us. And I held Darrie in friendly tenderness, much as the bourgeois business man holds the supernumerary women of his household, though she was by no means that, nor was she in any way dependent on me. . .

I was finding it very good to own, to possess, to take root; to be possessed and owned, in turn. I carried an obscure sense of triumph over Baxter.

*   *   *   *   *   *   *

Darrie, who had been to town the week before, had come back with a report of Penton's unhappiness, his belated acknowledgment that he was still, in spite of his battle against the feeling, deeply in love with his discarded wife. It was not so easy to tear her out of his heart, she had intertwined so deeply there . . eight years with a woman, and one child by her, and affection for her was no easy thing to root up from one's being.

"I sat there a long while with him in Riverside Park," Darrie reported, "it was chilly and he wore an old overcoat because he couldn't afford a new one. His hair was greying at the temples.

He looked stooped, aging, frail as if an extra wind might lift him up and carry him away from me. . .

"He was worried about my having been brought into what he called 'the mess' . . wondered how the papers had not scented 'the other woman' in me, no matter how innocent I was of that appellation.

"He seemed so lonely . . admitted he was so lonely. . .

"Johnnie, you're both poor, dear innocents, that's what you are——

"But of the two of you, you are the harder, the best equipped to meet the shock of life . . for you will grow wiser, where Penton never will."

"How did Penton speak of me?"

"Splendidly—said he considered that in a way, perhaps, he had worked you a wrong, done an injustice to you."

"Nonsense, the poor little chap!"

"He made me cry, he acted so pathetic . . he seemed like a motherless little boy that needed a woman's love and protection."

"Darrie, why don't *you* marry him?"

"Now you're trying to do with me as he tried to do with Ruth and you . . marry him . . no . . I'm—I think I'm—in love with 'Gene Mallows."

Penton was pleased to hear, she said, that Daniel and I had got on so nicely together, while he was down at West Grove. . .

.   .   .   .

So, as I rode in the dusty, bumping train, my mind reverted to our whole friendship together, and tenderness welled up in my heart for Penton Baxter.

.   .   .   .

In the office of the New York *Independent* sat William Hayes Ward, old, bent over, with his triple-lensed glasses behind which his dim, enlarged eyes floated spectrally like those of a lemur.

He greeted me with a mixture of constraint and friendliness.

"Well, my boy, you've certainly got yourself into a mess this time."

"A 'mess,' Dr. Ward?" I interrogated, quoting back to him the word he had used,—with rebuke in my voice.

"How else shall I phrase it?"

"—with the understanding that I expect from an old friend, one who bought my first poems, encouraged my first literary endeavours, —who enheartened and helped me at the inception of my struggle for recognition and fame."

"And now you've won too much of the baser coinage of fame, of a kind that a poet should never have."

"I have a poem with me . . one on the subject of what Christ wrote on the sand—after which he bade the woman go and sin no more . . and he who was without sin should cast the first stone."

Dr. Ward looked over the half-moons of his triple glasses at me . . he reached for the poem and read it.

"Yes, it's a fine poem, with that uniqueness in occasional lines, that occasional touch of power, that marks your worst effusions, Mr. Gregory! . . but," paused he, "we do not allow the *Woman Taken in Adultery* in the columns of the *Independent.*"

"Well," I shot back, pleased with myself at the retort I was makin, "well, I'm mighty glad Christ didn't keep her out of the pages of the New Testament, Dr. Ward!"

He barely smiled. He fixed me with a steadfast look of concern.

"Are you still with—with Mrs. Baxter?"

"Yes—since you ask it."

"The sooner you put that woman out of your life the better for you."

"Dr. Ward—one moment! . . understand that no woman I love can be spoken of as 'that woman' in my presence—if you were not an old man!——" I faltered, choking with resentment.

"Now, now, my dear boy," he replied very gently, "I am older than you say . . I am a very, very old man . . and I know life——"

"But do you know the woman you speak of?"

"I have met Mrs. Baxter casually with her husband several times." He stopped short. He paused, gave a gesture of acquiescence.

"Oh, come, Mr. Gregory, you're right . . quite right . . I had no right whatever to speak to you as I have——

"But please interpret it as my serious concern over your career as a poet . . it seems such a pity . . you had such a good start."

"You mean?——" I began, and halted.

"Precisely . . I mean that for the next two or three years all the reputable magazines will not dare consider even a masterpiece from your hands."

"In other words, if Shelley were alive to-day and were the same Shelley, he would be presented with a like boycott?"

"If his manner of living came out in the papers—yes."

"And François Villon?"

"Undoubtedly."

"I'm in good company then, am I not?"

"You should thank me for being frank with you."

"I do thank you .. that explains why the atmosphere up at the office of the *National* was as cold as the refrigerator-box of a meat car, when I was up there an hour ago .. but they were not as frank as you .. they acted like a company of undertakers officiating at my funeral."

   ·   ·   ·   ·   ·   ·

I was glad to find myself back in my little cottage, that same night—back in my little cottage, and in the arms of the woman who was everything to me, no matter if they said she spelled the ruination of my career.

For any man, I held, and still hold, who lets a woman ruin his career, ought to have it ruined.

I did not tell her of what Dr. Ward had told me. Why cause her unnecessary worry?

   ·   ·   ·   ·   ·   ·

After all, the magazine world was not the only medium to present my literary wares to the public. There remained the book world, a less narrow and prejudiced one.

Kennerley had written me that he waited eagerly the completion of my Biblical play.

And Zueblin, of the now defunct *Twentieth Century* had just sent me a twenty-five dollar check for a poem called *Lazarus Speaks*.

   ·   ·   ·   ·   ·   ·

I brought back with me from New York two books as a present for Hildreth .. Mary Wollstonecraft's *A Vindication of the Rights of Woman*, and *The Life of Mary Wollestonecraft* .. these were two books she had long desired. She was thoroughly pleased with her resemblance to the frontispiece picture of the celebrated woman radical, in the *Life*.

"You possess all her vivacity, all her intelligence .. but you are beautiful where she was plain .. she is like a plainer sister of yours."

   ·   ·   ·   ·   ·   ·

While in New York I had also paid a visit to the editor of one of the biggest sensational magazines in the city, and I had arranged with him, acting as Hildreth's agent, for a thousand dollars advance on her unfinished novel. The editor had dictated a letter in which he promised to deliver the thousand on receipt of two-thirds of the book. . .

Hildreth kissed me again and again when I gave her the letter. . .

"Johnnie, you really are wonderful . . and quite practical, after all."

.   .   .   .

"And now, my darling Hildreth, we'll take this old world and shake it into new life, into the vital thing I have dreamed!" I boasted grandiloquently. . .

"Here in this little sequestered dream-cottage of ours you and I will carry out, popularise, through novels, poems, plays, essays, and treatises, the noble work that Ellis, Key, and Rosa Von Mayerreder, and others, are doing in Europe . . and we ourselves will set the example of true love that fears nothing but the conventional legal slavery."

"It will soon be very cold down here," commented Darrie, irrelevantly, "this is only a summer cottage, and they say—the old settlers—that we are to have a severe winter . . the frost fish are already beginning to come ashore."

.   .   .   .

It was generally known, sub rosa, that Hildreth and I were living together. But, as long as she pretended it was not so, as long as I lived seemingly in another house, pretending, under another name, to be Mrs. Baxter's literary adviser, the hypocrisy of the world was satisfied.

I was, in other words, following the accepted mode.

It was a nasty little article by a fellow literary craftsman from the Pacific coast, that set me off, brought me to the full realisation that I was but playing the usual, conventional game,—that roused me to the determination that I must no longer sail under false colours.

This writer retailed how, after a brief, disillusioning few weeks together, Hildreth had grown tired of the poverty and spareness of the living a poet was able to make for her . . of how I was lazy, impliedly dirty . . of how, up against realities, we had parted . . I had, he stated, in fact, deserted her, and was now on my way back

to Kansas, riding the rods of freights, once more an unsavoury outcast, a knight of the road . . he ended with the implication, if I
remember correctly, that the reception that awaited me in Kansas,
would be, to say the least, problematical.

Of course this story was made up out of whole cloth.

'Gene Mallows afterward informed me that the big literary club
in San Francisco that this hack belonged to had seriously considered
disciplining him by expulsion for his unethical behaviour toward a
fellow-writer.

.   .   .   .

But I maintain that it was good that he penned the scurrilous
article. For I had allowed happiness to lull my radical conscience asleep. It was now goaded awake. I held a conference with
Hildreth.

"There is now only one thing for me to . . to come right out with
it that you and I are living here together in a free union, and that
the love we bear each other not only justifies, but sanctifies our doing
as we do—as no legal or ecclesiastical procedure could. . .

That here we are and here we intend to abide, on these principles—no matter what the rest of the world does or says or thinks."

"I admit, Johnnie, that that would be the ideal way, but——" in-
terrupted Darrie——

"But nothing—I'm tired of sneaking around, hiding from grocers
and butcher boys, when everybody knows——

"And besides, Hildreth," turning to her, taking her in my arms,
kissing her tenderly on the brow—"don't you see what it all means?

"As long as I pretend not to be living with you I'm considered a
sly dog that seduced his friend's wife and got away with it . . 'served
him right, the husband, for being such a boob!' . . 'rather a clever
chap, that Gregory, don't you know, not to be blamed much, eh?' . .
'only human, eh?' . . —'she's a deuced pretty little woman, they
say!'

"Can't you see the sly looks, the nudges they give each other, as
they gossip in the clubs?"

"Don't let your imagination get the better of you, please don't!"
urged Darrie. . .

"No," I went on, "I'm going to send right now for Jerome Miller,
a newspaper lad I knew in Kansas, who's now in New York on a
paper, and give him an interview that will set us right with the

stupid world once and for all. Miller was a fellow student of mine at Laurel .. he's a fine, square chap who will give me a clean break .. was president of our Scoop Club."

"Darling, darling, dearest," pleaded Hildreth, "I thought you had about enough of the newspapers .. you've seen how they've distorted all our ideals .. how our attempt to use them for propaganda has gone to smash .. how they pervert .. the filth and abuse they heap upon pioneers of thought in any direction—why wake the wild beasts up again?"

"What's the use believing in anything, if we don't stick up for what we believe?"

"Oh, go ahead, dear, if you feel so strongly about it, but—" and her tiny, dark head drooped, "I'm a little wearied .. I want quiet and peace a little while longer .. I'm getting the worst of it—not you so much, or Penton.

"I'm the woman in the case.

"Remember the invitation the other night, from the Congregational minister—for tea? He invited you for tea, you remember, and left me out?"

"—remember, too," I replied fondly, caressing her head, "how I didn't even deign to reply to the —— —— —— ——!"

"Sh!" putting her hand gently and affectionately over my mouth, "don't swear so .. very well, poke the wild beasts again! .. but we'll only serve as sport for another Roman holiday for the newspapers."

I wrote Miller to come down, that I had an exclusive interview for him.

He arrived the very night of the day he received my letter.

Darrie stepped out over to the Ronds', not to be herself brought into what she had so far managed to keep out of.

Hildreth consumed the better part of two hours fixing herself up as women do when they want to make an impression. ..

"Your friend from Kansas must see that you haven't made such a bad choice in picking me," she proclaimed, with that pretty droop of her mouth.

"No, no! be a good boy, don't muss me up now!"

She wore a plain, navy-blue skirt .. wore a white middy blouse with blue, flowing tie .. easy shoes that fitted snug to her pretty

little feet .. her eyes never held such depths to them, her face never
shone with such beauty before.

I wore a brown sweater vest with pearl buttons . . corduroy
trousers .. black oxfords .. a flowing tie. . .

A large log fire welcomed my former Kansas friend.

"Well, Johnnie, it's been a long time since I've seen you."

"Jerome, let me introduce you to the only woman that ever lived,
or shall live, for me .. Hildreth Baxter."

As Hildreth gave Miller her hand, I could see that he liked her,
and that he inwardly commented on my good taste and perhaps
said to himself, "Well, Johnnie is not so crazy after all!"

After I had given him the interview, he asked her a few questions,
but she begged to be left out, that it was my interview.

"Mr. Miller, you are a friend of Johnnie's . . I have often heard
him speak highly of you; can't you dissuade him from having this
interview printed .. no matter if you have been sent by your paper
all the way down here for it?"

Jerome liked what Hildreth had said, admired her for her common
sense. He offered to return to the city, and risk his job by
stating that he had been hoaxed.

"I will leave you to argue it out with him, Mr. Miller."   And
Hildreth excused herself and went off down the path to the Ronds'
too.

"Johnnie," my friend urged, putting his hand on my shoulder,
"your little lady has a lot of sense . . it *will* kick up a hell of a
row . . it's true what you say about them rather approving of you
now, some of them, considering you a sly dog and so forth. . .
Yes, I'm sorry to say, what you're doing, much of the world is
doing most of the time."

"I beg your pardon, Jerome, but there you've made my point . .
do you think I want a sneaking, clandestine thing kept up between
me and the woman I love?"

"Then why not stay apart till the divorce is granted, then marry
her like a regular fellow?"

"Damn it, Jerome, you don't understand, you don't get what we
radicals are driving at. . ."

"I'll take a chance with my job and quash this interview—that's
how much I like you, Johnnie."

"Oh, I know you mean well enough . . most of you boys have

treated me rather well, according to your lights .. it's the damned lead-writers and re-writers and editorial writers—they're the ones that do the damage."

"You want me to go ahead then?"

"Yes, that is the only way."

"It is a big story, a real scoop." Miller was again the newspaper man who had scored a beat on rival newspapers. . .

"Can't you stay over night, Jerome? We can make room."

"I must catch the next train back .. I'm off now .. there's the taxi I arranged to have come and take me .. it's out there now .. good-bye, Johnny, and God help you and your little girl."

.   .   .   .

Hildreth came in soon after Miller's departure, looking like a fresh-faced girl of twelve.

"Did—did your friend think I was good-looking?"

"Yes, I am sure he thoroughly approved of you."

"To-morrow another Roman holiday begins."

.   .   .   .

The result of that interview was worse than I could have surmised. All the batteries opened fire again. The Kansas papers called me "the shameless tramp" .. reporters spilled from autos and rigs all over the front stoop. After giving a few more interviews in the mad hope that this time they would get it straight, I saw that the harvest was even greater abuse and defamation .. and, as Hildreth had predicted, she came in for more than her share of the moral indignation of people who sold that precious ware at so much a line, or were paid salaries for such work. . .

We practically deserted our house so the reporters could not find us. . .

Many of the reporters never came near the house. Instead, lurid stories were concocted in the back rooms of nearby roadhouses. And, failing to find us at home, interviews were faked so badly that they verged on the burlesque .. where not vulgar, they were vicious .. words were slipped in that implied things which, expressed clearly, had furnished ample grounds for libel.

Hildreth and I were pictured as living on frost fish almost entirely; the fish that run along the ocean shore, and, growing numb with the cold of autumn, are tossed up on the sand by the waves. . .

I was depicted as strident-voiced .. belligerent .. waving my arms

wildly. It was said that, full of threats, I had taken a shotgun
menacingly from a rack . . that a vicious bull dog lay between my
feet, growling . . that I went, sockless, in sandals . . had long,
flowing, uncombed hair. . .

Once a party of three reporters, from a big metropolitan paper,—
two men and a woman, after stopping at a nearby road house till
they were well lit,—drove about in a livery rig till they finally
located us at the house of Mrs. Rond. . .

All the old nonsense was re-written . . things we had never said
or even had in our thought . . vulgarities alien to Hildreth's mouth
or mine. . .

The final insinuation—a sly touching on the fact that the Rond
family was on intimate terms with me, and that the young daughters
were attractive-looking, and seemed to favour the ideals I expressed
with murmurs of approval . . thus the story afterward appeared. . .

Mrs. Rond, after a peculiarly impertinent question of the woman
member of the party, realised by this time that the three reporters
were more than a little tipsy, and ordered these guardians of the
public morality out of the house. . .

In the first place, they had wormed admittance through a fraud
to Hildreth and me . . the woman falsely pretended that she was a
friend of Hildreth's mother . . a great stroke of journalistic
enterprise.

Mrs. Rond's rebuke was so sharply worded that it got through
even their thick skins. . .

I must say, though, that the behaviour of these three was not
characteristic . . generally the newspaper men and women were
most considerate and courteous . . even when they afterward wrote
unpleasant articles about us. And often I have had them blue-pencil
wild statements I had made, which, on second thought, I wished
withdrawn . . and during all the uproar I never had a reporter
break his word, once given.

"Say, Mr. Gregory, that's great stuff, do let us keep that in
the interview."

"Please, boys, draw your pencil through that . . it doesn't sound
the way I meant it."

"Oh, all right"—a sigh—"but it's a shame to leave it out."

.   .   .   .

The last and final outrage—perpetrated by the papers by orders from above, I am sure. . .

Even the second uproar had died down.

Always the "natives" in West Grove and round about, our neighbours, behaved considerately, let us alone . . we were greeted politely wherever we went. . .

But now, Mrs. Rond informed me, strange men were appearing on the street corners, conducting a regular soapbox campaign against us. . .

Some of them were seen to get on and off trains going to and coming from New York. . .

Goaded and spurred by these mysterious outsiders, the village people began to act aloof, and the more ignorant of them sullen toward us . . but as yet it was only in the air, nothing concrete to lay hold of.

   .   .   .   .

Mrs. Suydam had run away with her plumber . . the interviews she gave out showed that it was our case mainly that had impelled her to launch forth in imitation. . .

Others, in a wave of sex-radicalism, were running off together all about the country. . .

But it was Mrs. Suydam's case that interested me and Hildreth most . . she was a dainty, pretty little slight thing, as Hildreth was —I could judge by her pictures. . .

"Hildreth," I urged, "let's drop Mrs. Suydam a note encouraging her . . she's probably without a friend in the world, she and her man . . they're trying to oust her from her flat . . she's being hounded about."

"My God, Johnnie dear, let's *don't!* . . they'll only give our letter to the papers . . let's let well enough alone once more . . the grocer boy passed me in the street to-day and didn't tip his hat to me."

   .   .   .   .

I was sitting at Mrs. Rond's tea-table having afternoon tea with her. She had sent one of her girls over to the cottage to tell me she wished to see me "alone" . . "on a matter of great importance."

The cats, who had trailed her eldest daughter, Editha, across to our place, followed us back again with sailing tails in the air.

Mrs. Rond poured me a cup of strong tea.

"Drink that first, then I'll give you a little information that won't be so very agreeable to you."

The glimmer of satiric yet benevolent humour that was never long absent from her eyes, lightened there again, as she rolled and lit a "Plowboy."

"Have you noticed a change in the weather? A storm is blowing up. I'm speaking figuratively . . I might as well out with it, Johnnie,—there's a report, growing in strength, that a mob of townspeople is scheduled to come your way to-night, some time, and treat you to a serenade of protest and the traditional yokel hospitality of mobs . . a coat of tar and feathers and a ride on a rail beyond the town limits."

"So it's come to that, has it?"

"Johnnie, it isn't the townsfolk that started it . . of that I am certain . . left alone, they would still have been content to mind their business, and accept you and Hildreth on a friendly basis. . ."

She brought up the story of the strange men haranguing from street corners again. . .

"It's the New York newspapers, or one or two of the most sensational of them, that are back of this new phase."

"You mean, Mrs. Rond, that they would dare go so far as to instigate an attack on me and Hildreth . . with possibly fatal results?"

"Of course they would . . they need more news . . they want something more to happen . . to have all this uproar end tamely in happy, permanent love—that's what they couldn't endure. . ."

"Well," she resumed after a pause, "what are you going to do? You're not afraid, are you?"

"To tell the truth I am, very much afraid."

"You and Hildreth and Darrie would best take the three o'clock train back to New York then."

"I haven't the least intention of doing that."

"What are you going to do?"

"—just let them come."

"You won't—fight?"

"As long as I'm alive."

"You just said you were afraid."

"Where a principle is considered, one can be afraid and still stick by one's guns."

"You're a real man, John Gregory, as well as a real poet, and I'm going to help you .. if it was the townspeople alone I would hesitate advising you .. but it's dirty, hired outsiders who are back of this feeling. Here!" and she stepped over to the mantel and brought a six-shooter to me and laid it in my hand, "can you shoot?"

"A little, but not very well."

"It's loaded already .. here is a pocketful of extra bullets."

She filled my coat pocket till it sagged heavily. I slipped the gun in my hip pocket.

"You're really going to stand them off if they come?"

"As long as no one tries to break into my house I will lie quiet .. the minute someone tries to break in, I'll shoot, I'll shoot to kill, and I'll kill as many as I can before they take me. I'll admit I'm frightened, but I have principles of freedom and radical right, and I'll die for them if necessary."

Mrs. Rond put her hand on my shoulder like a man.

"You have the makings of a fine fanatic in you .. in the early Christian era you would have been a church martyr."

.   .   .   .

I held immediate consultation with Darrie and Hildreth and they were both scared blue .. but they were game, too.

Darrie, however, unfolded a principle of strategy which I put into immediate effect .. she advised me to try a bluff first.

When I walked downtown within the hour, to obtain the New York papers, there was no doubt, by the even more sullen attitude of the inhabitants that I passed on the street, that something serious was a-foot. . .

I sauntered up to the news stand, took my *Times* .. hesitated, and then tried the bluff Darrie had suggested:

"Jim," I began, to the newsdealer, who had been enough my friend for us to speak to each other by our first names, "Jim, I hear the boys are planning a little party up my way to-night!"

"Not as I've heard of, Johnnie," Jim answered, with sly evasion, and I caught him sending a furtive wink to a man I'd never seen in town before.

"Now, Jim, there's no use trying to fool me. I'm *on!*"

The newspaper stand was, I knew, the centre for the town's

dissemination of gossip. I knew what I said would sweep everywhere the moment I turned my back.

"As I said," I continued, "I'm on! And I looked about and spoke in a loud voice, while inwardly quaking, "Yes, I know all about it, and I want to drop just this one hint . . tell the boys they can come. Tell them they'll be welcome. . . So far I've had no trouble here . . everybody has been right decent with me," affecting a Western, colloquial drawl, "and I've tried to treat everybody, for my part, like a gentleman,—ain't that true?"

"That's true, Mr. Gregory" (it was suddenly "Mr. Gregory" now, not "Johnnie"). "As I was saying just the other day, there's lots worse in the world than Mr. Gregory that ain't found out."

"I want to leave this message with you, Jim. I'm from the West. I'm a good shot. I've got a six-shooter ready for business up at the cottage. I've got a lot of extra bullets, too. As I've said, I ain't the kind that looks for trouble, but when anybody goes out of their way—— Well, as I said before, as soon as the boys begin getting rough—I'll begin to shoot . . I'll shoot to kill, and I'll kill everybody I can get, till someone gets me."

"Yes, Mr. Gregory!"

"Mind you, Jim, I've always considered you as my friend. I mean what I say. I'm a householder. I'm in the right . . if the law wants me that's another matter . . but no group of private citizens——"

"Good-bye, Mr. Gregory."

.   .   .   .

I walked rapidly back to the cottage. I was thinking as rapidly as I walked. For the space of a full minute I thought of packing off ignominiously with my little household.

But before I stepped in at the door something murky had cleared away inside me.

"Oh, Hildreth! Darrie!"

The women came dragging forward. But with them, too, it was a passing mood.

My indignation at the personal outrage of the impending mob incited me as them . . till I think not one of the three of us would have stepped aside from the path of a herd of stampeding elephants.

"The yokels," and Darrie's nostrils flared, her blue blood showing, "to dare even think of such an action against their betters!"

.   .   .   .

We lit a roaring log fire. We sat reading aloud from Shelley. As the hours drew by . . eight . . nine . . ten . . eleven . . there is no doubt that our nerves grew to a very fine edge. . .

And at twelve o'clock———

Far off, at a respectful distance, a carol of rough, humorous voices sang the song, *"Happily Married"!*

"H-a-double-p-y," etc.

And we knew that my bluff had worked.

.   .   .   .

The next day we went through a let-down.

Hildreth was quite nerve-shaken, and so was Darrie.

But I strutted about with my chest out, the cock of the walk.

.   .   .   .

But, nevertheless, and despite their bravery and the fiasco of the mob's attack, the hearts seemed to have left the bodies of both "my" women.

.   .   .   .

The cold weather that Darrie and the old settlers had predicted was now descending on the countryside. . .

.   .   .   .

One morning Hildreth timidly and haltingly proposed returning to her mother's flat in New York. . .

I could stay and finish my play and, having disposed of it, come likewise to the city, and rent a flat, and she would come and live with me again. I am sure she was sincere in this. Or I could come to New York, rent a furnished room somewhere, and she would be with me daily, as now. . .

Darrie seconded Hildreth's proposal.

.   .   .   .

And yet my heart broke as Hildreth rode off in the carriage that came for her. I kissed her, and I kissed her . . despite the stern, unbending figure of the aged, moral coachman in the seat.

Then, after she had started off, I pursued the carriage, overtook it by a short cut, cried out that I had still something I had forgotten to give her . . it was more kisses . . and I kissed and kissed her again and again . . and we both wept, with aching hearts.

Then the moral coachman unbent.

"—beg pardon," he ventured, "but I'm sorry for you two children . . oh, yes, I know all about you . . everybody knows . . and I wish you good luck."

Darrie stayed over for the night, after Hildreth left, in order to see to packing the latter's clothes in her trunk . . Hildreth had been too upset to tend to the packing. . .

    .   .   .   .

The next day Darrie left, too.

"You have no more need of your chaperon," she laughed, a tear glinting in her eye. . .

    .   .   .   .

So now I was left utterly alone. . .

And a hellish winter descended upon the coast . bitter, blowing, frosty winds that ate into the very bone and made a fellow curse God as he leaned obliquely against them.

I learned how little a summer cottage was worth—in winter.

Mrs. Rond lent me a huge-bellied stove, the fireplace no longer proving of comfort.

But though I kept the stove so hot that it glowed red, I still had to hug it close, my overcoat on, and a pair of huge, woollen socks that I'd bought at the general store down in West Grove.

But, despite the intense cold, I worked and worked . . my play, *Judas* was nearing completion . . its publication would mean the beginning of my life as a man of letters, my "coming out" in the literary world.

I ate my food from open cans, not taking the trouble to cook.

At night (I had pulled my bed out close to the stove) I heaped all the blankets in the house over me, and still shivered . . I lived on the constant stimulus of huge draughts of coffee. . .

"Only a little while longer . . only a few days more . . and the play will then be finished . . and it will be published. And it will be produced.

"Then *the woman*, my first and only woman, she will be with me again forever . . I'll take her to Italy, away from all the mess that has cluttered about our love for each other."

    .   .   .   .   .   .   °

One day, in an effort to keep the house warm—the one room I confined myself to, rather,—I stoked the stove so hot that the stovepipe grew red to the place where it went through the roof into the attic. . .

My mind, at the time, was in far-off Galilee. I was on the last scene of the last act of my play . . the disciples, after the crucifixion, were gathered in the upper room again, waiting for the resurrected Christ to appear to take the seat left vacant for Him. . .

I looked up from the page over which my frosty fingers crawled. . .

The boards were smoking faintly. If I didn't act quickly the house would catch fire . . I laughed at the thought of the curious climax it would present to the world; I imagined myself among the embers.

I must lessen the heat in the stove. I ran and brought in a bucket of water. I pried open the red-hot door of the stove with a stick that almost caught flame as I pried.

With a backward withdrawal, a forward heave, I shot the contents of the pail into the stove. . .

There followed a detonation like a siege gun.

The stove-lid shot so close to my head it was no joke . . it took out the whole window-sash and lit in the outside snow. The stove itself, balanced on bricks under its four feet, slumped sidewise, fortunately did not collapse to the floor . . the stovepipe fell, but the wire that held it up at the bend also prevented it from touching the carpet . . the room was instantly full of suffocating soot and smoke.

I crawled forth like a scared animal . . found myself in the kitchen. In the mirror hanging there I looked like a Senegalese.

Then, finding myself unhurt, I laughed and laughed at myself. at the grotesqueness and irony of life, at everything . . but mostly at myself.

I righted the stove as best I could, brought the door in again from where it had bitten to the bottom of the snow drift, like an angry animal. It was still uncomfortably hot . . shifting it from hand to hand I managed to manœuvre it back to a slant position on its hinges. . .

Before I could light another and more moderate fire, unexpectedly the inspiration for the completion of the last scene of *Judas*—

the inspiration for which I had been waiting and hoping—rode in on me like a wave. . .

. . . .

Christ, in the spirit, unseen, comes to his waiting disciples.

Thomas. Someone has flung open the door. The wind has blown out the candles.

Andrew. Nay, I sit next the door. 'Tis closed!

John. He has risen. He is even now among us.

Thomas. Someone sits in the chair. I feel a presence by my side.

Peter. Brethren, 'tis the Comforter of which He spake! [*A misty light fills the room.*]

John. Ah, 'tis He! 'tis He! He is with us. He has not forsaken us. Verily, He has risen from the dead into a larger life than ever! Dear Lord, Beloved Shepherd of Souls, is it Thou?

Thomas. I believe, I believe! It is past speech! Thy Kingdom comes as I dreamed, but dared not believe!

John. He lives, He lives—the very Son of God!
Behold the Kingdom that He promised us;
'Tis no vain dream, 'tis everlasting truth!
He shall bind all the nations into one,
The love of him shall flood the world!
He shall conquer with love and gentleness, and not with the sword.
He shall live again in every heart that loves its fellow men.
Peace he will plant where discord grew before.
He will save and heal the souls of men forever and forever.
Ah, dear Master, forgive us, we beseech Thee,
For deeming Thou hadst ever died.

. . . .

And so, having nearly burnt a house down, and perhaps myself with it, I had written "finis" to my four-act play called *Judas*.

. . . .

Hildreth and I had written faithfully to each other twice a day . . the absurd, foolish, improper letters that lovers exchange . . I wrote most of my letters in the cave-language that we had invented between us. . .

And we marked all the interspaces with secret symbols that meant intimate caresses . . kisses . . everything. . .

. . . . . .

The play brought to a successful end, I realised that for one

day no letters had come from Hildreth. And the next none came
.. and the next. . .

I besieged the post office five and six times a day in a panic,
till the postmaster first pitied me, then grew a bit put out. . .

A week, and not a single letter from the woman I loved. . .

The day before, Mrs. Suydam and her plumber affinity, for
whom I felt myself and Hildreth and Penton largely responsible,
in the example we had set—the day before these two young people
had committed suicide.

As I walked about the cottage, alone, I had the uncanny feeling
that the place was haunted .. that maybe the ghosts of these two
poor children who had imitated us were down there haunting me
.. why had not Hildreth and I written that joint letter to them as
I had suggested!

—only a little thing, but it might have given them courage to go
on! . .

I was at the long-distance phone.

"Hildreth!" I cried, hearing her dear voice. . .

"Oh, how good, how sweet, my love, my life, it is to hear your
voice again .. tell me you still love me!"

"Hush, Johnnie, hush!" answered a far-away, strange voice ..
"I'm writing you a long letter .. somebody might be listening in."

"Did you see in the paper about Mrs. Suydam?"

"Yes, it was a terrible thing."

"—if we had only written to them!"

"—that was what I thought!"

"Shall I come to the city now? My book is finished. I'm a real
author now."

"The book is finished? That's fine, Johnnie .. but don't come to
the city now .. wait my letter."

When the bulky letter came, the roads rang like iron to my step.
I wouldn't allow myself to read it in the post office. I hugged the
luxury of the idea of reading it by the fire, slowly. I kissed the
still unopened envelope many times on the way home.

I broke the letter open .. it fell out of my hands as if a paralysis
had smitten me. . .

No, no, I would not believe it .. it could not be true .. in so short a time . . with hands that shook as with palsy I plucked it up from the chilly, draughty floor again. . .

"*Another man!*"

She had met, was in love with, another man!

Oh, incredible! incredible! I moaned in agony. I rocked like an old woman rocking her body in grief.

Now was my time to end it all!

Damn all marriage! Damn all free love! God damn to hell all women!

.   .   .   .   .   .

I thought of many ways of committing suicide. But I only *thought* of them.

I flung out into the night, meaning to go and tell Mrs. Rond of the incredible doom that had fallen upon me, the unspeakable betrayal.

"Poor Penton!" I cried. "Poor Penton!"

At last I sympathised fully with him.

.   .   .   .   .   .

Ashamed, in my slowly gathering new man's pride, I did not go in to see Mrs. Rond. Instead, I drove past her house with that curious, bent-kneed walk of mine,—and I walked and walked, not heeding the cold, till the ocean shouldered, phosphorescent, in the enormous night toward me.

.   .   .   .   .   .

Home again, I slept like a drunkard. It was broad day when I woke.

I had dreamed deliciously all night of Hildreth . . was strangely not unsatisfied—when I woke again to the hell of the reality her letter had plunged me into.

.   .   .   .   .   .

Mrs. Rond . . of course I finally took her into my confidence, and told her the entire story. . .

"Not to speak in disparagement of Hildreth, I knew it all along, Johnnie . . knew that this would be the result . . but come, come, you have bigger things in you. . . Penton Baxter will win his divorce sooner or later. Hildreth has another man, poor little girl! You have all that God means you to have at present: *Your first book!*"

.   .   .   .   .   .

THE END